THE WORKS OF COLONEL JOHN TRUMBULL

GEN. WASHINGTON

(Yale version)

THE WORKS OF
COLONEL JOHN TRUMBULL

ARTIST OF THE AMERICAN REVOLUTION

REVISED EDITION

---

by THEODORE SIZER

with the assistance of Caroline Rollins

NEW HAVEN AND LONDON

YALE UNIVERSITY PRESS   1967

To my son,

THEODORE RYLAND SIZER,

who dedicated his first book to me.

I now dedicate my last to him.

FOREWORD TO THE REVISED EDITION

Immediately upon its publication in 1950, Theodore Sizer's *The Works of Colonel John Trumbull* became one of the basic studies in the literature of the history of American art. To resolve any question involving Trumbull, one automatically turned to Sizer's *Works*. Because of its value, the book was soon out of print, and, ever since, art historians, libraries, museums, and collectors have had a difficult time obtaining copies. How fortunate we now are that Professor Sizer and Yale University Press have combined forces once more to bring out a new edition of the book, not only making available the contents of the original book but also bringing together many of Professor Sizer's subsequent writings on Trumbull and adding a greatly enlarged range of illustrations. The resulting volume affords a more comprehensive picture of Trumbull than has been previously available. When this book is considered in conjunction with Professor Sizer's other major Trumbull publication, *The Autobiography of Colonel John Trumbull* of 1953, a view of Trumbull as a more versatile, more creative, and more interesting individual than one would have suspected earlier, emerges.

Trumbull, the recipient of a classical education at Harvard (class of 1773), takes his place as one of those remarkable "Renaissance men" who ornamented the late eighteenth century. He was at various times a schoolteacher, a soldier, a military map-maker, a diplomat, an architect, an author, and a designer of all sorts of things from medals and badges to a mahogany casket for the remains of Major André. But above all he was an artist, proficient as well as prolific—and again his versatility is obvious: landscapes, miniatures, history paintings, portraits.

As impressive as Trumbull's diversity is the length of his creative span. As the reader inspects the panorama of illustrations made available in this book, he not only continues to marvel at Trumbull's early history pictures and miniatures but also grows increasingly aware of Trumbull's long dominance of the New York art scene in the early nineteenth century and of the quality of the pictures that he produced there. Even the latest history pictures, some of them qualitative fiascos, gain in interest within this expanded context and show themselves worthy of more than the automatic rejection that has been their previous lot.

The privilege of writing this introductory note also gives me the happy opportunity of being the first to thank Professor Sizer for bringing the *Works* up to date and presenting us with this enriched feast of Trumbulliana.

> JULES D. PROWN
> *Curator, Garvan and*
> *Related Collections of American Art*
> *Yale University Art Gallery*

Battle of Trenton

Through countless reproductions such as this, from Henry W. Harrison's *Battle-Fields of the Republic from Lexington to the City of Mexico* (Philadelphia, 1857), Trumbull's work became familiar to successive generations of school children. His scenes from the Revolutionary War thus became a part of the nation's pictorial tradition.

PREFACE TO THE REVISED EDITION

We Americans are fortunate to have had a group of highly intelligent, wise, and dedicated men to preside over the birth of this nation and to chart its future course. Our debt to the Founding Fathers is immeasurable. It was providential, too, that the Colonies produced a man worthy to record, pictorially, the chief actors and the salient events that took place at an epic period in our history.

Trumbull was the chief visual recorder of the American Revolution. What he saw and set down on paper, wood, and canvas—accurately and with grace—has created enduring impressions of men and dramatic episodes.

The first edition of this volume went out of print after being included in the "White House List" during the Kennedy administration. This revised version, published seventeen years after the original has given me a rare opportunity to bring the checklist up to date. An old subject has been looked upon with a fresh eye.

Many pictures, especially early ones, formerly listed from documentary sources—

inventories, packing and shipping lists, letters, and so on—as "unlocated" have been found. Perhaps the most exciting was the discovery of the miniature of Tom Paine, painted by the artist as a gift for the United States Minister to France, Thomas Jefferson (see Appendix). Many pictures have changed hands; there has been the constant flow from private to public ownership. Still there are many "lost" pictures—at least twenty in England, painted during the artist's long sojourns in that country, probably parading as "British School" (which, in reality, many of them are); I compiled a list of these in an article for *The Connoisseur* (London), December 1949 (pp. 121–22) with negative result. Misattributed work, together with more forgeries, have been brought to light (see Appendix). The compiling of checklists is a never-ending process, from which I have derived great and lasting satisfaction. I trust that this attempt to clarify further the work of an important American artist is sufficient justification for this revised edition.

The long list of acknowledgments in the 1950 book is not repeated here. I wish, however, to record with thanks the assistance of William P. Campbell, Assistant Chief Curator of the National Gallery of Art; and that of Miss Caroline Rollins, Public Relations Officer of the Yale University Art Gallery, for carrying on a vast and complicated correspondence with owners of Trumbulls, and, especially, for interpreting the scrawled changes in my interleafed copy of the original book. I also wish to thank my neighbor, Mrs. Russell D. VonBeren, Jr., for typing; and Mrs. Huntington P. Welch for keeping my files, correspondence, notes, and records in usable order, and for her generous and imaginative help throughout the editing of this book. Miss Barbara D. Simison of the Yale University Library has, as always, been of the greatest assistance. I am especially grateful to my colleagues, both old and new, who have been ever helpful with advice and generous with their time.

Finally, I wish to emphasize that this is a *reference* book—the record of one man's work at a critical moment in the nation's history—and it should be so regarded.

T. S.

Bethany, Connecticut
Fall 1966

The Trumbull Gallery on the Yale Campus

Opened to the public on Thursday, 25 October 1832; collections removed to a larger building in 1868; demolished in 1901.

PREFACE TO THE 1950 EDITION

In 1831 Benjamin Silliman, the scientist, negotiated the transfer to Yale of the paintings and miniatures in the possession of his seventy-five-year-old uncle-in-law, John Trumbull, in exchange for a thousand-dollar annuity. The life expectancy of the crusty old colonel was adjudged six years, but to the embarrassment of his Yankee underwriters he lived for twelve. As part of the agreement, a building to house the collection was constructed on the old Yale Campus after the aged painter's design. The little neoclassical "Trumbull Gallery," which opened its doors to the public in 1832, had the distinction of being one of the earliest art museums in the English-speaking world and the first to be connected with an educational institution in America. Professor Silliman became its first curator. Thus Yale has, for nearly a century and a half, possessed the largest and finest collection of the works of the chief recorder of the American Revolution.

I was in charge of the present Art Gallery, Yale's third, for a score of years and was perforce continually questioned, berated, and consulted about Trumbull and his real and supposed work. My resignation as Director of the Gallery, a sabbatical leave of absence, and the happy coincidence of a Guggenheim Fellowship made it possible to organize the mass of information I had unintentionally accumulated.

This task of organization necessitated much travel, chiefly up and down the Eastern seaboard, to ferret out Trumbull's work, true and false, and to locate letters, accounts, and other documentary evidence. I have attempted to see and study the complete *oeuvre* of the painter and to relate each painting to contemporary documentation.

In this I have fallen far short of an ideal yet impossible goal. Source material has, however, been related to the pictures, in consequence of which many "lost" works are herein recorded. Dates and places of execution, the *when* and the *where* of each portrait or historical composition, have been set down against each item listed. Far too often this has had to be based on stylistic and nondocumentary evidence. The matter of getting artist and sitter together (in which forgers often lamentably fail) has been arduous, but it is important for the collector, connoisseur, historian, and, incidentally, the philatelist.

This task of compilation has been undertaken with mingled zeal and righteousness. Trumbull's reputation as a painter has suffered grievously by misattribution. Like Copley and Stuart, before serious studies of their work were undertaken, Trumbull has been a sort of catchall. Pictures of Revolutionary worthies, especially if in uniform, have been indiscriminately ascribed to him in ignorance—and hope.

When I had completed my task, I found I had filled thirty-odd large, loose-leaf notebooks with lists of the real, supposed, and fraudulent work of the artist. I entertained the hope that a large and impressive *catalogue raisonné*, with the history of the individual pictures, accompanied by all the heavy baggage of biography, bibliography, and documentary information, might be published. Such monumental projects, however, cannot be undertaken in these days of uncertainty, much less underwritten at present high costs. Consequently, I reduced the catalogue to the bare minimum. The result was: "A Tentative 'Short-Title' Check List of the Works of Col. John Trumbull," which appeared serially in *The Art Bulletin* (September and December 1948 and March 1949). So convenient has this list proved to be that it is now republished substantially as it was, but with corrections and additions and with the keys of all the historical pictures added. The keys have been published many times but not always accurately; errors have crept in and have been perpetuated, ranks of the military were not those held at the time of the action depicted, and first names were often omitted, resulting in needless confusion.

Sketches and studies have been given the same importance in the listing as finished portraits and historical compositions. These are far from being inconsequential; in fact, they are often more informative than the more formal works. One frequently derives more aesthetic pleasure and gains a truer insight from artists' studies made directly from life than from the considered compositions of the studio; and Trumbull's work is no exception. All, therefore, and not a selected portion, of the artist's work has been included. One cannot anticipate in advance what trivial reference may yield the answer to a future problem.

Some of the portraits in the historical series were painted directly on small, easily transportable canvases (now at Yale), as noted in the *Autobiography*—the French officers in *Yorktown*, for instance. Trumbull explained to Robert Treat Paine (22 February 1837), "The portrait of your Grandfather was painted by me in Boston in 1791 and as I had the original picture with me, for the purpose, I painted Sam'l Adams, Mr. Paine & others in the original work—without any separate Sketch or Study . . ." (Yale University Library).

Few artists have recorded their own work. It is a tedious business uncongenial to the creative spirit. John Trumbull was more meticulous than most, for he kept intermittent memoranda. His *Autobiography* (New York and New Haven, 1841) contains a list of his work executed prior to his departure for London in 1779. This he based on an old list (in the Yale University Library and published in the *Gazette*, April 1948) of his paintings down to 1789, the year he left Benjamin West's studio for the second time. Neither manuscript nor printed version is complete.

Years later, in 1831, the artist supervised the publication of the catalogue of pictures turned over to Yale. This ultimately went through five editions (1832, 1835, 1852, 1860, and 1864), excellent evidence of popular interest. Other than these Trumbull Gallery catalogues, the earliest postmortem list was the auction sale of twenty-four pictures by the artist, held at New York on 1 December 1844, by W. H. Franklin of 15 Broad Street, off Wall Street, "without reserve, to close his estate."

John Ferguson Weir, Professor of Painting and Design at the Yale School of the Fine Arts from 1869 to 1913, listed a modest number of pictures additional to those contained in the 1831 collection, in his *John Trumbull*, published in 1901 on the occasion of Yale's bicentennial celebration. The next, in order, was John Hill Morgan's *Paintings by John Trumbull at Yale University* (New Haven, Yale University Press, 1926). Five years later Theodore Bolton, Librarian of the Century Association at New York, with Harry Lorin Binsse, compiled a list of Trumbull's portraits (*The Antiquarian*, July 1931) based on published and documentary sources.

In the preparation of this checklist the writer encountered hundreds of erroneously, and some fraudulently, attributed paintings and especially drawings. The interest initially engendered by such events as the Exposition of 1876 at Philadelphia and the centennial of Washington's inauguration held at New York in 1889 resulted in the creation of a body of eager collectors; in consequence, fraudulent paintings, often signed and dated, began to appear. But this was not all; importations were added to local manufacture. Genuine provincial European paintings were presented under spurious and ingenious American attributions. This transatlantic chicanery was not, of course, confined to Trumbull. Again, to meet a wide demand for less expensive portraits, quantities of drawings were produced as early as the 1880s. These are by several easily distinguishable hands. Most are signed or initialed and some are dated, though not always judiciously. In the writer's opinion the drawings listed in *Catalogue No. 128, The Trumbull Collection . . . Ed. Frossard . . . New York, 1894,* in the *Catalogue of the Trumbull Collection . . . Now on Exhibition at Dodd, Mead & Company . . .*

April 1894, and *The Frossard Revolutionary Collection, American Art Galleries, New York, March 1896,* are false. Doubts were cast upon the genuineness of the drawings by a lone writer in *The Nation* of 13 September 1894, and in the *New York Evening Post,* 19 September, and answered by Mr. Frossard in the latter on 27 September. This doubter, whose discerning eye saw what his contemporaries could not or did not see, was assuredly Kenyon Cox the mural painter and art critic—an identification for which I am indebted to the New York Public Library. To spot the forgeries of one's own day is difficult; it is comparatively easier to do so for the fraudulent productions of the past. (Dr. Hans Tietze has expounded this problem interestingly in "The Psychology and Aesthetics of Forgery in Art," *Metropolitan Museum Studies,* v, Part 1, 1–19, 1934.) The late John Hill Morgan's devastating analysis of the 1896 sale appeared in *Antiques* for February 1941. Forgeries of one kind or another abound whenever collecting is active and prices high.

The most extensive collection known to me of Trumbull forgeries of the Frossard variety, is that at the Yale University Art Gallery, consisting of twenty-two items on ivory, parchment, "on inside of book covers," and on paper—none, however, on irresistibly romantic "drumheads." All are framed and many are backed with contemporary newspaper. There is an interesting forged pencil sketch of Washington, by a different hand, likewise signed and dated, in the Print Room of the Museum of Fine Arts, Boston. Forgeries, used in comparison with genuine work, make excellent teaching material.

Professor Benjamin Silliman collected his uncle-in-law's (authentic) drawings, regarded in the 1830s and 40s as inconsequential. These were eventually sold by the professor's grandson—in the "Silliman Sales" (Stan. V. Henkel's Nos. 770 and 778, Philadelphia, 1896 and 1897). As these catalogues of original drawings (still the best source) are difficult to find, items in the sales have been identified in the following checklist by the original sales catalogue numbers.

It will be seen that the checklist presented here is by no means the first, but it is by far the most complete in that it includes all types of the many-sided, British-trained artist's work.

CONTENTS

ILLUSTRATIONS

The Artist

Silhouette in the Yale University Art Gallery

INTRODUCTION

Colonel John Trumbull was a faithful recorder of men and events at the birth of this nation, and therein lies his importance. Whether he was a great or mediocre portraitist and historical painter is of little moment. In spite of having but one good eye, at worst he was adequate. Being a soldier he understood with professional nicety what he was about; military gear and accoutrements are recorded with the punctiliousness and accuracy of a Meissonier. A camera clicked when the flag was raised at Iwo Jima, but it was the Revolutionary soldier-turned-painter who noted what banners were carried by friend and foe at Bunker's Hill. He came at a time of scant visual recording. It is through the eye of a Connecticut Yankee that we still envision the great events of our heroic epoch.

The colonel had a unique opportunity for the task to which he dedicated his long life—and wit enough to seize it. He was the son of the governor of Connecticut, Jonathan Trumbull, the "Brother Jonathan" of legendary fame; and brother of Joseph, the first Commissary General of the Continental forces, and of Jonathan, Jr., one of Washington's military secretaries. He himself was an aide-de-camp to the Commander-in-Chief, though only for a matter of weeks. Thus he was on familiar terms with the "top brass," as we should say today, of the Revolutionary army. On the civilian side, Jefferson took a deep interest in his work and Jay made him his diplomatic secretary. The colonel knew, for instance, the first six presidents of the United States, and the earliest the best. He painted the Founding Fathers; he was the foremost documentary artist at a critical moment in our national history.

Trumbull received a classical education at Harvard; indeed, he was the earliest American college graduate to become a professional painter. At Cambridge he acquired more than an academic education: friends, who were to be helpful in later years; some acquaintance with the fine arts, through books and prints at the College Library and the newly painted Copley portraits; and French, from a family of displaced Acadians. His ability to speak fluent French was a bridge to intimate friendships with David, Vigée-Lebrun, and other painters; consequently their influence on the young, impressionable artist was at firsthand. It is too often assumed that as a pupil of Benjamin West he developed his style exclusively on the British pattern, but such is not the case. The instrument of language, too, must have helped, if it did not actually make possible, the painting, at Jefferson's hospitable quarters in Paris, of the French officers who participated at Yorktown. At least, sprightly conversation must have gone far to relieve the restless Frenchmen of the tedium of posing.

In later years, too, Trumbull knew the "right people" in New York, though as he grew older he was forced to compete with the younger generation—Morse, Sully, Jarvis, Inman, and others. It is *who* he painted and not *how* he painted that is of primary interest to posterity. The colonel concerns us today not so much as a master of the brush, but as the portrayer of "Very Important Persons."

Like his master Benjamin West, Trumbull considered himself first and foremost a historical painter. His compositions represent the traditions of the day in pose, gesture, and grouping. The "Dying Spaniard," for example, in the *Sortie from Gibraltar*, for which Sir Thomas Lawrence obligingly posed, is inspired by the *Dying Gaul* (then known as the *Dying Gladiator*); Trumbull had studied a cast of it at the Royal Academy School at Somerset House. The disposition of the hands of the principal figures in this picture is derived from a similar arrangement in Tintoretto's *Bacchus and Ariadne* in the Ducal Palace at Venice, though the transference of influence was by means of an engraving, for Trumbull never visited Italy, as Jefferson once urged him to do. Trumbull's academically correct compositions, like those of West and Copley, are devoid of any suggestion of outdoor atmosphere or seasonal or weather conditions. For example, the Hessians captured Trenton in the dead of winter, but the setting of *Trenton* differs little from *Bunker's Hill*, which was assaulted on a fine June morning, or the surrenders at Saratoga and Yorktown, both of which occurred in October. We should not, however, blame the artist too severely for conforming to current conventions.

In spite of such limiting factors, the individuality of the painter—occasionally buoyant—is unconsciously reflected in his work. Though his figures may be studio-posed and grouped in the manner of West, violent action and the heat and turmoil of battle are successfully suggested in the *Attack on Quebec* and *Bunker's Hill*, which were painted in the quiet of West's far-removed London studio. There is a distinct

Rubenesque feeling in both these pictures, which is rather curious, since Trumbull was not exposed to much of Rubens' work until he visited the Continent a year or two later. He was enthusiastic about that master's small compositions, as we are today. It is odd that an admirer and follower of the Jesuit baroque, stylistically speaking, should have been a Connecticut Puritan.

Trumbull was a traditionalist, in spite of being a revolutionist. He had fought for political freedom, not for social change. Formal, correct, a man of property and an ardent Federalist, he lacked the fiery passion of a Goya or Delacroix. He reflected honestly, and unconsciously, the beliefs of his day.

Although his "national history" series, as he called it, which occupied half his life span, is familiar to every American schoolchild through countless schoolbook reproductions, Trumbull's preliminary sketches and early versions of the paintings are little known. The first painting of the series was done under the inspiration and encouragement of both Jefferson and West at a time when life was sweet and untrammeled. The last was completed nearly forty years later for the Capitol at Washington. It is tragic that the later—dull, heavy, but celebrated—replicas painted by a disillusioned, querulous, debt-ridden old man should be the pegs on which his reputation hangs.

Happily, however, for Trumbull's good name and fame, his religious and classical compositions are little known. Like similar works of his master West, they have received scant approbation from later generations—to put it mildly. They were the products of his classically inspired youth, middle-aged idleness (when commissions failed as they did in England during the War of 1812), and faltering old age.

Edmund Burke urged Trumbull to study architecture (of which the young painter already had some knowledge), pointing out that a new country would require buildings before paintings to decorate them. This sound advice was but partially heeded. To judge from the Lebanon Meetinghouse, which still stands, he might have gone far in that profession. Charles Bulfinch, Ithiel Town, and Alexander J. Davis (of the celebrated architectural firm of Town and Davis) were all close friends. Davis regarded himself as Trumbull's pupil. The painter's delicate architectural drawings in the New-York Historical Society, of which he was vice-president, bear out this conviction.

Still less familiar than his architectural efforts are such things as Trumbull's designs for Indian peace medals and badges, his maps, and his student work.

As a portraitist Trumbull displayed slight psychological insight, except when he held the mirror to himself. Corporal realities were rendered with knowledge and skill in the conventional manner of the day. He used few accessories; formal composition played but little part. The likenesses satisfied his sitters—in those innocent, bygone days when ignorance of photographic exactitude was bliss. A certain characterization and individualization added to the usual three-quarter head—turned sometimes to the left and sometimes to the right but always at the same level to the beholder—was all that was necessary.

Though many of his life-size effigies are dull, Trumbull's miniatures, especially those of the early 1790s, are enchanting. Considerable aesthetic pleasure may be derived from these lovely little oils (always on mahogany, never the customary watercolor on ivory), in which the lack of compositional pattern and the limitations of monocular vision are unnoticed. William Dunlap, the author and miniature painter, who detested Trumbull, confessed that they were "among the most admirable miniatures in oil that ever were painted." The colonel knew and admired the work of the most celebrated English miniaturist of his time, Richard Cosway, fourteen years his senior. He also thought highly of that of his fellow countryman and junior by twenty-one years, Edward Greene Malbone. (Incidentally, as a young man, this finest of American miniaturists painted the colonel.) Trumbull is therefore bracketed midway between the two best English-speaking practitioners on both sides of the Atlantic.

Toward the end of the artist's long life a newfangled contraption, the clumsy box camera, began seriously to compete with the gentle art of miniature painting. It was in the decade of the 1840s that daguerreotypes reached their greatest popularity. When the old colonel died in 1843 the charming, delicate mode of portrait painting "in the little" had sadly declined, replaced by cheap photography.

The tragedy of the bilingual, one-eyed soldier-turned-painter was that most of his good work was produced before he was forty and he lived to be eighty-eight. His best was behind him by the pivotal year 1800, which marked exactly the halfway point in his long life. He absorbed little of what Europe had to offer—technically, spiritually, or

This decoration is taken from *Thrilling Incidents of the Wars of the United States . . .* by the Author of *The Army and Navy of the United States*, New York, Robert Sears, 1851.

intellectually—after the years of the French Revolution. He remained until his death, in thought, word, and deed, a proud and punctilious eighteenth-century gentleman.

It has been given to few, in the long history of Western painting, to become the creators of the visual symbols of an epoch. Our image of Martin Luther is derived from the paintings and prints made by his friend Lucas Cranach. Henry VIII and his court live today through the scrupulous recordings of Hans Holbein the Younger. It is by the means of the canvases of Sir Anthony Van Dyck that we envision the court of Charles I, and our image of the Emperor Napoleon comes by way of the paintings of Jacques Louis David. In like manner, our visual conception of the events surrounding the birth of this republic are due to the documentation of a certain Connecticut Yankee.

View of Lebanon, Connecticut

(From John Warner Barber, *Historical Connecticut* [New Haven, 1838], drawn by the author in June 1835), showing the Meetinghouse (center) designed by Colonel Trumbull and (to the right) Master Tisdale's School where Trumbull both studied and taught.

Electrotype of Barber's original woodblock in possession of Yale University Library.

CHRONOLOGY

THE EARLY NEW ENGLAND OR COPLEY PERIOD, 1756–1780

Born in Lebanon, Conn. (6 June 1756); damage to left eye resulting in the near loss of its sight (1760); attends Master Tisdale's School (to 1772); begins to draw, copies engravings; enters Harvard College in middle of junior year and graduates, youngest member of his class (1773); influenced there by Hogarth's *Analysis of Beauty* (London, 1753), Piranesi's prints of Imperial Rome, and Copley's newly painted portraits; returns to Lebanon, teaches school, paints classical subjects; an officer in the Continental Army (1775–1777), aide-de-camp to General Washington at Boston for some weeks; resigns commission, returns to Lebanon, paints portraits; takes John Smibert's old painting rooms at Boston and copies his copies of Italian masters; volunteers in the Rhode Island campaign; Boston again, "resumes his pencil"; there is no one to teach him.

THE WEST PERIOD, 1780–1789

Accepted as a pupil of Benjamin West in London (1780); is the earliest American college graduate to become a professional painter; incarcerated in England in reprisal for the hanging of Major André, studies a little architecture in prison; returns to America, desultory occupations; becomes a contractor for army supplies, paints a few portraits and landscapes, and returns to London and West (1784) as soon as possible after the Treaty of Paris; attends Royal Academy School, begins his "national history" series (1786) at the suggestion of West and with the encouragement of Jefferson; Paris (1787 and 1789), visits Jefferson; meets David, Mme. Vigée-Lebrun, and other French artists, is much influenced by their work and to a lesser degree by that of the old masters; travels on the Continent "with the object of finding proper engravers" for his battle pictures; returns to America to secure necessary portraits and other documentary evidence for his historical paintings.

THE "BEST" PERIOD, 1789–1794

Travels up and down the Eastern seaboard, from New Hampshire to South Carolina, collecting "heads" for his historical series and subscriptions for his engravings, studies the terrain of battlefields; paints many miniatures and some large portraits; years of feverish activity and promise.

THE PERIOD OF DISTRACTION, 1794–1804

Accompanies John Jay as secretary on diplomatic mission to London, and remains as fifth commissioner to settle the seventh article of the Jay Treaty; travels to the Continent; the French Revolution; speculates in old masters and, disastrously, in French brandy; marries Sarah Hope Harvey, an Englishwoman who is not a social asset, in London (1800); paints few portraits, chiefly of Americans, and religious pieces; the ten-year life of the commission ended (1804), he returns to America, his "political as well as [his] military glory departed."

THE FIRST NEW YORK PERIOD, 1804–1808

Intends to set up as a portrait painter in Boston, but as Gilbert Stuart is there, establishes himself in New York instead; does many posthumous portraits of Alexander Hamilton, who was killed two weeks after Trumbull's arrival; designs Meetinghouse at Lebanon, Conn.; paints panoramas of Niagara Falls and other landscapes; few portrait commissions except those for City Hall; Napoleonic wars and the Embargo Act bring depression; disappointedly returns to England with his wife and "nephew," John Trumbull Ray, concerned over the "alarming decay" of his eyesight.

THE LONDON EXPERIMENT, 1808–1816

Establishes himself handsomely in London but fails to become a fashionable portrait painter; Americans unpopular as political tension increases; commissions in the enemy country cease with the outbreak of the War of 1812; paints religious and literary subjects and a few landscapes and copies portraits after Van Dyck—probably out of boredom; heavily in debt, returns to America.

THE LONG NEW YORK PERIOD, 1816–1837

Secures highly paid commission for historical pictures in Rotunda of the new Capitol at Washington; busy with affairs of American Academy of Fine Arts (founded 1802; dissolved 1839); quarrels with the younger members who withdraw and establish the National Academy of Design (1825); Mrs. Trumbull dies (1824); few portrait commissions; copies his earlier historical series; financial difficulties; gives his pictures to Yale College in exchange for an annuity (1831); the Trumbull Gallery opened (1832)—the earliest art museum connected with an educational institution in America; a tomb constructed beneath the Gallery and his wife's remains buried there (1834); claims to be the senior surviving officer of the Revolutionary army (1832); does some traveling.

THE NEW HAVEN PERIOD, 1837–1841

Lives with his nephew-in-law, Professor Benjamin Silliman of Yale, and writes his defensive *Autobiography* (published in 1841) at his home; makes heavy-handed, large-scale copies of earlier religious pictures.

THE END AT NEW YORK, 1841–1843

Moves back to be near his medical friend, Dr. James Augustine Washington; dies 10 November 1843, and is buried beside his wife in the "Trumbull Gallery" beneath his full-length military portrait of Washington.

Tailpiece from John Frost, *An Illuminated History of North America . . .*, New York, Henry Bill, 1854.

From the *New-York Annual Advertiser*, containing "Longworth's New-York Directory," for 1819–1820, in which the painter is listed: Trumbull col. John, 27 Park-place.

BIBLIOGRAPHICAL NOTE

MANUSCRIPTS

The most extensive collection of manuscripts is in the Yale University Library; much additional information is to be found in the papers of the artist's devoted nephew-in-law, Professor Benjamin Silliman. Other manuscript material is in the Library of Congress, The Historical Society of Pennsylvania, the New York Public Library, the New-York Historical Society, the Connecticut State Library, the Wadsworth Athenaeum and the Connecticut Historical Society (both in Hartford), the Boston Athenaeum and the Massachusetts Historical Society, the Boston Public Library, the Clements Library at the University of Michigan, and the Huntington Library at San Marino, California. Many letters are in private hands.

PRINTED WORKS

William Dunlap, *History of the Rise and Progress of the Arts of Design*, 1834 (edited and reprinted in 1918) is illuminating and spirited but biased and derogatory. Trumbull's defensive reply, the *Autobiography, Reminiscences and Letters*, 1841, written when he was eighty-two and published when he was eighty-five—two years before his death—is an uneven work. Much information is to be found, curiously, in the early pages of the *American Journal of Science*, founded in 1818 by Professor Silliman of Yale (at whose New Haven home the *Autobiography* was written). John Ferguson Weir, Dean of the Yale School of the Fine Arts, adds little in his *John Trumbull*, except aesthetic appreciation and an early checklist. This slim volume was published in 1901 for the Yale Bicentennial Celebration that year. John Hill Morgan's *Early Amer-*

ican Painters, 1921, and his *Paintings by John Trumbull at Yale University*, 1926, are both scholarly and helpful contributions.

In 1953 the present author made two major contributions, the history of the American Academy (of which the old colonel was the dictatorial and domineering president) in Mary Bartlett Cowdrey's two-volume *American Academy of Fine Arts and American Art-Union* (vol. 1, pp. 2–94), published by the New-York Historical Society, and the editing of Col. Trumbull's invaluable *Autobiography* of 1841. This long out-of-print volume was the earliest extended account of an individual American artist to be written and published in this country. The annotated edition (Yale University Press) contains much information omitted—overlooked, deemed inconsequential, forgotten, or suppressed—from the 1841 life.

Ideally the Yale edition of the *Autobiography* of 1953 should be used as a companion piece to this newly revised checklist.

The present author has written over the years some forty articles for various journals having to do with different phases of Col. Trumbull's long and active life. Some were reprinted in the Yale edition of the *Autobiography,* and others—having to do with the artist's creative work—appear in the appendix of this volume.

Among these independent articles, neither reprinted in the *Works* nor in the *Autobiography,* the following may be noted:

"An Early Check List of the Paintings of John Trumbull" (valuable for chronological sequence and place where painted), *Yale University Library Gazette, 22* (April 1948), 116–23.

"Sketches by Trumbull," *Bulletin of the Metropolitan Museum of Art, 6* (June 1948), 261–63.

"John Trumbull, Colonial Limner," *Art in America, 36* (Oct. 1949), 190–201 (contains much the same information as the article directly above).

"John Trumbull Cartographer" (with Alexander O. Vietor), *Yale University Library Gazette, 23* (Jan. 1949), 137–39.

"Trumbull's Lost London Work," *The Connoisseur,* London, *74* (Dec. 1949), 121–22.

"John Trumbull, 'Patriot-Painter' in Northern New York," *New York History,* Cooperstown, N.Y., *31* (July 1950), 283–93.

"Benjamin West to His Former Pupil, John Trumbull," *Yale University Library Gazette, 25* (Jan. 1951), 104–09.

"Trumbull's List of American Historical Painters," *Yale University Library Gazette, 26* (April 1952), 193–94.

CHECKLIST

The following catalogue represents the best knowledge and judgment of the compiler. In collecting information of scattered and constantly shifting material, such as this, it is difficult to avoid sins of commission and omission, great or small. I trust they may be confined to the latter.

View of the New York City Hall in 1825

Courtesy of the Museum of the City of New York

Begun in 1803 and finished in 1812. For twenty-seven years Trumbull lived near City Hall Park. He painted thirteen portraits for the City, which still hang in their original settings at City Hall.

EXPLANATION

Portraits are painted in oils and are on canvas unless otherwise stated. A dozen or more are on wooden panels, less than a half-dozen on academy board, and a few are early attempts on copper. Bust size is usually about 30 by 25 inches, and half-, three-quarter-, and full-lengths are correspondingly greater.

Miniatures are painted in oils on wood (mahogany). There are a few exceptions (copper and heavy paper); none, so far as I know, is painted in watercolor on ivory. All but a few are cut oval in shape, approximately $3\frac{7}{8}$ by $2\frac{7}{8}$ inches. Copley used, though not exclusively, oil on copper; miniatures of the sixteenth century are usually in opaque watercolor on vellum or paper; in the seventeenth century, oil on wood or metal was often employed; and in the eighteenth, transparent watercolor on ivory was the favorite medium. There are a great many "Trumbull" miniatures on ivory, usually initialed "J.T.," all of which I believe are fraudulent.

Portrait sketches are on paper, usually in pencil. The heads, the chief source for those in the historical paintings, are approximately the same size as those in the miniatures. Many of these drawings were used, without change of size, for the portrait engravings.

Signatures are rare; only a few of the paintings are signed; some are also dated. Note is made of this except in the case of the too numerous drawings. None of the miniatures is signed or initialed, but some have notations in the artist's hand pasted on the back. Some of the drawings bear information of time and place. Fraudulent paintings, miniatures, and drawings are usually signed or initialed and dated.

Historical pictures are designated by the following shortened forms. The numbers given after each portrait correspond to the key.

> *Bunker's Hill: The Battle of Bunker's Hill, Boston, 17 June 1775*
> *Declaration: The Declaration of Independence, Philadelphia, 4 July 1776*
> *Gibraltar: The Sortie Made by the Garrison of Gibraltar, 27 November 1781*
> *Princeton: The Death of General Mercer at the Battle of Princeton, 3 January 1777*
> *Quebec: The Death of General Montgomery, in the Attack on Quebec, 31 December 1775*
> *Resignation: The Resignation of General Washington, Annapolis, 23 December 1783*
> *Saratoga: The Surrender of General Burgoyne at Saratoga, 16 October 1777*
> *Trenton: The Capture of the Hessians at Trenton, 26 December 1776*
> *Yorktown: The Surrender of Lord Cornwallis at Yorktown, 19 October 1781*

The combat units or staff assignments of officers represented in the battle pictures at the time of the event are indicated, so far as possible.

Abbreviated military titles are included only if the subject was painted in uniform. If the subject is in one of the historical pictures, the rank is that of the date of the event, otherwise it is that of the time the portrait was painted.

In some instances it is impossible to determine the source for the portraits in the historical pictures. Trumbull's usual practice was to paint his subjects from life, either in miniature on mahogany (in oils) or in pencil on paper (most of the forged portrait drawings are pen-and-ink or pen-and-wash). For the deceased and for those who for some reason were not available, he had recourse to memory, to description by friends, prints, and family portraits. He made use, for example, of the portraits of the prolific Charles Willson Peale at Philadelphia when he was in that city in the early 1790s; the likeness of General Mercer for the *Battle of Princeton* was derived from the study of the general's sons. For the *Declaration of Independence* Trumbull did thirty-six members of the Continental Congress from life, nine from portraits by others, one from memory, and one "from description aided by memory." The source of General Putnam in *Bunker's Hill* is debatable; how many of the high-ranking British officers sat for the ex-rebel presents an insoluble problem. During his long years in England he probably relied to some extent on engravings. The scrupulous artist, we may be certain, employed the best sources within reach.

Civilian titles (governor, judge, representative, etc.), except ecclesiastical and medical, are omitted, as they too often require chronological qualifications.

Portraits of women are listed under their maiden or married names, depending on when they were painted, and are cross-referenced in all but a few cases.

Foreign nationality is indicated.

Trumbull, a Harvard graduate (having the unique distinction of being buried at Yale beneath the Yale University Art Gallery, successor of the old Trumbull Gallery), painted thirty-four members of his own college, plus fifteen recipients of honorary degrees, making a total of forty-nine Harvard men. He did portraits of twenty-four graduates of Yale and nineteen recipients of honorary degrees, a total of forty-three.

It is interesting to note that Trumbull, the painter of "V.I.P.s," did the portraits of thirty-seven members of the American Philosophical Society (Philadelphia, founded in 1743), of which he was a member (No. 570); thirty-two of the American Academy of Arts and Sciences (Boston, 1780), of which he was a member; nineteen of the Massachusetts Historical Society (Boston, 1791); thirty-one of the American Academy of the Fine Arts (New York, 1802 to 1839), of which he was both a founding member and, for nineteen years, its president; fourteen of the Connecticut Academy of Arts and Sciences (New Haven, 1799), of which he was a member; and forty-two of the New-York Historical Society (New York, 1804), of which he was also a member and vice-president. Naturally, there are duplications in college, academy, and society membership.

Trumbull painted ninety-five members of the Society of the Cincinnati (in the affairs of which he was active), including George Washington, Alexander Hamilton, Charles Cotesworth Pinckney, Thomas Pinckney, and Morgan Lewis, all presidents-general; Horatio Gates, Thomas Mifflin, Henry Knox, and John Brooks, vice-presidents-general; and Otho Holland Williams, assistant secretary-general.

Additional information, if available, has been added for lost pictures, as an extra means of identification.

Since the artist painted chiefly prominent personages, other biographical data have been kept to a minimum and usually omitted for those represented in the historical scenes.

Note has been made of portraits and scenes used on United States postage stamps and paper currency—whereby Trumbull's work has become familiar to millions (see Generals George Washington, Nathanael Greene, and Rufus Putnam, the *Declaration* and *Saratoga* for the former and Alexander Hamilton for the latter). To cite all the engravings, on metal and wood, after the artist's paintings, confined even to those produced during his lifetime, would overburden this short-title list and is left for the catalogue raisonné—should such ever be published.

A detailed catalogue raisonné, including a record of erroneously and fraudulently attributed pictures, is maintained at the Yale University Art Gallery. Record of previous ownership, frequently long and involved, included in the catalogue raisonné, has been omitted for the sake of brevity in the following list, except in a few instances, as an added means of identification, involving replicas of the same original picture.

Reference is made by number to the sixty-eight early works painted before 1779, listed in the not-always-trustworthy *Autobiography,* pp. 59–62, of which but twenty-two have been located. Other than maps and architectural drawings (which Trumbull did not regard as "art"), ten portraits and two classical and two religious subjects, all painted before the artist's first voyage to Europe in May 1780, unrecorded in the *Autobiography,* are included herein. Much of Trumbull's *juvenilia,* like that of most artists, has disappeared.

Place abbreviations: Words in parentheses are omitted.

    Art Institute of Chicago (Chicago, Illinois)
    Chicago Historical Society (Chicago, Illinois)
    Columbia University (New York, New York)
    Connecticut Historical Society (Hartford, Connecticut)
    Detroit Institute of Arts (Detroit, Michigan)
    Fordham (University Library, New York, New York)
    Harvard (University, Cambridge, Massachusetts)
    Massachusetts Historical Society (Boston, Massachusetts)
    Metropolitan Museum of Art (New York, New York)
    Museum of the City of New York (New York, New York)
    New-York Historical Society (New York, New York)
    New York Public Library (New York, New York)
    Pennsylvania Academy (of Fine Arts, Philadelphia, Pennsylvania)
    The Historical Society of Pennsylvania (Philadelphia, Pennsylvania)
    Princeton (University Library, Princeton, New Jersey)
    Yale (University, New Haven, Connecticut)

The indenture made between the artist and the President and Fellows of Yale College on 19 December 1831 comprises the "eight original paintings of the American revolution" (historically the most important of all of the painter's work), thirty "miniature portraits of persons distinguished during the Revolution" ("painted in the artist's best days . . . only rivaled by the exquisitely beautiful heads painted in the small historical pictures"—William Dunlap), the bust portraits of Washington, Hamilton, King, and Gore, *Peter the Great at Narva* ("a picture of no merit"—William Dunlap), and eight dull religious pieces: a total of fifty-one items. These can be readily recognized in the following list by the Yale catalogue numbers "1832. — —." As it was agreed that "said paintings shall never be sold, alienated, divided or dispersed, but shall always be kept together," they may not be lent. Other Trumbull paintings in the Yale University Art Gallery are not subject to this restriction. It should be noted that Trumbull refers to the eight historical paintings as the *originals*. (One of the two original copies of the indenture, printed in the *Autobiography,* is in the Yale University Library.)

Most of the following attributions can be documented, and dates and places of execution verified; some, however, cannot, and attributions are based on stylistic evidence alone. In some instances pictures which I have been unable to see and study, or concerning which I have some reservations, have been included with an interrogation mark in parentheses directly after the subject. Dates and places have been questioned in the same way. I wish to emphasize that attributions unsupported by documentary evidence, as well as omission of hundreds of paintings and drawings which I believe are erroneously ascribed to the artist, represent only my personal—and fallible—opinion.

All but a few of the quotations in the checklist are from Trumbull's scattered papers. To cite each one would overburden the text, which has purposely been kept to a minimum. Others are from the Silliman sales catalogues or from the 1844 auction sale broadside.

PORTRAITS

A

LIEUT. COL. SIR ROBERT ABERCROMBY (1740–1827), British, 37th Regt. of Foot.
No. 13 in *Bunker's Hill* (not from life). (See Figs. 145 and 146)

ELIZA ACKLEY (see MRS. JOSEPH CONSTANT).

JOHN ADAMS (1735–1826), Signer, first Vice President and second President of the United States.
1787, London, painted in directly; *Autobiography*, pp. 147–48.
No. 31 in *Declaration*. (See Figs. 158 and 159)

Miniature, 1793, Philadelphia, signed and dated on back.
From the artist for the Trumbull Gallery, New Haven, Conn.
Yale, Trumbull Collection, no. 1832.22. (Fig. 108)

Bust, probably 1793, Philadelphia.
Gift of Andrew Craigie in 1794 to Harvard, no. H73. (Fig. 1)

Bust, probably at the same time and place.
Formerly property of John Jay.
Now owned by the children of the late Mrs. William J. Iselin, on loan to "Bedford House," Katonah, N.Y.

"A full length portrait of the late president, Mr. Adams, by Trumbull executed in good style and a faithful likeness," exhibited (no. 16) at the "Columbian Gallery at the Pantheon, no. 80, Greenwich Street, near the Battery," New York, owned by Edward Savage 1802–03.
Unlocated.

SAMUEL ADAMS (1722–1803), Revolutionary Statesman, Signer.
No. 7 in *Declaration*, 1791, Boston. (See Figs. 158 and 159)

MAJ. ROGER ALDEN (1748?–1836), Revolutionary officer.
"Small head—not bad," signed "J.T." and dated "1778," Lebanon, Conn. (red sash across shoulder by another hand); *Autobiography*, no. 34.
Mrs. Roger Alden Derby, New York, N.Y. (Fig. 2)

SARAH ALLEN (see MRS. JULIUS SMITH).

WILLIAM ALLEN (1784–1868), clergyman, author, President of Bowdoin College.
Miniature, 1827, New York.
Yale, Trumbull Collection, no. 1832.73. (Fig. 109)

FISHER AMES (1758–1808), statesman, political writer.
Miniature, 1792, Philadelphia, signed and dated on back.
Yale, Trumbull Collection, no. 1832.31. (Fig. 107)

SARAH ANNIS (see MRS. THOMAS SULLY).

MISS S. (for Susan?) APTHORP.
"Small head," on oval copper plate, 1778, Boston; *Autobiography,* no. 61.
Unlocated.

JANE ARDEN (see MRS. ALEXANDER HOSACK).

MAJ. JOHN ARMSTRONG (1758–1843), aide-de-camp to Gen. Gates.
No. 22 in *Saratoga, ca.* 1816, New York(?). (See Figs. 184 and 185)

B

EUNICE BACKUS (see MRS. JONATHAN TRUMBULL, JR.).

SARAH BACKUS (see MRS. DAVID TRUMBULL).

FRANCIS BACON (1561–1626), English philosopher and statesman.
From a print, 1772–73, at Cambridge, Mass.; possibly one of the "six small portraits of eminent men ... given to Isaiah Doane"; *Autobiography,* nos. 10–15.
Unlocated.

GOLDSBROW BANYAR (1724–1815), Deputy Secretary of the Colony of New York.
Half-length, 1806, New York.
New-York Historical Society, no. 1957.48. (Fig. 3)

Replica, approximately same date.
Albany Institute of History and Art, Albany, N.Y., no. 1953.20.

CAPT. JOSÉ BARBOZA (d. 1781), Spanish Artillery.
No. 17 in *Gibraltar;* the "Dying Spaniard," for which Sir Thomas Lawrence posed. (See Figs. 198 and 199)

JOEL BARLOW (1754–1812), poet, statesman, "Hartford Wit," Minister to France.
Miniature.

Museum of Fine Arts, Boston (Ellen Kelleran Gardner Fund), no. 58.526. (Fig. 116)

ADMIRAL LOUIS, COMTE DE BARRAS (d. 1788), French.
No. 12 in *Yorktown*, 1787, Paris. (See Figs. 187 and 188)

JOSIAH BARTLETT (1729–95), physician, Signer, Governor of New Hampshire.
Pencil sketch, 1790, Exeter, N.H., dated.
New Hampshire Historical Society, Concord, N.H.

Bust, posthumous, from the sketch, 1824, New York.
Hugh and Paul Bartlett, Hillsdale, Ill., in 1949.

JOSIAH BARTLETT.
No. 3 in *Declaration*, from the sketch. (See Figs. 158 and 159)

WILLIAM BAYARD (?) (1761–1826), New York financier.
Probably after 1816 and before 1826 (copy in New-York Historical Society).
Unlocated.

EGBERT BENSON (1746–1833), statesman, Commissioner under Jay Treaty, Justice of the Supreme Court of New York.
Miniature, 1792, Philadelphia, signed and dated on back.
Yale, Trumbull Collection, no. 1832.63. (Fig. 112)

Possibly the "Portrait of a Gentleman, Lent by E. Benson," (American Academy Cat., 1817, no. 149), bust (?).
Unlocated.

Miniature, 1792, Philadelphia.
Children of the late Mrs. William J. Iselin, on loan to "Bedford House," Katonah, N.Y.

ROBERT BENSON (1739–1823), brother of the above, Clerk of the City and County of New York.
Bust, 1804, New York, signed and dated on back.
New-York Historical Society, no. 1885.3. (Fig. 4)

CARDINAL GUIDO BENTIVOGLIO (1579–1644), Italian churchman.
Bust, 1778, Boston, Mass., after John Smibert's copy (now lost) of Sir Anthony Van Dyck's full-length portrait of *ca.* 1623 in the Pitti Palace, Florence; *Autobiography*, no. 37.
Gift of Trumbull to Harvard College in 1791.
Harvard, no. H24. (Fig. 5)

DUC DE BIRON (see DUC DE LAUZUN).

SAMUEL BLODGET, JR. (1757–1814), Revolutionary officer from New Hampshire, merchant, architect, first Superintendent of Public Buildings in the District of Columbia.
> "Small whole length of Mr. Sam Blodget, sitting, in a purple morning gown . . . done in London 1784 . . . 10 Gns."
> Rev. I. Harding Hughes, Raleigh, N.C.

> An identical picture, in a harder manner, probably painted shortly before the above (in 1784, a year of abrupt stylistic change, from the "early Copley manner" to that of the current British school), unrecorded by the artist.
> Insurance Company of North America (of which the subject was a director in 1792), Philadelphia.

> (?) Pencil drawing, head only, labeled by the artist on reverse "Capt. L. Blodget, Princeton," most probably Capt. Samuel Blodget, Jr., of the 8th Continental Foot (formerly the 2d New Hampshire), which unit was present at Princeton.
> Possibly intended for inclusion in *Princeton*.
> Probably 1786, London.
> Yale, gift of Mrs. Winchester Bennett, no. 1931.66.

> "Portrait, Mr. Blodget in a Rifle dress—Recd 15 Gns . . . a beautiful little picture . . . finished in 1786," London, probably after the above study.
> Destroyed by fire about 1925.

ELIAS BOUDINOT (1740–1821), Revolutionary statesman.
> Half-length, *ca.* 1805 in New Jersey(?).
> Archibald S. Alexander, Bernardsville, N.J.

ELIZABETH BOWDOIN (see LADY TEMPLE).

MARIE BOWNE (see MRS. SAMUEL OSGOOD).

ELEANOR BOYD (see MRS. THEODORE DWIGHT, JR.).

MRS. ABRAHAM (DOROTHEA REMSEN) BRINCKERHOFF (1750–1834).
> Half-length, *ca.* 1804, New York.
> Remsen Brinckerhoff, Englewood, N.J.

> Bust, *ca.* 1804, New York.
> Mrs. Samuel Robinson Knight, Spring Lake, N.J., on loan to Monmouth County Historical Society, Freehold, N.J.

ISAAC BRONSON (1760–1839), junior surgeon Revolutionary War, banker.
> Bust, *ca.* 1805, New York.
> Bronson W. Griscom, Phillips, Me. (Fig. 6)

MRS. ISAAC (ANNA OLCOTT) BRONSON (*ca.* 1764–1850).
Same as above. (Fig. 7)

LIEUT. COL. JOHN BROOKS (1752–1825), Revolutionary officer, physician, Governor of Massachusetts.
Miniature, 1790, Philadelphia, signed and dated on back.
Yale, Trumbull Collection, no. 1832.29. (Fig. 104)

LIEUT. COL. JOHN BROOKS, 8th Massachusetts Regt.
No. 18 in *Saratoga,* from the above. (See Figs. 184 and 185)

JOHN BROWN (1757–1837), Revolutionary soldier, first Senator from Kentucky.
Miniature, 1792, Philadelphia, signed and dated on back.
Yale, Trumbull Collection, no. 1832.34. (Fig. 107)

WILLIAM BROWN (1753–1816), merchant of Norwich, Conn.
Half-length, 1804 or 1806, Norwich, Conn.
Addison Gallery, Andover, Mass., no. 1930.381.
Half-length, before 1808, probably at Norwich, Conn.
Art Institute of Chicago, no. 23.920. (Fig. 8)

MARQUESS OF BUCKINGHAM (see GEORGE NUGENT-TEMPLE-GRENVILLE).

JOSEPH TINKER BUCKINGHAM (1779–1861), editor, Senator in Massachusetts legislature.
Miniature, *ca.* 1825, New York.
Stephen Alvord Buckingham, Boston, on loan to the Museum of Fine Arts, Boston.

REV. JOSEPH BUCKMINSTER, D.D. (1751–1812), nephew of Rev. Elisha Williams and cousin of Rev. Jonathan Edwards, Yale tutor, clergyman.
Three-quarter length, between 1777 and 1779, Lebanon, Conn., or Boston, Mass.; formerly attributed to Ralph Earl.
Yale, gift of Mrs. Eliza Buckminster Lee, no. 1864.1.

CAPT. JOSEPH BUDWORTH (1756–1815), British, 72d Regt. of Foot (Royal Manchester Volunteers), aide-de-camp to Gen. Ross (changed his name to Joseph Palmer in order to inherit his wife's estates).
No. 15 in *Gibraltar,* 1784–87, London. (See Figs. 198 and 199)

ESTHER MARGARET BULL (see MRS. THOMAS CHESTER).

MRS. FREDERIC BULL (see MARY HUNTINGTON LANMAN and her sister, ABIGAIL LANMAN).

JOSEPH BULL (1736/7–1797), of Hartford, Conn.
Half-length, posthumous, after "a miserable old crayon portrait and 2 small miniatures," New Haven.
James Chetwood Beatty, San Juan, Puerto Rico.

WILLIAM GEDNEY BULL (1781–1859).
Bust, 1820s, New York.
Sir Alfred Chester Beatty, Dublin, Ireland, on exhibition at the Chester Beatty Library, Dublin. (Fig. 9)

LIEUT. GEN. JOHN BURGOYNE (1722–92), British.
No. 11 in *Saratoga,* probably not from life. (See Figs. 184 and 185)

BRIG. GEN. RICHARD BUTLER (1743–91), Revolutionary officer, Indian agent.
Miniature, 1790, Philadelphia, signed and dated on back.
Yale, Trumbull Collection, no. 1832.78. (Fig. 106)

C

COL. JOHN CADWALADER (1742–86), Pennsylvania militia.
No. 4 in *Princeton,* posthumous. (See Figs. 169 and 170)

JOHN CALDWELL CALHOUN (1782–1850), statesman, Vice President of the United States.
Miniature, 1827, New York.
Yale, Trumbull Collection, no. 1832.72. (Fig. 109)

BEN CALL, merchant.
"Head size of life," 1778, Boston; *Autobiography,* no. 51.
Unlocated.

COL. DONALD CAMPBELL, Deputy Quartermaster General, New York Dept.
Pencil sketch, idealized, London, 1785, for no. 4 in *Quebec.*
Yale, gift of Mrs. Robert F. Jefferys, no. 1952.3.2a.
No. 4 in *Quebec,* from the above. (See Figs. 152 and 153)

RACHEL CARMER (see MRS. ROBERT LENOX).

CATHERINE CARROLL (later MRS. ROBERT GOODLOE HARPER) (1778–1861).
No. 29 in *Resignation,* probably not from life. (See Figs. 203 and 204)

CHARLES CARROLL of "Carrollton" (1737–1832).
No. 16 in *Declaration, ca.* 1790, Philadelphia(?). (See Figs. 158 and 159)
No. 29 in *Resignation.* (See Figs. 203 and 204)

Mrs. Charles Carroll of "Homewood" (see Harriet Chew).

Mary (Molly) Carroll (later Mrs. Richard Caton) (1770–1846).
    No. 29 in *Resignation,* probably not from life. (See Figs. 203 and 204)

Mrs. Richard Caton (see Mary Carroll).

Giuseppe Ceracchi (1751–1802), Italian sculptor.
    Miniature, 1792, Philadelphia, signed and dated on back.
    Yale, Trumbull Collection, no. 1832.40. (Fig. 110)
    Miniature, 1792, Philadelphia.
    Metropolitan Museum of Art, no. 36.35.

Children of Charles I, "Heads of Two Boys" (Charles, 1639–85, later Charles II, and James, 1633–1701, later James II), British, after John Smibert's copy (now lost) of one of the many Van Dyck portraits.
    1778, Boston, Mass.; *Autobiography,* no. 38.
    Unlocated.

Charles II (1639–85) (see above).

Jeremiah Townley Chase (1748–1828), Member of Congress from Maryland.
    No. 19 in *Resignation, ca.* 1820 in Maryland(?). (See Figs. 203 and 204)

Samuel Chase (1741–1811), Revolutionary leader, Signer, Justice of the United States Supreme Court.
    Pencil sketch, probably *ca.* 1790 in Maryland (1st Silliman sale, no. 50).
    Estate of Hall Park McCullough, Bennington, Vt. (Fig. 131)
    No. 10 in *Declaration.* (See Figs. 158 and 159)

Maj. Gen. François Jean, Marquis de Chastellux (1734–88), French.
    No. 10 in *Yorktown,* 1787, Paris. (See Figs. 187 and 188)

Capt. Jacob Cheeseman, aide-de-camp to Gen. Montgomery (killed in action at Quebec, 1775).
    Pencil sketch, posthumous, 1785, London, for no. 2 in *Quebec.*
    Yale, gift of Mrs. Robert F. Jefferys, no. 1952.3.2b.
    No. 2 in *Quebec,* from the above. (See Figs. 152 and 153)

Mrs. John Chenevard (see Julia Seymour).

Mrs. Thomas (Esther Margaret Bull) Chester (1777–1844), of Wethersfield and Hartford, Conn., daughter of Col. Joseph Bull, wife of Thomas Chester (1764–1831,

Yale 1780, Clerk of the Court of Common Pleas in 1796 and of the Superior Court in 1806).

> 1838, New Haven.

HARRIET CHEW (later MRS. CHARLES CARROLL of "Homewood") (1775–1861).

> Miniature, 1793, Philadelphia, signed and dated on back.
> Yale, Trumbull Collection, no. 1832.59. (Figs. 114 and 117; see also Fig. 118)

SOPHIA CHEW (later MRS. HENRY PHILIPS) (1769–1841).

> Miniature, 1793, Philadelphia, signed and dated on back.
> Yale, Trumbull Collection, no. 1832.58. (Fig. 114)

LIEUT. GEN. CLAUDE GABRIEL DE CHOISY, French.

> No. 5 in *Yorktown,* 1787, Paris. (See Figs. 187 and 188)

MRS. JOHN BARKER (ANGELICA SCHUYLER) CHURCH (married 1777), CHILD (PHILIP CHURCH), AND SERVANT.

> 1784, London.
> Peter Butler Olney, Andover, Mass.

PHILIP CHURCH (1778–1861), son of the London banker.

> "Small whole length," 1784, London.
> Mrs. Philip Schuyler Church, Dayton, Ohio. (Fig. 10)

> "Smaller copy of whole length," 1784, London.
> Unlocated.

COL. JOSEPH CILLEY (1734–99), 1st New Hampshire Regt.

> No. 2 in *Saratoga,* if from life before 1794. (See Figs. 184 and 185)

ABRAHAM CLARK (1726–94).

> No. 29 in *Declaration, ca.* 1790, Philadelphia. (See Figs. 158 and 159)

JOHN INNES CLARKE (1745–1808), Rhode Island merchant.

> Half-length, *ca.* 1793, Providence, R.I.
> Chauncey Stillman, Amenia, N.Y.

MAJ. MATTHEW CLARKSON (1758–1825).

> No. 26 in *Saratoga, ca.* 1816, New York(?). (See Figs. 184 and 185)

DUCHESS OF CLEVELAND, Barbara Villiers, Countess of Castlemaine and Duchess of Cleveland (1641–1709).

> After (a copy of?) a portrait by Sir Peter Lely (ex coll. Sir Joshua Reynolds and

Charles Wilkes of New York, exhibited at the American Academy 1820, no. 36; 1824, no. 57; and 1825, no. 74).

Unlocated.

Half-length (Trumbull's copy American Academy Cat., 1825, no. 106 or 108. "Portrait of a Lady"); probably painted between 1820 and 1824.

Unlocated.

DE WITT CLINTON (1769–1828), Senator from New York, Mayor of New York City, Governor of New York, chief promoter of the Erie Canal, incorporator and third president of the American Academy of the Fine Arts.

Half-length, 1805, New York.

City Hall, New York, no. 59. (Fig. 11)

1806, New York.

Unlocated.

Replica of City Hall version, 1807, New York.

Chamber of Commerce, New York.

MRS. DE WITT (CATHERINE JONES) CLINTON (second wife, married 1819).

Half-length, to left, seated, in low-necked dress, right arm resting on chair, 1806, New York.

Unlocated.

GEORGE CLINTON (1739–1812), Revolutionary officer, seven times Governor of New York, Vice President of the United States.

Full-length, 1791, New York, signed and dated.

City Hall, New York. (Fig. 12)

GEORGE CLINTON.

No. 8 in *Declaration*, probably from the above. (See Figs. 158 and 159)

LIEUT. GEN. SIR HENRY CLINTON (1738–95), British.

No. 12 in *Bunker's Hill*, if from life between 1782 and 1786, London. (See Figs. 145 and 146)

BRIG. GEN. JAMES CLINTON (1733–1812), Continental Army.

No. 23 in *Yorktown*, 1790(?), before 1808. (See Figs. 187 and 188)

GEORGE CLYMER (1739–1813).

No. 25 in *Declaration, ca.* 1790, Philadelphia(?). (See Figs. 158 and 159)

LIEUT. COL. DAVID COBB (1748–1830), aide-de-camp to Gen. Washington.

No. 21 in *Yorktown, ca.* 1790, Massachusetts(?). (See Figs. 187 and 188)

REV. WILLIAM COCHRAN (*ca.* 1757–1833), educator, professor of classics.
  Half-length, 1821, New York.
  Columbia University, New York. (Fig. 13)

GEORGE CODWISE (173?–1816), New York merchant and shipowner.
  Half-length, *ca.* 1805, New York.
  The Mattatuck Museum, Waterbury, Conn.

MRS. GEORGE (ANNA MARIA VAN RANST) CODWISE (1740–1805), daughter of Luke van Ranst, of New York, and Elizabeth Beekman.
  Mr. and Mrs. Hubert E. Codwise, Swampscott, Mass.

JAMES CODWISE (1772, married 1797, d.?), son of George Codwise of New York and later of the Island of St. Croix, West Indies.
  Half-length, *ca.* 1805, New York.
  New-York Historical Society, no. 1952.92.

MRS. JAMES (REBECCA RODGERS) CODWISE, daughter of John Rodgers of "Mt. Victory Plantation," St. Croix.
  New-York Historical Society, no. 1952.93.

JOHN BUTLER COLES (1760–1827), New York merchant, builder of turnpikes, Alderman of New York City.
  Bust, 1805, New York.
  Deerfield Academy, Deerfield, Mass.

JOSEPH CONSTANT (1773–1819), New York merchant of French Huguenot extraction.
  Half-length, *ca.* 1816, New York.
  Walter Rumsey Marvin, Columbus, Ohio.

MRS. JOSEPH (ELIZA ACKLEY, originally Aclée) CONSTANT (married 1778).
  Same as above.

MAJ. SAMUEL COOPER (d. 1840), "formerly Captain in the Artillery of the U.S., 72 Old, full of Colour—White hair—dressed in Black."
  1828, Norwich, Conn.(?).
  Unlocated.

1ST LIEUT. SAMUEL COOPER, 2d Connecticut Regt. (killed in action at Quebec 1775).
  No. 11 in *Quebec,* posthumous. (See Figs. 152 and 153)

WILLIAM COOPER (1754–1809), founder of Cooperstown, N.Y., first judge of Otsego County, Member of Congress.

Probably "head with hands," as the artist received $150, the price for that size portrait, 1806, Albany.

Lost in the destruction of "Otsego Hall," Cooperstown, in 1852(?).

Bust, somewhat damaged, possibly the above, but more likely a copy of the lost(?) original made by Ezra Ames (1768–1836) of Albany.

Dr. H. S. Fenimore Cooper, Cooperstown, N.Y.

1ST LIEUT. WILLIAM CUPPAGE, British, Royal Regt. of Artillery.
No. 11 in *Gibraltar*, 1784–87, London. (See Figs. 198 and 199)

COMMODORE SIR ROGER CURTIS (1746–1816), British.
No. 3 in *Gibraltar*, 1784–87, London. (See Figs. 198 and 199)

SAMUEL CURZON(?) (1753–86), West Indian merchant of Baltimore and London.
Bust(?), 1786, London.
Unlocated. (A possible copy by an unknown hand of this lost portrait was owned by a descendant, the late Dr. J. Hall Pleasants of Baltimore, Md.)

BRIG. ADAM PHILIPPE, COMTE DE CUSTINE (1740–93), French.
No. 3 in *Yorktown*, 1787, Paris. (See Figs. 187 and 188)

ELEANOR (NELLY) PARKE CUSTIS (later MRS. LAWRENCE LEWIS) (1779–1852).
Miniature, 1792, Philadelphia, signed and dated on back.
Yale, Trumbull Collection, no. 1832.55. (Fig. 114)

Miniature, 1792, Philadelphia.
"Kenmore," Fredericksburg, Va.

ELEANOR PARKE CUSTIS.
No. 30 in *Resignation*, probably not from life. (See Figs. 203 and 204)

ELIZABETH PARKE CUSTIS (later MRS. THOMAS B. LAW) (1776–1832).
No. 30 in *Resignation*, probably not from life. (See Figs. 203 and 204)

MARTHA PARKE CUSTIS (later MRS. THOMAS PETER) (1777–1854).
No. 30 in *Resignation*, probably not from life. (See Figs. 203 and 204)

MR. (———?) CUTLER.
"Small," 1778, Boston, Mass.; *Autobiography*, no. 43.
Unlocated.

D

TRISTRAM DALTON (1738–1817), Senator from Massachusetts.
Miniature, 1792, Philadelphia, signed and dated on back.
Yale, Trumbull Collection, no. 1832.41. (Fig. 110)

Col. Joseph François Louis Charles, Comte de Damas (1758–1829), French.
>No. 9 in *Yorktown*, 1787, Paris. (See Figs. 187 and 188)

Bartholomew Dandridge (1773/4–1802), secretary to Rufus King, American Legation, London.
>Bust, *ca.* 1800, London.
>Yale, bequest of Gherardi Davis, no. 1941.807. (Fig. 14)

>(?) Half-length, similar to the above.
>Mrs. Hollis E. Suits, Kirkwood, Mo.

Thomas Dawes (either Col. Thomas Dawes, 1733–1809, Boston architect, or his son, Thomas Dawes, 1757–1825, Massachusetts jurist).
>"Head," 1779, Boston; *Autobiography*, no. 66.
>Unlocated.

Lieut. Col. Henry Dearborn (1751–1829), 3d New Hampshire Regt., *ca.* 1790(?).
>No. 7 in *Saratoga*. (See Figs. 184 and 185)

Capt. Daniel Delevan (1757–1835), Revolutionary officer.
>Bust, *ca.* 1805, New York.
>New-York Historical Society, no. 1895.2.

Elias Hasket Derby (1766–1826), merchant of Salem, Mass.
>Bust, *ca.* 1816, New York (?).
>Mrs. Richard Derby, Oyster Bay, N.Y.

Col. Christien(?) (b. 1752), or Col. Guillaume(?) (b. 1754), both Marquis des Deux-Ponts, French.
>No. 1 in *Yorktown*, 1787, Paris. (See Figs. 187 and 188)

John Dickinson (1732–1808).
>No. 45 in *Declaration, ca.* 1792, Philadelphia. (See Figs. 158 and 159)

Brig. Gen. Philemon Dickinson (1739–1809), New Jersey Militia.
>No. 13 in *Trenton, ca.* 1790. (See Figs. 164 and 165)

James Duane (1733–97), jurist, Mayor of New York.
>Bust, 1805, New York, copied from the Robert Edge Pine portrait now in the New-York Historical Society.
>City Hall, New York. (Fig. 15)

Asher Brown Durand (1796–1886), engraver of Trumbull's *Declaration of Independence*, landscape painter.
>Half-length, on wood, 1826, New York.
>New-York Historical Society, no. 1895.13. (Fig. 16)

HENRY WILLIAM DWIGHT (1788–1845), member of Congress from Massachusetts.
Miniature, 1827, New York.
Yale, Trumbull Collection, no. 1832.71. (Fig. 109)

THEODORE DWIGHT, SENIOR (1764–1846), brother of Rev. Timothy Dwight of Yale, lawyer, editor, author.
Bust, 1828, New York, "high expansive forehead almost bald—a little white hair—sallow complexion—peculiar black penetrating Eye—Dress Black—background Umber and white—architecture—Five Sittings."
Unlocated.

THEODORE DWIGHT, JR. (1796–1866), son of the above, author, educator.
Half-length, on composition board, 1828, New York.
Miss Isobel Ferris, Bronxville, N.Y.

MRS. THEODORE (ELEANOR BOYD) DWIGHT, JR. (1805–70), married 1827.
Same as above.

REV. TIMOTHY DWIGHT (1752–1817), Congregational minister, President of Yale College.
Bust, 1807, New York.
Yale, a gift of T. Dwight Partridge, no. 1948.5.
Replica, three-quarter length, posthumous, 1817, New York, painted for Yale College.
Yale, no. 1817.1. (Fig. 17)

AMELIA DYER (see MRS. JOSEPH TRUMBULL).

JAMES DYER, British, Benjamin West's bodyservant.
"Head," 1784, London.
Unlocated.
"Large head," 1784, London.
Unlocated.
"Small full length—in the uniform of the Horse Grenadier Guards, with his horse."
Unlocated.

E

LIEUT. GEN. GEORGE AUGUSTUS ELIOTT, later Lord Heathfield and Baron of Gibraltar (1717–90), British officer, Governor of Gibraltar.
Drawing, 1784–87, London (1st Silliman sale, no. 105).
Connecticut Historical Society.
No. 1 in *Gibraltar,* from the above. (See Figs. 198 and 199)

WILLIAM ELLERY (1727–1820), Signer, Member of Congress from Rhode Island.
> Pencil sketch, 1791, Newport, R.I., dated (1st Silliman sale, no. 47).
> Unlocated.

> No. 24 in *Declaration,* before 1794, probably from the above. (See Figs. 158 and
> > 159)
> No. 18 in *Resignation,* same. (See Figs. 203 and 204)

EDWARD ELLICE, British, probably Edward Ellis, Sr. (1781–1863), merchant and M.P.
> "Head," before 1815, London.
> Unlocated.

"MR. ELLIS, an English merchant."
> 1844 auction sale, no. 17, purchased by "Lanman"; probably the above.
> Unlocated.

"MR. ELIS, now a member of Parliament, taken when young" (1844 auction sale, no.
21), probably Edward Ellis, Jr. (1810–80), M.P., son of the above.
> Before 1815, London.
> Unlocated.

WILLIAM ELLICE, British watercolorist.
> Half-length, *ca.* 1800, London (compare with "Mr. Palmer an Artist of London").
> Mrs. Alexander M. White, Oyster Bay, N.Y.

OLIVER ELLSWORTH (1745–1807), Senator from Connecticut, Chief Justice of the
United States Supreme Court.
> Miniature, 1792, Philadelphia.
> Yale, Trumbull Collection, no. 1832.44. (Fig. 110)

MRS. JOHN ERVING (see MISS A. SHEAFFE).

LIEUT. COL. BENJAMIN G. EYRE (d. 1781), 2d Battalion (Philadelphia) Pennsylvania
Militia.
> No. 8 in *Princeton.* (See Figs. 169 and 170)

F

T. FARMAR(?), possibly THOMAS FARMER, New York merchant.
> Bust(?), "Portrait of a Gentleman, Lent by T. Farmar" (American Academy Cat.,
> > 1818, no. 167).
> Unlocated.

WILLIAM FARNUM (1760–1829), volunteer at Lexington and Concord, a gentleman of
no profession; "his peculiar excellence . . . lies in the science of politeness" (John
Quincy Adams).

Half-length, 1784, London.
Miss Louisa Farnham Cobb, Barnstable, Mass.

COL. HANS AXEL, COMTE DE FERSEN (1755–1810).
No. 8 in *Yorktown,* French, 1787, Paris. (See Figs. 187 and 188)

MAJ. NICHOLAS FISH (1758–1833), 2d New York Regt.
No. 34 in *Yorktown,* before 1794. (See Figs. 187 and 188)

WILLIAM FLOYD (1734–1821).
No. 13 in *Declaration, ca.* 1791. (See Figs. 158 and 159)

ABIEL FOSTER (1735–1806).
No. 11 in *Resignation,* before 1794. (See Figs. 203 and 204)

DR. JOHN WAKEFIELD FRANCIS (1789–1861), physician, antiquarian.
Half-length, 1819, New York.
Presbyterian Hospital, New York. (Fig. 18)

BENJAMIN FRANKLIN (1706–90), Signer, author, statesman, diplomat, scientist, philan-
thropist.
"Head . . . a fur cap—from a French print" (after the 1777 engraving by Augustin
de Saint-Aubin after Charles Nicolas Cochin), 1778, Boston; *Autobiography,*
no. 39.
Yale, John Hill Morgan Fund, no. 1960.13. (Fig. 19)
No. 35 in *Declaration,* 1790, Philadelphia. (See Figs. 158 and 159)
See *Treaty of Paris,* 1783.

MARIA FRANKLIN (see MRS. DE WITT CLINTON).

MRS. WALTER FRANKLIN (see MRS. SAMUEL OSGOOD).

WILLIAM TEMPLE FRANKLIN (*ca.* 1760–1823), grandson of Benjamin Franklin, his sec-
retary in Paris.
Miniature, 1790, Philadelphia, signed and dated on back.
Yale, Trumbull Collection, no. 1832.24. (Fig. 108)

LIEUT. EDWARD BOSCAWEN FREDERICK (b. 1762), British, 72d Regt. of Foot (Royal Manchester Volunteers), aide-de-camp to Gen. Ross.
No. 14 in *Gibraltar,* 1784–87, London. (See Figs. 198 and 199)

G

GAHN, probably HENRY GAHN (d. 1834), Consul General for Sweden at New York.
Portrait of "Gahn" mentioned in packing list of 23 June 1808, included item 46,

New-York Historical Society, before 1808, New York.
Unlocated.

MISS (———?) GALE, "the betrothed of Mr. Hudson [Jonathan Trumbull Hudson],
Italian Complexion, dark & rich Colour—full dark expressive Eye—black hair—Dress
black Silk—with a lace kerchief. Sitting on a deep red Settee—Umber coloured. Archi-
tecture background—both hands grouped together."
Half-length, 1828, Hartford.
Unlocated.

GEORGE GALLAGHER (b. 1786), New York merchant.
Half-length, on wood, 1826, New York.
Mrs. Robert A. Eyerman, Bear Creek, Pa.

COL. THOMAS GARDNER, Massachusetts Regt. (mortally wounded at Bunker's Hill
1775).
No. 4 in *Bunker's Hill,* from memory. (See Figs. 145 and 146)

MAJ. GEN. HORATIO GATES (1728/9–1806), Revolutionary officer, Trumbull's superior
at Ticonderoga.
Pencil sketch, 1790, New York (1st Silliman sale, no. 35).
Metropolitan Museum of Art, no. 06.1346.1. (Fig. 132)
No. 14 in *Saratoga,* from the above. (See Figs. 184 and 185)

CORNELIUS VAN DER GEEST (1577–1647), Dutch.
Copied after the portrait by Sir Anthony Van Dyck, now in the National Gallery,
    London (there known as "Gervartius" until 1864), 1815, London, hands
    added by Trumbull.
New-York Historical Society, no. 68.

GEORGE III (1738–1820).
"Small head," 1784, London, copy after Benjamin West (possibly that in Bucking-
    ham Palace).
Unlocated.

ELBRIDGE GERRY (1744–1814), Member of Congress from Massachusetts.
No. 20 in *Declaration, ca.* 1789. (See Figs. 158 and 159)
No. 3 in *Resignation.* (See Figs. 203 and 204)

GERVARTIUS or "GOVITUS" (see CORNELIUS VAN DER GEEST).

BRIG. GEN. MORDECAI GIST (1742/3–92), Continental Army.
No. 24 in *Yorktown, ca.* 1790. (See Figs. 187 and 188)

BRIG. GEN. JOHN GLOVER (1732–97), Revolutionary officer.
  Pencil sketch, 1790, Marblehead, Mass.
  Estate of Hall Park McCullough, Bennington, Vt.

COL. JOHN GLOVER, 14th Continental Infantry.
  No. 14 in *Trenton,* before 1797, probably from the above. (See Figs. 164 and 165)

BRIG. GEN. JOHN GLOVER, Continental Army.
  No. 24 in *Saratoga,* same. (See Figs. 184 and 185)

WILLIAM GILES GODDARD (see *Portrait of an Unknown Man*).

CHAUNCEY GOODRICH (1759–1815), Senator from Connecticut.
  Bust, *ca.* 1804, Hartford, Conn.(?).
  Mrs. Henriette de S. Lehman, Saratoga, Calif.

CHAUNCEY ALLEN GOODRICH (1790–1860), clergyman, educator, lexicographer, Yale professor.
  Bust, on wood, 1827, New Haven.
  Bowdoin College Museum of Art, Brunswick, Me., no. 1954.29. (Fig. 20)

CHRISTOPHER GORE (1758–1827), fellow member with the artist on the commission for the adjustment of claims under Article 7 of the Jay Treaty at London, Governor of Massachusetts.
  Miniature, 1790 or 1793, Boston.
  Mrs. John Morse Elliot, Boston, Mass.

  Half-length, 1800, London.
  From the artist for the Trumbull Gallery, New Haven. (American Academy Cats.,
    1816, no. 17, and 1831, no. 15).
  Yale, Trumbull Collection, no. 1832.18. (Fig. 21)

  On wood, half-length, 1800, London.
  Purchased by subscription in 1844, the year after the artist's death, Massachusetts
    Historical Society.

  Bust, after 1815.
  Destroyed by fire 1949, belonged to Mrs. Edward King Davis, Tuxedo Park, N.Y.
  "Head size," exhibited at the American Academy of Fine Arts in 1824, possibly the
    above.
  Unlocated.

  Half-length, posthumous replica of Yale portrait, 1834, New York.
  Harvard, no. H56.

Mrs. Christopher (Rebecca Amory Payne) Gore (1759–1834).
>   Bust, *ca.* 1800, London.
>   Mrs. John Morse Elliot, Boston, Mass.

John Gore, Jr.
>   Letter, 13 April 1844, Vienna, from Horatio Greenough, the sculptor, and the husband of Eliza Ingersoll Gore, daughter of John Gore, Jr., to his brother Henry Greenough, painter: "My wife desires me to thank you for your beautiful copy of her father's portrait, which she prefers to the original by Trumbull, that being stiff and hard" (*Letters of Horatio Greenough*, Boston, 1887, p. 174).
>   Unlocated.

Children of Archibald Gracie(?) (Archibald Gracie, 1755–1829, married Esther Rogers by whom he had eight children).
>   Possibly the "Portrait of Children. Lent by A. Gracie, Esq." (American Academy Cat., 1817, no. 96).
>   Unlocated.

Mrs. William (Elizabeth Stoughton Wolcott) Gracie (1795–1814).
>   Half-length, *ca.* 1816, posthumous, New York.
>   New-York Historical Society, no. 1941.486.

Edward Gray (d. 1805 or 1806).
>   "Size of life," 1778, Boston; *Autobiography,* no. 41.
>   Unlocated.

Mrs. Edward (possibly Mary Paddock(?), d. 1789) Gray.
>   Same as above, *Autobiography,* no. 42.
>   Unlocated.

Admiral François Joseph Paul, Comte de Grasse-Tilly (1723–88), French.
>   No. 13 in *Yorktown,* 1787, Paris. (See Figs. 187 and 188)

Col. John Greaton (1741–83), 3d Massachusetts Regt.
>   No. 6 in *Saratoga,* posthumous. (See Figs. 184 and 185)

Maj. Gen. Nathanael Greene (1742–86), Revolutionary officer.
>   Miniature, 1792, Philadelphia, "from the only original picture remaining," probably after Charles Willson Peale's 1783 portrait, signed and dated on back (used on U.S. postage stamp, no. 785, 1¢, green, 1936).
>   Yale, Trumbull Collection, no. 1832.25. (Fig. 104)

Same, replica of the above.

Mrs. Brenton G. Meader, Cranston, R.I.

Drawing, 1791, Providence, R.I.

Estate of Hall Park McCullough, Bennington, Vt. (Fig. 133)

No. 11 in *Trenton,* from the above. (See Figs. 164 and 165)

MLLE. GRENIER DE BREDA, French.

Pencil drawing, 1786 on the Rhine; *Autobiography,* pl. 12.

The Five Daughters of Mrs. Winchester Bennett, New Haven, Conn.

GEORGE NUGENT-TEMPLE-GRENVILLE, first Marquess of Buckingham (1753–1813), British, Lord Lieutenant of Ireland.

Small full-length, begun at London, finished in 1828, New York.

Yale, gift of Robert Gilmor, no. 1845.1.

LIEUT. COL. JOHN FACHERAUD GRIMKÉ (1752–1819), Revolutionary officer, statesman, jurist.

Miniature, 1791, Charleston, S.C., signed and dated on back.

Yale, Trumbull Collection, no. 1832.54. (Fig. 111)

ELIZABETH GRIMKÉ (see MRS. JOHN RUTLEDGE).

2D LIEUT. THOMAS GROSVENOR (1744–1825), 3d Connecticut Regt.

No. 9 in *Bunker's Hill,* before 1786 in Connecticut. (See Figs. 145 and 146)

In "Lieutenant Grosvenor and his Negro Servant," study for *Bunker's Hill.*

Yale, Mabel Brady Garvan Collection, no. 1932.302.

H

ALEXANDER HAMILTON (1757–1804), Aide and Military Secretary to Gen. Washington, leader of the Federalist party, first secretary of the United States Treasury.

Jay Type

Bust, painted for John Jay probably before July 1792 at Philadelphia(?).

John Jay and descendants, "Bedford House," Katonah, N.Y.; more recently William Jay Iselin.

Gift of the Avalon Foundation, in 1952, to the National Gallery of Art, Washington, D.C., no. NGA 1081. (Fig. 22)

"An original, painted at Washington in 1792, now in the possession of the family of the late Gov. Wolcott." (*Autobiography,* p. 433, 1841, when the artist was 85 years. Note: Washington was not planned until 1791); possibly one of the following.

Lost(?).

"Copied in 1832" (item 38, p. 433 *Autobiography*) from the above, at New York,
   for the Trumbull Gallery at Yale College, New Haven, Conn. (opened to the
   public in 1832).
Yale, no. 1832.11. (Fig. 23)

Head of Hamilton . . . left at Mr. West's, Newman Street, London . . . 1797.
Unidentified; lost(?).

Replica, full-length, in gray coat, from above in 1792 (engraved by Robert Field,
   1806).
Painted for the Chamber of Commerce, New York, no. 50.

Later replica, bust.
Gift of George Atkinson Ward to the Essex Institute, Salem, Mass., no. 106,821.

Replica, bust, but coat dark, after 1804.
Metropolitan Museum of Art, no. 81.11.

Replica, bust; for Gov. Wolcott.
Unlocated.

Ceracchi Type

Posthumous (from one of the marble busts of 1791 by the visiting Italian sculptor,
   Giuseppe Ceracchi [Fig. 24]), full-length, in black coat, 1805, New York.
Painted for City Hall, New York. (Fig. 27)
Head from full-length portrait used on:
   $1,000 gold notes, series of 1907, 1922, and 1928
   $1,000 Federal Reserve note, series of 1918
   $50 certificate of indebtedness, series of 1907
   $10 national currency, series of 1929
   $10 Federal Reserve notes, series of 1928 and 1934
   $10 silver certificates, series of 1933 and 1934
   U.S. postage stamp, no. 1053, $5.00, black, 1956

Replica, bust, 1806, New York.
S. S. Perkins, Boston, 1806, to Robert C. Winthrop, to the Museum of Fine Arts,
   Boston (bequest of Robert C. Winthrop), no. 94.167. (Fig. 25)

Replica, bust, 1806, New York.
Senator George Cabot of Massachusetts, to Henry Cabot, to Anna Cabot Lodge, to
   Henry Cabot Lodge, Beverly, Mass.

Replica, bust 1806, New York.
Painted for Dr. David Hosack, the surgeon in attendance at Hamilton's fatal duel
   with Aaron Burr.

Mellon Educational and Charitable Trust to the National Gallery of Art, Washington, D.C., no. NGA 494.

Replica, "head," 1806, New York, "Received from J. P. Davis of Boston [Isaac P. Davis, 1771–1855, of Boston?]—$100"; probably one of the above or following.
Unlocated.

Replica, bust, 1804–08, New York.
Gift of Thomas J. Bryan to the New-York Historical Society, no. 1867.305.

Replica, bust, 1804–08, New York, presented by the artist to David B. Ogden, law partner of Alexander Hamilton, in 1829.
To Rev. Charles Hoffman, to Charles F. Dillon, to Silas Wodell, to Katherine Wodell, to Edsel B. Ford, to Ford Motor Company.
The White House, Washington, D.C. (Fig. 26)

Replica (partially restored), bust, 1804–08, New York.
Belonging to the Hamilton family; anonymous loan to the Museum of the City of New York.

Late replica, bust with hand, New York.
Arthur Meeker, Chicago, to Albert H. Wiggin, New York.
Lynde Selden, New York, on loan to The Chase Manhattan Bank, New York.

(?) Bust, possibly a late replica finished by another hand.
Unlocated.

Type Unknown

Full-length, life-size (American Academy Cats., 1817, no. 94; 1819, no. 25; 1820, no. 29; 1821, no. 31; 1822, no. 12; and 1823, no. 13); possibly one of the above.
Unlocated.

"Feby. 19th. Recd. of Mr. Vaughan for Hamilton's portrait—£31"; possibly one of the above.
Unlocated.

"Mr. Hamilton," probably one of the above (Royal Academy, London, 1811, no. 427).
Unlocated.

"Weaver's Hamilton," so listed by the artist, possibly one of the above.

No. 31 in *Yorktown, ca.* 1790, as lieut. col. and principal aide-de-camp to Gen. Washington. (See Figs. 187 and 188)

A. (ABIJAH?) HAMMOND (Abijah, Lieut., Continental Artillery, d. 1832).
    1806, New York.
    Unlocated.

GEORGE HAMMOND (1763–1853), British, peace commissioner, first British Minister to the United States.
    Miniature, 1793, Philadelphia, signed and dated on back.
    Yale, Trumbull Collection, no. 1832.23. (Fig. 108)
    (?) Another.
    Unlocated.

JOHN HANCOCK (1736/7–93), Boston merchant, Treasurer of Harvard College, President of the Continental Congress, first Signer, first Governor of the Commonwealth of Massachusetts.
    Pencil sketch, 1790, Boston, dated (1st Silliman sale, no. 48).
    Unlocated.
    No. 43 in *Declaration,* probably from the above. (See Figs. 158 and 159)

BRIG. GEN. EDWARD HAND (1744–1802), Adjutant General Continental Army.
    No. 26 in *Yorktown,* 1791, Philadelphia. (See Figs. 187 and 188)

"LIEUT. COL. HUGO HANOVERIAN" (see LIEUT. COL. ERNST AUGUST VON HUGO).

MAJ. JOHN HARDY, British, 56th Regt. of Foot.
    No. 7 in *Gibraltar,* 1784–87, London. (See Figs. 198 and 199)

SAMUEL HARDY (1758–85), Member of Congress from Virginia.
    No. 20 in *Resignation,* posthumous. (See Figs. 203 and 204)

MRS. ROBERT GOODLOE HARPER (see CATHERINE CARROLL).

BENJAMIN HARRISON (1726?–91).
    No. 5 in *Declaration,* "from description aided by memory." (See Figs. 158 and 159)

LIEUT. COL. ROBERT HANSON HARRISON (1745–90), Military Secretary to Gen. Washington.
    No. 7 in *Trenton,* from memory. (See Figs. 164 and 165)
    Tracing of head.
    Yale, no. 1947.504.

MAJ. ELNATHAN HASKELL (1755–1825), Revolutionary officer.
    Miniature, 1791, Charleston, S.C., signed and dated on back.
    Yale, Trumbull Collection, no. 1832.61. (Fig. 112)

1ST LIEUT. ELNATHAN HASKELL, Adjutant, 14th Massachusetts Regt.
　　No. 21 in *Saratoga,* from the above. (See Figs. 184 and 185)

MARQUESS OF HASTINGS (see FRANCIS RAWDON).

BENJAMIN HAWKINS (1754–1818), Member of Congress from North Carolina.
　　No. 10 in *Resignation, ca.* 1790. (See Figs. 203 and 204)

2D LIEUT. LOUIS HAY (d. 1799), British, Royal Engineers.
　　No. 16 in *Gibraltar,* 1784–87, London. (See Figs. 198 and 199)

LORD HEATHFIELD (see GEN. GEORGE AUGUSTUS ELIOTT).

CAPT. HELMSTADT (see BARON VON HELMSTADT).

CAPT. WILLIAM HENDRICKS, Thompson's Pennsylvania Regt. (died of wounds received
at Quebec 1776).
　　No. 8 in *Quebec,* posthumous. (See Figs. 152 and 153)

BISHOP OF HEREFORD (see JOHN LUXMORE).

JOSEPH HEWES (1730–79).
　　No. 26 in *Declaration,* posthumous. (See Figs. 158 and 159)

JAMES HEWLETT (1789–1836), British, "the eminent flower painter of Bath."
　　Bust(?) (American Academy Cat., 1817, no. 130 and note to Dr. Hosack, 9 May
　　　　1828), probably 1813, Bath, England.
　　Unlocated.

THOMAS HEYWARD, JR. (1746–1809), Signer, Revolutionary officer, jurist.
　　Sketch or miniature(?), 1791, Charleston, S.C.
　　Unlocated.
　　No. 15 in *Declaration,* from the above, 1793, Charleston, S.C. (See Figs. 158 and
　　　　159)

"RALPH HICKLEY" (see RALPH KIRKLEY).

REV. ENOS HITCHCOCK (1744–1803), Chaplain, 10th Massachusetts Regt.
　　Drawing, 1791 in New England(?).
　　Yale, gift of Mrs. Winchester Bennett, no. 1931.64.
　　No. 19 in *Saratoga,* from the above. (See Figs. 184 and 185)

COL. BENJAMIN HITCHBOURN (also HICHBORN) (1746–1817), Boston lawyer.
　　"Half-length," 1779, Boston; *Autobiography,* no. 65.
　　Unlocated.

REV. EDWARD HOLYOKE (1689–1769), tenth President of Harvard College.
> After John Singleton Copley's portrait of *ca.* 1760, Harvard, no. H6, 1772–73,
>> Cambridge, Mass.; *Autobiography,* no. 9.
> Unlocated.

WILLIAM HOOPER (1742–90).
> No. 22 in *Declaration, ca.* 1789. (See Figs. 158 and 159)

"JOHN HOPKINS" (see STEPHEN HOPKINS).

DR. LEMUEL HOPKINS (1750–1801), physician, "Hartford Wit."
> Miniature, 1793, Hartford, Conn.
> Yale, Trumbull Collection, no. 1832.68. (Fig. 113)
> Half-length, signed and dated 1793(?) Hartford(?).
> Yale, gift of Miss Elizabeth Sill, no. 1914.1. (Fig. 28)
> Replica, half-length, posthumous, 1827, New York.
> Mrs. Robert A. (Alice Gardner Hopkins) Eyerman, Bear Creek, Pa.

MARY ELIZABETH HOPKINS, daughter of Samuel Miles Hopkins, married William Gordon ver Planck, 1826.
> Bust, *ca.* 1805, New York.
> Miss Jane Lesley ver Planck, Geneva, N.Y., 1949.

SAMUEL MILES HOPKINS (1772–1837), Judge of the New York State Circuit Court, incorporator of the American Academy of the Fine Arts.
> Bust, *ca.* 1805, New York.
> Mrs. George E. (Virginia Murray Hopkins) Mayakis, Castleton-on-Hudson, N.Y.
> Replica(?).
> Mrs. James Scribner Hopkins, Roxbury, N.Y.

MRS. SAMUEL MILES (SARAH ELIZABETH ROGERS) HOPKINS (1774–1866).
> Mrs. George E. Mayakis, Castleton-on-Hudson, N.Y.

STEPHEN HOPKINS (1707–85), Colonial Governor of Rhode Island, Signer.
> Pencil sketch, posthumous, 1796 (1st Silliman sale, no. 49).
> Fordham.
> No. 23 in *Declaration,* from the above. (See Figs. 158 and 159)

FRANCIS HOPKINSON (1737–91).
> No. 30 in *Declaration, ca.* 1790. (See Figs. 158 and 159)

HOPOTHLE (HOP-HITHLI MIKO), or the Talasee King of the Creeks.
Pencil sketch, 1790, New York (1st Silliman sale, no. 66).
Fordham. (Fig. 129)

ALEXANDER HOSACK (1736–1826), born in Scotland, sergeant in Lord Jeffrey Amherst's army in America, later a New York merchant, father of David Hosack.
Bust, probably 1806, New York.
John Hampton Barnes, Jr., "Mount Pleasant Farm," Middletown, Del., in 1949.

MRS. ALEXANDER (JANE ARDEN) HOSACK (1743–1828), married 1768 at New York.
Half-length, probably same time and place as above.
Connecticut Historical Society, no. 140.

DR. DAVID HOSACK (1769–1835), attending physician at the New York Hospital, botanist, professor at Columbia College, philanthropist, art patron, incorporator and chief backer of the American Academy of Fine Arts.
"Cash recd. From Dr. Hosack for a portrait 140 [dollars]," accounts for 15 November 1806; possibly the same as "Portrait of a Gentleman. Lent by Dr. Hosack" (American Academy Cat., 1817, no. 128), or possibly the following.
Unlocated.
"Portrait of the late David Hosack, M.D., F.R.S., Painted by Col. John Trumbull for Richard Pennell, M.D." (Royal Academy, London, 1818, no. 275; Apollo Association, New York, 1839, October Exhibition, no. 38).
Presented in 1866 by Mary C. and George C. Pennell to the New York Hospital.
Half-length, on wood, 1806, New York.
Society of the New York Hospital, New York. (Fig. 29)

LIEUT. COL. JOHN EAGER HOWARD (1752–1827), Revolutionary officer, Governor of Maryland, United States Senator.
Pencil sketch, 1792, Philadelphia (1st Silliman sale, no. 44).
Unlocated.
No. 28 in *Resignation*, from the above. (See Figs. 203 and 204)

MAJ. GEN. SIR WILLIAM HOWE, K.B. (1729–1814), British.
No. 11 in *Bunker's Hill*, if from life before 1786, London (after Benjamin West?).
(See Figs. 145 and 146)

DAVID HOWELL (1747–1824), educator, professor at Brown University (Rhode Island College), jurist, member Continental Congress, Commissioner under Jay Treaty.
Pencil drawing, 1793, Newport, R.I.
Unlocated.
Miniature.
Unlocated.

No. 14 in *Resignation,* after the drawing above. (See Figs. 203 and 204)

HARRIET TRUMBULL HUBBARD (see below).

OLIVER PAYSON HUBBARD (1809–1900), HIS WIFE FAITH WADSWORTH SILLIMAN (1812–1887), AND THEIR DAUGHTER, HARRIET TRUMBULL (1838–91).
>Group, 1839, New Haven, Conn., signed and dated on back. Dr. Hubbard, scientist, assistant to Prof. Benjamin Silliman of Yale, professor at Dartmouth College; Mrs. Hubbard, the second daughter of Professor and Mrs. (Harriet Trumbull) Silliman.
>Mrs. David A. Campbell, Falls Village, Conn.

JONATHAN TRUMBULL HUDSON (1805–52), grandson of the artist's brother, Jonathan Trumbull, Jr.
>"Age 22—brown Complexion Dark brown hair—Dress Blue Coat, & white vest—both hands—one holding a Letter—Background Umber & White—Column &c."
>Half-length, 1828, Hartford.
>Unlocated.

MRS. JONATHAN TRUMBULL HUDSON (see MISS GALE).

ROBERT BALL HUGHES (1806–68), British-trained sculptor.
>Bust, probably 1839, New Haven.
>Frederic R. Brown, Jr., Ridgefield, Conn.

MRS. ROBERT BALL (ELIZA WRIGHT) HUGHES (1807–92).
>Bust, on academy board, 1839, New Haven.
>Mr. Landsdell K. Christie, Syosset, N.Y.

LIEUT. COL. ERNST AUGUST VON HUGO (1725–88), of the 6th Hanoverian Infantry Regt.
>No. 4 in *Gibraltar,* probably after Copley's sketch (at the Fogg Museum, Harvard University) of 1783 (for the *Repulse of the Floating Batteries at Gibraltar,* now at the Guildhall, London), 1784–87, London. (See Figs. 198 and 199)

BRIG. GEN. WILLIAM HULL (1753–1825), Revolutionary officer, Governor of Michigan Territory.
>Miniature, 1790, Boston, signed and dated on back.
>Yale, Trumbull Collection, no. 1832.26. (Fig. 104)

>No. 5 in *Saratoga,* from the above, as major, 8th Massachusetts Regt. (See Figs. 184 and 185)

GEN. DAVID HUMPHREYS (1752–1818), aide-de-camp to Gen. Washington, Revolutionary officer, statesman, poet.

Bust, posthumous before 1824, New York.
Wadsworth Atheneum, Hartford, no. 1848.8.

Study, *ca.* 1800, London(?).
Unlocated.

No. 24 in *Resignation,* as lieut. col. (See Figs. 203 and 204)

1ST LIEUT. JOHN HUMPHRIES, Morgan's Company of Virginia Riflemen, killed in action.

No. 10 in *Quebec* (though possibly 2d Lieut. William Humphrey, 1st Rhode Island Regt., taken prisoner at Quebec). (See Figs. 152 and 153)

BRIG. GEN. EBENEZER HUNTINGTON (1754–1834), 3rd Connecticut Regt., Revolutionary officer, son of Gen. Jabez Huntington.

Bust, 1806, Norwich, Conn.
James Graham and Sons, New York. (Fig. 30)

Posthumous replica, bust, on wood, 1835, New York.
Oliver Wolcott, Hamilton, Mass.

(?) Miniature.
Unlocated (Miss S. H. Perkins, Norwich, Conn., in 1895).

No. 29 in *Yorktown,* before 1794, Norwich, Conn., as lieut. col. (See Figs. 187 and 188)

"GEN. E. HUNTINGTON(?)" (see BRIG. GEN. SAMUEL BLACHLEY WEBB).

MAJ. GEN. JABEZ HUNTINGTON (1719–86), West Indian merchant of Norwich, Conn., Colonial and Revolutionary officer, father of Jedediah Huntington.

Full-length, 1777, Lebanon, Conn.; *Autobiography,* no. 27.
Connecticut State Library, Hartford, Conn., on loan to the State Capitol. (Fig. 31; see also Fig. 32)

JABEZ HUNTINGTON (1767–1848), grandson of above.

Bust, 1777, Lebanon, Conn.; *Autobiography,* no. 36.
Yale, a gift of Yale University Art Gallery Associates, no. 1938.272. (Fig. 33)

JEDEDIAH HUNTINGTON (1743–1818), of Norwich, Conn., Revolutionary officer, married Faith Trumbull, the artist's sister.

Miniature, *ca.* 1790, Connecticut.
Connecticut Historical Society, no. 125.

JOSHUA HUNTINGTON (b. 1751), merchant, son of Jabez Huntington.

Pencil sketch, *ca.* 1808, Norwich, Conn.(?).
Unlocated.

SAMUEL HUNTINGTON (1731–96).
>No. 39 in *Declaration, ca.* 1790, Philadelphia(?). (See Figs. 158 and 159)

HYSAC, of "The Woman's Man," a Creek Indian.
>Pencil study, 1790, New York (*Autobiography,* pl. 19; 1st Silliman sale, no. 68).
>Unlocated.

I

"THE INFANT," chief of the Seneca Indians.
>Miniature, 1792, Philadelphia, signed and dated on back.
>Yale, Trumbull Collection, no. 1832.32. (Fig. 107)

RALPH IZARD (1741/2–1804), Revolutionary patriot, diplomat, Senator from South Carolina.
>Miniature, 1793, Philadelphia, signed and dated on back.
>Yale, Trumbull Collection, no. 1832.53. (Fig. 111)

J

JAMES II (see CHILDREN OF CHARLES I).

JOHN JAY (1745–1829), jurist, statesman, diplomat, negotiated "Jay's Treaty" with Great Britain (Trumbull was his secretary), first Chief Justice of the United States Supreme Court, Governor of New York.
>Miniature, 1793, Philadelphia, signed and dated on the back.
>Yale, Trumbull Collection, no. 1832.21. (Fig. 108)

>Bust, 1794 or 1795, London.
>Property of John Jay.
>Now owned by the children of the late Mrs. William J. Iselin, on loan to "Bedford House," Katonah, N.Y.

>Full-length, 1805, New York.
>City Hall, New York. (Fig. 34)

>Half-length (American Academy Cat. 1824, no. 60).
>Unlocated.

>Head by Gilbert Stuart, *ca.* 1782, London, balance of three-quarter, seated figure by Trumbull *ca.* 1785, London.
>Used for the engraving by Asher B. Durand, 1835.
>John Clarkson Jay, Williamstown, Mass.

MARY RUTHERFURD JAY (see MRS. FREDERICK PRIME).

THOMAS JEFFERSON (1743–1826), third President of the United States, Signer, author, architect, scientist, educator.

"In the autumn of 1787, I again visited Paris, where I painted the portrait of Mr. Jefferson in the original small Declaration of Independence . . . at Mr. Jefferson's house"; *Autobiography,* pp. 150–51.

No. 34 in *Declaration,* in the original version at Yale, used for the engraving by Asher B. Durand. (See Figs. 158 and 159)

Miniature, replica of the portrait painted in the original *Declaration* at Paris in 1787; 1787, London.

Presented by the artist to Jefferson's oldest daughter, Martha.

"Monticello," Thomas Jefferson Memorial Foundation, Charlottesville, Va., no. 58–38. (Fig. 119)

Miniature, a replica, 1788, London.

For Mrs. John Barker (Angelica Schuyler) Church, of London, to Mrs. Bertram P. (Catherine Church) Cruger, to John Church Cruger, to Cornelia Cruger, to the Metropolitan Museum of Art, no. 24.19.1.

Miniature, a replica, 1788, London.

For Maria (Hadfield) Cosway, 1759–1838, wife of the English miniature painter Richard Cosway.

Collegio Maria S.S. Bambina (founded by Maria Cosway), Lodi, Italy.

No. 12 in *Resignation,* from the portrait in *Declaration,* then in Trumbull's hands, after 1816 at New York. (See Figs. 203 and 204)

DANIEL OF ST. THOMAS JENIFER (1723–90).

No. 31 in *Resignation,* probably posthumous. (See Figs. 203 and 204)

JOHN—A CREEK.

Pencil sketch, 1790, New York (1st Silliman sale, no. 64).

Yale, no. 1947.496.

K

CHARLES KING (1789–1867), second son of Rufus King, later President of Columbia College, New York.

Bust, 1801, London.

Estate of Mrs. Joseph H. (Alice King) Bigley, Elizabeth, N.J.

EDWARD KING (1795–1836), fourth son of Rufus King.

Bust, 1801, London.

New-York Historical Society, no. 1958.11.

JAMES GORE KING (1791–1853), third son of Rufus King.

Bust, 1801, London.

Joseph Larocque, Jr., Bernardsville, N.J., in 1949.

JOHN ALSOP KING (1788–1867), eldest son of Rufus King, Governor of New York.
> Bust, 1801, London.
> New-York Historical Society, no. 1909.21.

RUFUS KING (1755–1827), statesman, Senator from New York, Minister to Great Britain.
> Miniature, 1792, Philadelphia, signed and dated on back.
> Yale, no. 1832.30. (Fig. 107)
> Bust, 1800, London (American Academy Cat., 1831, no. 14).
> Yale, Trumbull Collection, no. 1832.17. (Fig. 35)
> Bust, 1800, London.
> Charles King Lennig, Jr., Chestnut Hill, Philadelphia, Pa.

MRS. RUFUS (MARY ALSOP) KING (1769–1819).
> Half-length.
> Charles King Lennig, Jr., Chestnut Hill, Philadelphia, Pa. (Fig. 36)
> Posthumous replica, half-length, without necklace, 1820, New York.
> Charles King, Jr., Wilton, Conn. (Color chart for this portrait dated 1820; Yale, gift of Gherardi Davis, no. 1922.4.)

"MRS. K———," so listed by the artist.
> Probably the posthumous portrait of Mrs. Rufus King.

RALPH KIRKLEY, British, Sir Joshua Reynolds' bodyservant.
> Half-length, *ca.* 1800, London.
> David H. Lanman, Jr., Bellport, N.Y.

CAPT. THOMAS KNOWLTON (1749–76), 3d Connecticut Regt.
> No. 6 in *Bunker's Hill,* posthumous. (See Figs. 145 and 146)

BRIG. GEN. HENRY KNOX (1759–1806), Chief of Artillery, Continental Army.
> No. 12 in *Trenton, ca.* 1790, Philadelphia(?). (See Figs. 164 and 165)
> No. 28 in *Yorktown,* same as above. (See Figs. 187 and 188)

2D LIEUT. GEORGE FREDERIC KOEHLER (d. 1800), British, Royal Regt. of Artillery.
> No. 13 in *Gibraltar,* 1784–87, London. (See Figs. 198 and 199)

L

MAJ. GEN. MARIE JOSEPH PAUL YVES ROCH GILBERT DU MOTIER, MARQUIS DE LAFAYETTE (1757–1834), French.
> No. 19 in *Yorktown,* Paris. (See Figs. 187 and 188)

JOHN LANGDON (1741–1819), merchant, Senator from New Hampshire, Governor of New Hampshire.
>   Miniature, 1792, Philadelphia, signed and dated on back.
>   Yale, Trumbull Collection, no. 1832.33. (Fig. 107)

MARY HUNTINGTON LANMAN (later MRS. FREDERICK BULL (1804–80), AND HER SISTER, ABIGAIL TRUMBULL LANMAN (1806–91).
>   Double portrait, *ca.* 1824, Norwich, Conn.
>   Mrs. Edward Welch Clucas, Oldwick, N.J.

DAVID TRUMBULL LANMAN (1802–66), of Norwich, Conn., son of Peter Lanman.
>   Bust, on wood, 1820s, New York.
>   Mrs. Edwin L. Keiffer, Wakefield, R.I.

PETER LANMAN (1771–1854), Norwich merchant.
>   Half-length, on wood, 1828, Norwich, Conn.
>   Yale, gift of Henry W. Bull, no. 1941.75. (Fig. 37)

MRS. PETER (ABIGAIL TRUMBULL) LANMAN (1781–1861), daughter of David Trumbull, the artist's brother (see also MARY HUNTINGTON LANMAN).
>   Half-length, on wood, 1828, Norwich, Conn.
>   Yale, gift of Henry W. Bull, no. 1941.76. (Fig. 38)

JANE ELIZA LATHROP (see MRS. JONATHAN G. W. TRUMBULL).

JOHN LAURANCE (1750–1810), Judge Advocate General during Revolution, Senator from New York.
>   Miniature, 1792, Philadelphia.
>   New-York Historical Society, no. 1886.2.

HENRY LAURENS, SR. (1724–92), planter and merchant of Charleston, S.C., President, Continental Congress, the prisoner exchanged for Lord Cornwallis.
>   Miniature, 1791, Charleston, S.C., signed and dated on back.
>   Yale, Trumbull Collection, no. 1832.20. (Fig. 108)

MRS. HENRY LAURENS, JR. (see ELIZA RUTLEDGE).

LIEUT. COL. JOHN LAURENS (1754–82), aide-de-camp to Gen. Washington.
>   No. 32 in *Yorktown,* posthumous. (See Figs. 187 and 188)

BRIG. DUC DE LAUZUN (after 1788 known as Armand-Louis de Gontaut, Duc de Biron) (1747–93), French.
>   No. 4 in *Yorktown,* 1787, Paris. (See Figs. 187 and 188)

BRIG. MATTHIEU PAUL LOUIS, VICOMTE DE LAVAL (later, Comte de Montmorency) (1748–1809), French.
> No. 2 in *Yorktown*, 1787, Paris. (See Figs. 187 and 188)

MRS. THOMAS B. LAW (see ELIZABETH PARKE CUSTIS).

SIR THOMAS LAWRENCE (1769–1830), British portrait painter.
> Head, pencil sketch, for the "Dying Spaniard" (José Barboza).
> Boston Athenaeum, Boston, Mass. (Fig. 200)
>
> No. 17 in *Gibraltar*, 1789, London. (See Figs. 198 and 199)

ARTHUR LEE (1740–92), diplomat.
> Miniature, 1790, New York, signed and dated on back.
> Yale, Trumbull Collection, no. 1832.79. (Fig. 106)
>
> No. 13 in *Resignation*, from the above. (See Figs. 203 and 204)

BILLY LEE, Negro bodyservant to Gen. Washington.
> In the 1780 portrait of Washington. (Fig. 90)

MAJ. GEN. CHARLES LEE (1713–82).
> Pencil sketch, posthumous, 1785, London; probably for the projected *Attack on Charleston, South Carolina*.
> Yale, gift of Mrs. Robert F. Jefferys, no. 1952.3.5.

RICHARD HENRY LEE (1732–94).
> No. 6 in *Declaration*, ca. 1790, Philadelphia. (See Figs. 158 and 159)

LIEUT. LE FIEVRE, French.
> Sketch (1st Silliman sale, no. 127, as "Lt. L'Fever Dying").
> Unlocated.

ROBERT LENOX (1759–1839), New York merchant, President of the Chamber of Commerce; his country retreat, "Five Mile Farm."
> Half-length, 1805, New York.
> New York Public Library. (Fig. 39)

MRS. ROBERT (RACHEL CARMER) LENOX (1763–1843).
> Half-length, 1805, New York.
> New York Public Library. (Fig. 40)
>
> Half-length, 1806, New York.
> New-York Historical Society, no. 1950.226.

CATHERINE LENTNER (1771–1851), a friend of the artist in his old age.
　　　Bust, 24 by 20 inches, 1836, New York.
　　　Mrs. John Proudfoot, Mobile, Ala., in 1949.

　　　Bust, 23 by 20½ inches, in a lace cap, late 1830s, New York.
　　　Unlocated.

LOUISA LENTNER (in her early twenties), also thought to be LOUISA MONROE.
　　　Miniature, *ca.* 1836, New York.
　　　Mrs. Rufus Lentner Sewall, Boston, Mass.

KATHARINA(?) LENTNER (sister of the above, about two years older), also thought to be
SUSAN MONROE.
　　　Miniature, *ca.* 1836, New York.
　　　Same as above.

MISS LENTNER AND HER SISTERS (group portrait?).
　　　1836, New York.
　　　Unlocated.

CAPT. HON. WILLIAM LESLIE, 17th Regt. of Foot, British (1751–77), killed at Battle of
Princeton.
　　　No. 7 in *Princeton*. (See Figs. 169 and 170)

FRANCIS LEWIS (1713–1802).
　　　No. 37 in *Declaration, ca.* 1790, Philadelphia(?). (See Figs. 158 and 159)

"COL. JOSEPH LEWIS" (or "Louis"), chief of the Oneida Indians.
　　　Pencil sketch, idealized, 1785, London, for no. 6 in *Quebec*.
　　　Yale, gift of Mrs. Robert F. Jefferys, no. 1952.3.4.

　　　No. 6 in *Quebec,* from the above. (See Figs. 152 and 153)

MRS. LAWRENCE LEWIS (see ELEANOR PARKE CUSTIS).

COL. MORGAN LEWIS (1754–1844), Deputy Quartermaster General, Northern Dept.
　　　No. 9 in *Saratoga, ca.* 1790(?), New York(?). (See Figs. 184 and 185)

MORGAN LEWIS, Revolutionary officer, Governor of New York.
　　　Full-length, 1808, New York.
　　　City Hall, New York. (Fig. 41)

MAJ. GEN. BENJAMIN LINCOLN (1733–1810).
　　　No. 15 in *Yorktown, ca.* 1790, Boston. (See Figs. 187 and 188)

HANNAH LINDLEY (see MRS. JOHN MURRAY).

MAJ. WILLIAM LITHGOW (1750?–96), Revolutionary officer, 11th Massachusetts Regt.
  Pencil sketch, 1791, Boston.
  Yale, gift of Mrs. Winchester Bennett, no. 1931.63.
  No. 1 in *Saratoga,* from the above. (See Figs. 184 and 185)

SAMUEL LIVERMORE (1732–1803), jurist, Senator from New Hampshire.
  Miniature, 1792, Philadelphia.
  Yale, Trumbull Collection, no. 1832.76. (Fig. 106)
  Same.
  Currier Gallery of Art, Manchester, N.H.

EDWARD LIVINGSTON (1764–1836), Mayor of New York, statesman, diplomat, art patron,
founder and first President of the American Academy of the Fine Arts.
  Bust, 1805, New York.
  City Hall, New York. (Fig. 42)

MRS. JOHN R. LIVINGSTON (see MISS P. SHEAFFE).

PHILIP LIVINGSTON (1716–78).
  No. 48 in *Declaration,* posthumous. (See Figs. 158 and 159)

ROBERT R. LIVINGSTON (1746–1813).
  Ca. 1790, New York(?).
  No. 33 in *Declaration.* (See Figs. 158 and 159)

EDWARD LLOYD (1744–96), Member of Congress from Maryland.
  No. 8 in *Resignation,* probably posthumous. (See Figs. 203 and 204)

JOHN LOCKE (1632–1704), British philosopher.
  From a print, 1772–73, Cambridge, Mass.; *Autobiography,* no. 11.
  Unlocated. (See "Unidentified Men.")

COL. JOSEPH "LOUIS" (see "COL. JOSEPH LEWIS").

JOHN LUXMORE (1756–1830), British, Bishop of Hereford, England, 1808–15, and
Bishop of St. Asaph, Wales, 1815–30.
  Half-length, before 1815 in England (American Academy Cat., 1824, no. 101).
  Unlocated.

THOMAS LYNCH (1749–79), member Continental Congress, Signer.
  Pencil sketch, posthumous.
  Yale, no. 1931.68.
  No. 4 in *Declaration,* from the above. (See Figs. 158 and 159)

M

MAJ. ANDREW MCCLARY (*ca.* 1730–75), 1st New Hampshire Regt., killed at Bunker's Hill.

> No. 7 in *Bunker's Hill,* posthumous. (See Figs. 145 and 146)

REV. SAMUEL MCCLINTOCK (1732–1804), Chaplain of the 2d New Hampshire Regt.
> No. 10 in *Bunker's Hill,* not from life. (See Figs. 145 and 146)

ELEAZER MCCOMB (d. 1798), Member of Congress from Delaware.
> No. 6 in *Resignation,* probably posthumous. (See Figs. 203 and 204)

JANE MCCREA (see MURDER OF JANE MCCREA).

THOMAS MCKEAN (1734–1817).
> *Ca.* 1790, Philadelphia(?).
> No. 47 in *Declaration.* (See Figs. 158 and 159)

CAPT. ALEXANDER MCKENSIE, British, 73d Regt. of (Highland) Foot.
> No. 12 in *Gibraltar,* 1784–87, London. (See Figs. 198 and 199)

CAPT. JOHN MACPHERSON (1754–75), killed in action at Quebec, aide-de-camp to Gen. Montgomery.
> Pencil sketch, posthumous, 1785, London; for no. 3 in *Quebec.*
> Yale, gift of Mrs. Robert F. Jefferys, no. 1952.3.3.

> No. 3 in *Quebec.* (See Figs. 152 and 153)

JAMES MADISON (1750–1836), fourth President of the United States.
> No. 17 in *Resignation,* probably after Gilbert Stuart's 1804 portrait or one of the
> replicas. (See Figs. 203 and 204)

LAURENCE MANNING (1756–1804), Revolutionary officer.
> Miniature, 1791, Charleston, S.C., signed and dated on back.
> Yale, Trumbull Collection, no. 1832.77. (Fig. 106)

DR. EDWARD PREBLE MARCELLIN (M.D., 1829, d. 1863), New York physician.
> *Ca.* 1830, New York.
> Thomas M. Evans, New York, and Gainesville, Va. (Fig. 43)

MARIE ANTOINETTE (1755–93) AND HER CHILDREN, French.
> Ink sketch, after Vigée-Lebrun, 1787, Paris.
> Yale, no. 1947.478.

GEN. EBENEZER MATTOON of Amherst, Mass., Revolutionary officer.
> 1838, New Haven (noted by Prof. Benjamin Silliman).
> Unlocated.

LIEUT. COL. HAMILTON MAXWELL (d. 1800), British, 73d Regt. of (Highland) Foot.
No. 6 in *Gibraltar*, 1784–87, London. (See Figs. 198 and 199)

GEORGE MEADE (1741–1808), Philadelphia merchant and philanthropist.
Bust, *ca.* 1790, Philadelphia.
John Paulding Meade, Rye, N.Y., on loan to Mrs. Richard Worsam Meade, Mt. Kisco, N.Y.

MAJ. RETURN JONATHAN MEIGS (1740–1832), 2d Connecticut Regt.
No. 7 in *Quebec*, not from life. (See Figs. 152 and 153)

BRIG. GEN. HUGH MERCER (*ca.* 1725–77), Colonial and Revolutionary officer.
Posthumous, pencil study made of his eldest son, John (1772–1817), 1791, Fredericksburg, Va. (1st Silliman sale, no. 40).
Metropolitan Museum of Art, no. 96.1346.2.
Same (1st Silliman sale, no. 41).
Fordham. (Fig. 182; see also Figs. 169–181)
(?) Same, but probably of one of Mercer's younger sons (1st Silliman sale, no. 52).
Fordham.
No. 6 in *Princeton*, after the above. (See Figs. 169 and 170)

ARTHUR MIDDLETON (1742–87), Signer, Revolutionary leader.
Miniature(?), 1790, "Middleton Place," Charleston, S.C., posthumous, copied after the Benjamin West group portrait of 1771 (now owned by Henry Middleton Drinker, Jenkintown, Pa.).
Unlocated.
No. 14 in *Declaration*, from the above. (See Figs. 158 and 159)

THOMAS MIFFLIN (1744–1800), Philadelphia merchant, Revolutionary officer, Governor of Pennsylvania.
Miniature, head three-quarters to right, 1790, Philadelphia, signed and dated on back.
Yale, Trumbull Collection, no. 1832.75. (Fig. 106)
Slightly more full-faced, 1790, Philadelphia.
Mr. and Mrs. J. William Middendorf, II, Greenwich, Conn. (Fig. 120)
No. 1 in *Princeton*, from the miniature. (See Figs. 169 and 170)
No. 1 in *Resignation*, from the miniature. (See Figs. 203 and 204)

STEPHEN MINOT (born 1772/3), Boston merchant.
Bust, 1806, New York.
Museum of Fine Arts, Boston (gift of Miss Susan I. Minot), no. 79.333. (Fig. 44)

Mrs. Stephen (Sarah or "Sally") Minot (married 1805).
  Bust, 1806, New York.
  Museum of Fine Arts, Boston (gift of Miss Susan I. Minot), no. 79.334. (Fig. 45)
  Bust, same as above but somewhat idealized, 1806, New York.
  Mrs. John E. Boit, Brookline, Mass., on loan to American Academy of Arts and Sciences, Brookline, Mass.

Mrs. Mitchel, "wife of an English clergyman."
  Before 1815, England (1844 auction sale, no. 19).
  Unlocated.

Earl of Moira (see Lord Rawdon).

1st Lieut. James Monroe (1758–1831), 3d Virginia Regt.
  No. 4 in *Trenton, ca.* 1790, Philadelphia(?). (See Figs. 164 and 165)

Louisa and Susan Monroe (see The Misses Lentner).

Duc de Montmorency (see Vicomte de Laval).

Maj. Gen. Richard Montgomery (1738–75), (killed in the assault on Quebec), Continental Army.
  Pencil sketch, posthumous, 1785, London, for no. 1 in *Quebec.*
  Yale, gift of Mrs. Robert F. Jefferys, no. 1952.3.1b.
  No. 1 in *Quebec,* from the above. (See Figs. 152 and 153)

Alexander Moore(?) (d. 1791), Boston merchant.
  Small full-length, on copper, 1784, London.
  Mrs. John Insley Blair, Tuxedo Park, N.Y., in 1949.

Maj. Willard Moore (killed at Bunker's Hill, 1775), Doolittle's Massachusetts Regt.
  No. 8 in *Bunker's Hill,* posthumous. (See Figs. 145 and 146)

Brig. Gen. Daniel Morgan (*ca.* 1736–1802), Revolutionary officer.
  Miniature, 1792, Philadelphia, after Charles Willson Peale's portrait now in Independence Hall, Philadelphia; signed and dated on back.
  Yale, Trumbull Collection, no. 1832.62. (Fig. 112)
  Sketch for engraving.
  Unlocated.
  No. 16 in *Saratoga,* from the miniature, as col., 11th Virginia Regt. (See Figs. 184 and 185)

Cadwalader Morris (1741–95), Member of Congress from Pennsylvania.
  No. 21 in *Resignation.* (See Figs. 203 and 204)

LEWIS MORRIS (1726–98).

> No. 12 in *Declaration, ca.* 1790, Philadelphia. (See Figs. 158 and 159)

ROBERT MORRIS (1734–1806), Philadelphia merchant and banker, financier of the Revolution.

> Miniature, 1790, Philadelphia.
> Mrs. Philip L. Poe, Ruxton, Md. (Fig. 121)
>
> No. 17 in *Declaration,* from the above. (See Figs. 158 and 159)

MRS. ROBERT (MARY WHITE) MORRIS (married 1769).

> Miniature, 1790, Philadelphia.
> Mrs. Philip L. Poe, Ruxton, Md. (Fig. 122)
>
> Half-length to right, engraved by H. Wright Smith.
> Unlocated.

MRS. WASHINGTON MORTON (see CORNELIA SCHUYLER).

COMTE DE MOSLOY (see LOUIS GUILLAUME OTTO).

MAJ. GEN. WILLIAM MOULTRIE (1730–1805), Revolutionary officer, Governor of South Carolina.

> Miniature, 1791, Charleston, S.C., signed and dated on back.
> Yale, Trumbull Collection, no. 1832.49. (Fig. 105)

BRIG. GEN. JOHN PETER GABRIEL MUHLENBERG (1746–1807), Continental Army.

> No. 27 in *Yorktown,* before 1807. (See Figs. 187 and 188)

JOHN MURRAY (1737–1808), younger brother of Robert Murray of "Murray Hill," New York, merchant, President of the New York Chamber of Commerce.

> Half-length, *ca.* 1806, New York (previously misidentified as Robert Murray, 1721–86).
> Metropolitan Museum of Art, no. 22.76.1. (Fig. 46)

MRS. JOHN (HANNAH LINDLEY) MURRAY (married 1766; previously misidentified as Mrs. Robert [Mary Lindley] Murray, married 1733).

> Metropolitan Museum of Art, no. 22.76.2. (Fig. 47)

THE MISSES MURRAY (Mary and Hannah, daughters of the above).

> Wash drawing, 1806, New York (1st Silliman sale, no. 131).
> Mrs. Harold K. English, New Haven, Conn.
>
> Large double portrait, 1806, New York.
> Mrs. Thomas A. (Elizabeth Hoffman McVickar) Fransioli, Jr., Cambridge, Mass.

N

JOHN NEILSON(?) (1745–1833), Revolutionary officer, member of the Continental Congress.

> Bust, 1807, New York, damaged and repainted by another hand.
> Rutgers, The State University, New Brunswick, N.J.

THOMAS NELSON, JR. (1738–89).

> No. 36 in *Declaration,* not from life. (See Figs. 158 and 159)

> No. 18 in *Yorktown,* not from life. (See Figs. 187 and 188)

SIR ISAAC NEWTON (1642–1727), British scientist.

> From an engraving, 1772–73, Cambridge, Mass.; *Autobiography,* no. 10.
> Unlocated. (See "Unidentified Men.")

O

THOMAS JACKSON OAKLEY (1783–1857), Member of Congress, Chief Justice of the Superior Court of New York, N.Y.

> Miniature, 1827, New York.
> Yale, Trumbull Collection, no. 1832.70. (Fig. 109)

DAVID BAYARD OGDEN (1775–1849), New York lawyer.

> Miniature, 1827, New York.
> Yale, Trumbull Collection, no. 1832.74. (Fig. 109)

LIEUT. MATTHIAS OGDEN (1754–91), volunteer.

> No. 12 in *Quebec,* not from life. (See Figs. 152 and 153)

LIEUT. COL. JEREMIAH OLNEY (1750–1812), Revolutionary officer, Collector of Customs, Providence, R.I.

> Portrait drawing, 1793, Newport or Providence, R.I.
> Unlocated.

SAMUEL OSGOOD (1747/8–1813), Revolutionary officer, Member of the Continental Congress, Postmaster General.

> No. 5 in *Resignation.* (See Figs. 203 and 204)

SUSAN KITTREDGE OSGOOD (see MRS. MOSES FIELD).

LOUIS GUILLAUME OTTO, Comte de Mosloy (1754–1817), French.

> Half-length, *ca.* 1800, London (stipple engraving in color, 1802, by P. Roberts, undoubtedly Percy Roberts 1795–1828 of London).
> Unlocated.

MME. LOUIS GUILLAUME (AMERICA FRANCES—or "FANNY"—SAINT-JOHN DE CRÈVE-COEUR) OTTO (1770–1823), married 1790, French.
>   Bust, companion portrait.
>   Louis Saint-John de Crèvecoeur, LaPlagne, Montesquiou-sur-Losse, Gers, France.

P

WILLIAM PACA (1740–99).
>   No. 9 in *Declaration, ca.* 1790 in Maryland. (See Figs. 158 and 159)

MARY PADDOCK (see MRS. EDWARD GRAY).

ROBERT TREAT PAINE (1731–1814).
>   No. 21 in *Declaration,* 1791, Boston, Mass. (See Figs. 158 and 159)

THOMAS PAINE (1737–1809), pamphleteer, author of *Common Sense.*
>   Miniature, 1788, once belonged to Thomas Jefferson, "Monticello."
>   Thomas Jefferson Memorial Foundation, Charlottesville, Va., no. 57–28. (Fig. 123)

JOSEPH PALMER (see LIEUT. JOSEPH BUDWORTH).

THOMAS PALMER, possibly T. Palmer, Jr., London architect, who exhibited designs at the Royal Academy in 1798 and 1799 and a painting(?) in 1804; or Thomas Palmer (1754?–1833), engraver from Hounslow, near London (note to Dr. David Hosack, 9 May 1828).
>   Probably the same picture as that of "MR. PALMER, an Artist of London" (1844 auction sale, no. 40, purchased by a Mr. Lanman), *ca.* 1800 or *ca.* 1810, London.
>   Unlocated.

MRS. WILLIAM L. PALMER (see AUGUSTA TEMPLE).

JOSIAH PARKER (1751–1810), Isle of Wight County, Va., Revolutionary officer and politician.
>   Sketch(?) or portrait(?), possibly 1791, Virginia.
>   Unlocated.
>   No. 3 in *Trenton,* from the above, as lieut. col., 5th Virginia Regt. (See Figs. 164 and 165)

LIEUT. COL. MOSES PARKER (died of wounds received at Bunker's Hill, 1775), Bridge's Massachusetts Regt.
>   No. 5 in *Bunker's Hill,* posthumous. (See Figs. 145 and 146)

GEORGE PARTRIDGE (1740–1828), statesman, Member of Congress from Massachusetts.
"Profile" (a sketch?), 1823, New York.
Unlocated.

"Portrait," same date (from the above?).
Unlocated.

MME. PAYEN, French.
Sketch, 1786 on the Rhine; *Autobiography,* pl. 11.
The Five Daughters of Mrs. Winchester Bennett, New Haven, Conn.

JOHN HOWARD PAYNE (1791–1852), dramatist, editor, and actor (played in England).
Bust(?), exhibited at the Liverpool Academy of Arts (no. 68), Liverpool, England, in August 1813; probably painted earlier that year, London.
Unlocated.

REBECCA AMORY PAYNE (see MRS. CHRISTOPHER GORE).

"GOOD PETER," chief of the Oneida Indians.
Miniature, 1792, Philadelphia, signed and dated on back.
Yale, Trumbull Collection, no. 1832.67. (Fig. 113)

MRS. THOMAS PETER (see MARTHA CUSTIS).

MRS. HENRY PHILIPS (see SOPHIA CHEW).

MAJ. GEN. WILLIAM PHILLIPS (1731–81), British, Royal Regt. of Artillery.
No. 10 in *Saratoga,* posthumous. (See Figs. 184 and 185)

COL. TIMOTHY PICKERING (1745–1829), Quartermaster General of the Continental Army.
No. 30 in *Yorktown, ca.* 1790, Philadelphia. (See Figs. 187 and 188)

BRIG. GEN. CHARLES COTESWORTH PINCKNEY (1746–1825), Revolutionary officer, statesman, diplomat.
Miniature, 1791, Charleston, S.C., signed on back.
Yale, Trumbull Collection, no. 1832.48. (Fig. 105)

Miniature, 1791, Charleston.
Mrs. Edward Rutledge Pinckney, Charleston, S.C.

MAJ. THOMAS PINCKNEY (1750–1828), Revolutionary officer, diplomat, Governor of South Carolina.
Miniature, 1791, Charleston, S.C., signed and dated on back.

Yale, Trumbull Collection, no. 1832.46. (Fig. 105)

Miniature, same time and place, pose slightly different, head tilted back, uniform
   coat unbuttoned disclosing waistcoat.

Langbourne M. Williams, Jr., Rapidan, Va., and New York.

Miniature, presumably same time and place.

Mrs. Edward Rutledge Pinckney, Charleston, S.C.

WILLIAM PINKNEY (1764–1822), Maryland lawyer, statesman, diplomat, fellow member with the artist on the commission for the adjustment of claims under Article 7 of the Jay Treaty at London, United States Attorney General, Minister to Russia.

Half-length, *ca.* 1800, London.

Mrs. Guy (Elizabeth Pinkney Gray) McCoy, Oakland, Calif.

MRS. WILLIAM (ANNE MARIA RODGERS) PINKNEY (married 1789, d. 1849).

Half-length, *ca.* 1800, London.

H. McCoy Jones, Washington, D.C.

JOHN PINTARD (1759–1844), merchant, philanthropist, founder of the New-York Historical Society in 1804, incorporator and treasurer of the American Academy of the Fine Arts.

Bust, 1817, New York.

New-York Historical Society, no. 1817.3. (Fig. 48)

DR. DAVID PITCAIRN (1749–1809), British physician, eldest son of the following.

Drawing, 1786, London (1st Silliman sale, no. 46).

Unlocated.

MAJ. JOHN PITCAIRN (1722–75) (died from wounds received at Bunker's Hill), British, Royal Marines.

No. 14 in *Bunker's Hill,* posthumous. (See Figs. 145 and 146)

LIEUT. WILLIAM PITCAIRN, son of Maj. Pitcairn, British, Royal Marines.

No. 16 in *Bunker's Hill,* if from life 1784–87, London. (See Figs. 145 and 146)

JONAS PLATT (1769–1834), Member of Congress from New York, Justice of the New York Supreme Court.

Half-length, 1826, New York (engraved by Asher B. Durand) (American Academy
   Cat., 1826, no. 47).

Once owned by Washington Allston.

Unlocated.

MISS POGGI (probably a daughter of Antonio C. de Poggi of London, publisher of Trumbull's engravings; note to Dr. David Hosack, 9 May 1828).

> *Ca.* 1786(?), London.
> Unlocated.

SAMUEL POWEL (1739–93), Mayor of Philadelphia.

> Miniature on wood (copy on ivory; Samuel Powel, Utica, N.Y.), *ca.* 1790, Philadelphia.
> Unlocated.

COL. WILLIAM PRESCOTT (1726–95), Massachusetts Militia.

> No. 3 in *Bunker's Hill,* not from life. (See Figs. 145 and 146)

> No. 15 in *Saratoga,* if from life before 1794. (See Figs. 184 and 185)

NATHANIEL PRIME (1768–1840), Boston merchant.

> Half-length, 1805, New York.
> Estate of Lincoln Baylies, Brookline, Mass.

MRS. NATHANIEL (CORNELIA SANDS) PRIME (1773–1852), mother of Frederick Prime.

> Half-length, 1805, New York.
> Same as above.

MRS. FREDERICK (MARY RUTHERFORD JAY) PRIME (1810–35), granddaughter of John Jay.

> Half-length, 1829, Norwich, Conn.(?).
> Mrs. Howland Russell, New York. (Color chart for portrait, dated 1829; Yale, no. 1900.40.)

MAJ. GEN. ISRAEL PUTNAM (1718–90), Revolutionary officer, 3d Connecticut Regt., patriot.

> Pencil sketch, possibly a posthumous portrait from a print, if from life early 1790 at Brooklyn, Conn. (1st Silliman sale, no. 37).
> The Putnam Phalanx, Wethersfield, Conn.; on loan to the Wadsworth Atheneum, Hartford, Conn., no. 37.45.
> No. 2 in *Bunker's Hill,* from the above, as colonel. (See Figs. 145 and 146)

BRIG. GEN. RUFUS PUTNAM (1738–1824), cousin of Israel Putnam, Revolutionary officer, 5th Massachusetts Regt.

> Miniature, 1790, New York, signed and dated on back.
> Yale, Trumbull Collection, no. 1832.51. (Fig. 111). (U.S. postage stamp no. 795, 3¢, violet, 1937).
> No. 17 in *Saratoga,* from the above, as colonel. (See Figs. 184 and 185)

R

JACOB RADCLIFF (1764–1841), lawyer, Mayor of New York.
Bust, 1816, New York.
City Hall, New York. (Fig. 49)

COL. JOHANN GOTTLIEB RALL (1725–76) (killed at the Battle of Trenton 1776), of the Hessians.
No. 5 in *Trenton*. (See Figs. 164 and 165)

LIEUT. FRANCIS, LORD RAWDON (later second Earl of Moira and still later first Marquess of Hastings) (1754–1826), British, 63d Regt. of Foot.
No. 17 in *Bunker's Hill,* not from life. (See Figs. 145 and 146)

GEORGE READ (1733–98).
No. 44 in *Declaration, ca.* 1790, Philadelphia. (See Figs. 158 and 159)

JACOB READ (1753–1816), lawyer, Revolutionary officer, Senator from South Carolina.
Miniature, 1793, Charleston, signed and dated on back.
Yale, Trumbull Collection, no. 1832.52. (Fig. 111)
No. 16 in *Resignation,* from the above. (See Figs. 203 and 204)

BRIG. GEN. JAMES REED(?) (1722 O.S.–1807), Revolutionary officer.
Copy "after Trumbull" in the State House, Concord, N.H.
Unlocated.

MAJ. GEN. FRIEDRICH ADOLF RIEDESEL, Baron Eisenbach (1738–1800), German.
No. 12 in *Saratoga*. (See Figs. 184 and 185)

DOROTHEA REMSEN (see MRS. ABRAHAM BRINCKERHOFF).

DAVID RITTENHOUSE (1732–96), astronomer, mathematician.
Miniature, 1790, Philadelphia.
Miss Elizabeth Sergeant Abbot, Philadelphia, Pa.
Bust, posthumous replica, 1816, New York.
Pennsylvania Academy.

DEBORAH RIVERS (see MRS. BARTHOLOMEW SKAATS).

ALTHEA ROBINSON (see MRS. ABEL STILES).

FAITH ROBINSON (see MRS. JONATHAN TRUMBULL, SR.).

LIEUT. GEN. JEAN-BAPTISTE DONATIEN DE VIMEUR, Comte de Rochambeau (1725–1807), French.

Painted sketch, 1787, France.
Unlocated.
No. 14 in *Yorktown*, from the above. (See Figs. 187 and 188)

ANNE MARIA RODGERS (see MRS. WILLIAM PINKNEY).

MOSES ROGERS (1750–1825), New York merchant.
Bust, 1806, New York.
Possibly the same as "Portrait of a Gentleman, Lent by M. Rogers, Esq." (American Academy Cat., 1817, no. 133).
Mrs. H. Schuyler Cammann, Cold Spring Harbor, N.Y.

MRS. MOSES (SARAH WOOLSEY) ROGERS(?) (1750–1816), possibly the "Portrait of a Lady, Lent by M. Rogers, Esq." (American Academy Cat., 1817, no. 135).
Bust(?).
Unlocated.

REBECCA ROGERS (see MRS. JAMES CODWISE).

WILLIAM ROGERS (1761–1817), New York merchant.
Bust, 1804–08, New York.
National Gallery of Art, Washington, D.C., no. NGA 921.

MLLE. ROSAMONDE, French, pupil of Mme. Guiard.
Pen and crayon, 1787, Paris (1st Silliman sale, no. 114).
Yale, no. 1947.494. (Fig. 134)

MAJ. GEN. CHARLES ROSS (d. 1797), British.
No. 2 in *Gibraltar;* "In the autumn of 1787, I again visited Paris, where I painted . . . Major General Ross in the small Sortie of Gibraltar"; *Autobiography,* pp. 150–51. (See Figs. 198 and 199)

BRYAN (BRIAN) ROSSETTER (Rossiter, Roseter) (1760–1834), Revolutionary soldier, sergeant (Connecticut Line), sergeant-at-arms of the Society of the Cincinnati, State of New York.
Bust "in the uniform of the Revolutionary Army," *ca.* 1808, New York (American Academy Cat., 1827, no. 50).
New York State Society of the Cincinnati, Washington, D.C. (Fig. 50)

PETER PAUL RUBENS (1577–1640), Flemish, painter and diplomat.
"Miniature," from a print, 1772–73, Cambridge, Mass.; *Autobiography,* no. 19.
Unlocated.

"Head, copied from a picture in possession of Gov. Hancock," 1778, Boston, Mass.; *Autobiography*, no. 49.
Unlocated.

DR. BENJAMIN RUSH (1745–1813).
No. 19 in *Declaration, ca.* 1790, Philadelphia. (See Figs. 158 and 159)
No. 3 in *Princeton*, as military surgeon. (See Figs. 169 and 170)

THOMAS RUSSELL (1746–96), one of the leading merchants of Boston, and his third wife, ELIZABETH WATSON RUSSELL (1767–1809).
Double portrait, full-length, small, 1793, Boston.
Mrs. James Amory Sullivan, Rindge, N.H.

EDWARD RUTLEDGE (1749–1800), Signer, Governor of South Carolina.
Sketch(?), possibly one of the twenty "heads" painted or drawn at Charleston, S.C., in 1791.
Unlocated.
No. 46 in *Declaration,* from the above. (See Figs. 158 and 159)

ELIZA (ELIZABETH) RUTLEDGE(?) (1776–1842), daughter of John Rutledge (later Mrs. Henry Laurens, Jr.).
Miniature, 1791.
Gibbes Art Gallery, Charleston, S.C.

JOHN RUTLEDGE (1739–1800), statesman, jurist.
Miniature, 1791, Charleston, S.C., signed and dated on back.
Yale, no. 1832.47. (Fig. 105)
Replica, 1791, Charleston, S.C.
James R. Rutledge, Jr., Greenville, S.C.
(?); Mrs. Charles Cotesworth Pinckney, Charleston, S.C.
(?); Mrs. Horace Holt, Stony Creek, Conn.

MRS. JOHN (ELIZABETH GRIMKÉ) RUTLEDGE (married 1763, d. 1792).
Miniature(?), 1791, Charleston, S.C.
Unlocated.

STATES RUTLEDGE (1783–1829), son of John Rutledge.
Miniature(?), 1791, Charleston, S.C.
Unlocated.

S

"THE YOUNG SACHEM," Chief of the Six Nations.
    Miniature, 1792, Philadelphia, signed and dated on back.
    Yale, Trumbull Collection, no. 1832.42. (Fig. 110)

BISHOP OF ST. ASAPH (see JOHN LUXMORE).

MAJ. GEN. ARTHUR ST. CLAIR (1736–1818), Revolutionary officer, Governor of the
Northwest Territory.
    Pencil sketch, 1790, New York (1st Silliman sale, no. 39).
    Metropolitan Museum of Art, no. 06.1346.3. (Fig. 135)

LIEUT. GEN. CLAUDE ANNE, MARQUIS DE ST. SIMON (1749–1819), French.
    No. 7 in *Yorktown*. (See Figs. 187 and 188)

PETER SALEM.
    In "Lieutenant Grosvenor and His Negro Servant," study for *Bunker's Hill;* in
        Bunker's Hill (on extreme right, no key number). (See Figs. 145 and 146)

MR. SANDERSON.
    "Kit-kat size," 1811, London.
    Unlocated.

MRS. SANDERSON.
    Same as above (Royal Academy, London, 1811, no. 87).
    Unlocated.

CORNELIA SANDS (see MRS. NATHANIEL PRIME).

MAJ. WINTHROP SARGENT (1753–1820), soldier, administrator, first Governor of Missis-
sippi Territory.
    Pencil sketch, 1790, New York (1st Silliman sale, no. 45).
    The late Lord Killearn (a descendant of Gov. Sargent), of "Haremere Hall," Etch-
        ingham, Sussex, England; M. Knoedler & Co., Inc., New York. (Fig. 51)

COL. ALEXANDER SCAMMELL (1747–81), 3d New Hampshire Regt.
    No. 8 in *Saratoga,* not from life. (See Figs. 184 and 185)

ANGELICA SCHUYLER (see MRS. JOHN BARKER CHURCH).

CORNELIA SCHUYLER (later Mrs. Washington Morton) (1776–1808).
    Miniature, 1792, Philadelphia, signed and dated on back.
    Yale, Trumbull Collection, no. 1832.56. (Fig. 114)

MAJ. GEN. PHILIP JOHN SCHUYLER (1733–1804), Revolutionary officer, statesman.

    Miniature, 1792, Philadelphia, signed and dated on back.

    Yale, Trumbull Collection, no. 1832.64. (Fig. 112)

    Miniature, 1792, Philadelphia.

    New-York Historical Society, no. 1915.13. (Fig. 124)

    No. 23 in *Saratoga,* from the above. (See Figs. 184 and 185)

    See also Miniature of an Unknown Man.

THEODORE SEDGWICK (1746–1813), lawyer, Member of Congress from Massachusetts, United States Senator, Judge, Massachusetts Supreme Court.

    Miniature, 1792, Philadelphia, signed and dated on back.

    Yale, Trumbull Collection, no. 1832.43. (Fig. 110)

MRS. SEWALL AND HER TWO SONS.

    Bequeathed by the artist to Catherine Lentner, sister of Mrs. Sewall.

    Unlocated.

JULIA SEYMOUR (later Mrs. John Chenevard) (1769–1843).

    Miniature, 1792, Lebanon, Conn., signed and dated on back.

    Yale, Trumbull Collection, no. 1832.39. (Fig. 115)

CAPT. THOMAS YOUNGS SEYMOUR (1757–1811), Revolutionary officer, 2d Continental Dragoons.

    Miniature, 1793, Hartford, signed and dated on back.

    Yale, Trumbull Collection, no. 1832.28. (Fig. 104)

    No. 4 in *Saratoga,* from the above. (See Figs. 184 and 185)

MISS A. SHEAFFE (Ann, later Mrs. John Erving), daughter of William Sheaffe, Deputy Collector of Customs at Boston.

    "Small head," on oval copper plate, 1778, Boston; *Autobiography,* no. 60.

    Unlocated.

MISS P. SHEAFFE ("Polly," Margaret, later Mrs. John R. Livingston), younger sister of the above.

    Also small head on copper, same date; *Autobiography,* no. 59.

    Unlocated.

COL. WILLIAM SHEPARD (also spelled Shepherd) (1737–1817), 3d Continental Infantry.

    No. 2 in *Trenton, ca.* 1793 in Massachusetts. (See Figs. 164 and 165)

ROGER SHERMAN (1721–93).

    No. 32 in *Declaration, ca.* 1790, Philadelphia. (See Figs. 158 and 159)

CAPT. THOMAS SHUBRICK (1756–1810), aide-de-camp to Gen. Greene.
    Miniature, 1791, Charleston, S.C., signed and dated on back.
    Mrs. George Clymer, Longmeadow, Mass.

MR. SHUTTLEWORTH (possibly Samuel Shuttleworth, Harvard, A.B. [1777, d. 1834], or Ashton Ashton Shuttleworth [1754–1830], British, Major, Royal Artillery).
    "Small whole length," before 1784, London.
    Unlocated.

MRS. CHARLES (LYDIA HUNTLEY) SIGOURNEY (1791–1865).
    Poetess, "the Sweet Singer of Hartford."
    Half-length, 1838, New Haven, Conn.
    Wadsworth Atheneum, Hartford, no. 1863.7. (Fig. 52)

BENJAMIN SILLIMAN (1779–1864), of New Haven, scientist, Yale professor, editor of the *American Journal of Science,* nephew-in-law of the painter, first Curator of the Trumbull Gallery.
    Bust, on wood, *ca.* 1805, New Haven or New York.
    Mrs. Forbes Hawkes, Coconut Grove, Fla.

    1825, New York.
    Unlocated.

MRS. BENJAMIN (HARRIET TRUMBULL) SILLIMAN (1783–1850), the artist's niece, daughter of Jonathan Trumbull, Jr.
    1825(?), New York(?).
    Miss Angelica Schuyler Church, Ossining, N.Y., in 1949.

    Replica, 1834, New York.
    Unlocated.

FAITH WADSWORTH SILLIMAN (see MRS. OLIVER PAYSON HUBBARD).

"L. SIMOND, for a portrait of himself with hands," probably Lewis (Louis) Simond, New York, West Indian merchant, incorporator of the American Academy of the Fine Arts in 1808, member of the New-York Historical Society in 1812, married Frances Wilkes at New York in 1791.
    1806, New York.
    Unlocated.

SAMUEL SITGREAVES (1764–1827), Member of Congress from Pennsylvania, Commissioner on the Jay Treaty.
    Bust, *ca.* 1820, New York.
    Mrs. Edgar Grim Miller, Jr., New York.

BARTHOLOMEW SKAATS (New York Dutch family formerly spelled Schaets or Schaats) (1754–1830), silversmith, "welcomer" of New York City, Keeper of New York City Hall in 1812, occupied apartments there (Trumbull painted thirteen portraits for City Hall between 1790 and 1816).

Bust, *ca.* 1816, New York.
City Art Museum of St. Louis, no. 26:56. (Fig. 53)

MRS. BARTHOLOMEW (DEBORAH RIVERS) SKAATS, married 1794.
Half-length, *ca.* 1816, New York.
International Business Machines, New York, on long-term loan to the American Embassy in The Hague. (Fig. 54)

MAJ. JOHN SMALL (1726–96), British, 84th Regt. of Foot (Royal Highland Emigrants).
No. 15 in *Bunker's Hill,* if from life *ca.* 1784, London. (See Figs. 145 and 146)

"REV. D. SMALLEY" (see MAURICE SWABEY).

MAJ. GEN. WILLIAM SMALLWOOD (1732–92), Revolutionary officer, Governor of Maryland.
Miniature, 1792, Philadelphia, after Charles Willson Peale, signed and dated on back.
Yale, Trumbull Collection, no. 1832.60. (Fig. 112)
No. 25 in *Resignation,* from the above. (See Figs. 203 and 204)

MRS. JUNIUS (SARAH ALLEN) SMITH.
Half-length, *ca.* 1816, New York(?).
Chicago Historical Society.

LIEUT. COL. SAMUEL SMITH (1752–1839), Lee's Additional Continental Regt.
No. 27 in *Resignation, ca.* 1790, Maryland(?). (See Figs. 203 and 204)

WILLIAM LOUGHTON SMITH (*ca.* 1758–1812), lawyer, Member of Congress from South Carolina, Minister to Portugal.
Miniature, 1792, Philadelphia, signed and dated on back.
Yale, gift of Herbert L. Pratt, no. 1936.116. (Fig. 111)

LIEUT. COL. WILLIAM STEPHENS SMITH (1755–1816), Revolutionary officer, Secretary of the Legation at London in 1785, Member of Congress from New York.
Bust (partly ruined, face completely restored), probably 1785, London.
Amherst College, Amherst, Mass., no. 1945.79.

WILLIAM STEPHENS SMITH (1755–1816).
No. 6 in *Trenton,* 1787, London, as major. (See Figs. 164 and 165)

RICHARD DOBBS SPAIGHT (1758–1802), Member of Congress from North Carolina.
> No. 9 in *Resignation, ca.* 1790. (See Figs. 203 and 204)

DAVID SPROAT (1734–99), British, uncle of James and Robert Lenox of New York, Loyalist, merchant of Philadelphia, Commissary General of Naval Prisoners of War in North America, later Provost of Kirkcudbright, Scotland.
> Three-quarter length, small, 1806, New York (a posthumous copy, with slight variations, after a portrait painted in 1788 by an unknown hand, now in the Lenox Collection, New York Public Library).
> New-York Historical Society, no. 1950.224.

BRIG. GEN. JOHN STARK (1728–1833), New Hampshire Militia.
> No. 3 in *Saratoga, ca.* 1790(?), New Hampshire(?). (See Figs. 184 and 185)

MAJ. GEN. FRIEDRICH WILHELM LUDOLF GERHARD AUGUSTIN, Baron von Steuben (1730–94), German, Continental Army.
> No. 20 in *Yorktown, ca.* 1790, New York(?). (See Figs. 187 and 188)

LIEUT. COL. EBENEZER STEVENS (1751–1823), Revolutionary officer, Independent Battalion of Artillery, Continental Army.
> Miniature, 1790, New York, signed and dated on back.
> Yale, Trumbull Collection, no. 1832.27. (Fig. 104)

> No. 27 in *Saratoga,* from the above, as major. (See Figs. 184 and 185)

> No. 16 in *Yorktown,* 2d Continental Artillery, from the above, as lieut. col. (See Figs. 187 and 188)

COL. WALTER STEWART (*ca.* 1756–96), 2d Pennsylvania Regt.
> No. 33 in *Yorktown.* (See Figs. 187 and 188)

REV. ABEL STILES (1708/9–83), uncle of Ezra Stiles (President of Yale), Congregational minister of Woodstock, Conn.
> Bust, *ca.* 1777, Woodstock, Conn.(?).
> Unlocated.

MRS. ABEL (ALTHEA ROBINSON) STILES (1710–86), sister of Mrs. Jonathan Trumbull, Sr.
> Same as above.

STIMAFUTCHKE, or "Good Humor of the Coosades," Creek Indian chief.
> Drawing, 1790, New York (1st Silliman sale, no. 67); *Autobiography,* pl. 20.
> Unlocated.

RICHARD STOCKTON (1730–81), lawyer, Signer.
>   Pencil sketch, posthumous.
>   Yale, gift of Mrs. Winchester Bennett, no. 1931.67.
>   No. 11 in *Declaration,* from the above. (See Figs. 158 and 159)

WILLIAM LEETE STONE (1792–1844), journalist, historian, editor of the New-York *Commercial Advertiser*.
>   Bust, *ca.* 1821, New York.
>   Mrs. Charles H. Higgins, New York. (Fig. 55)

MRS. WILLIAM LEETE (SUSANNAH PRITCHARD WAYLAND) STONE (1798–1852).
>   Bust, on wood, *ca.* 1821, New York.
>   Newark Museum, Newark, N.J.

PETER STUYVESANT (1592–1672), Director-General of New Netherland.
>   Copied from the *Stuyvesant Limner,* 1808, New York.
>   City Hall, New York. (Fig. 56)

MAJ. GEN. JOHN SULLIVAN (1740–95), Revolutionary officer, statesman.
>   Pencil sketch, 1790.
>   Unlocated.
>   Miniature.
>   Mrs. James Amory Sullivan, Rindge, N.H.
>   No. 10 in *Trenton,* from the above. (See Figs. 164 and 165)

MRS. THOMAS (SARAH ANNIS) SULLY (1779–1867), wife of the painter.
>   Bust, 1806, New York, signed and dated on back.
>   Amherst College, Amherst, Mass., no. 1945.83. (Fig. 57)

MAURICE SWABEY (1752?–1826), British associate of the artist on the commission for the adjustment of claims under Article 7 of the Jay Treaty (previously misidentified as "Dr. Smalley" and "Rev. D. Smalley").
>   Bust, *ca.* 1800, London.
>   New-York Historical Society, no. 1858.74. (Fig. 58)

LIEUT. COL. BENJAMIN TALLMADGE(?) (1754–1835), Revolutionary officer, Member of Congress from Connecticut.
>   Pencil sketch, *ca.* 1790 in Connecticut.
>   Unlocated.

AUGUSTA GRENVILLE TEMPLE (1779–1852), British, married William L. Palmer of the British Army in 1797.

    "Small portrait," 1783, Boston, Mass.
    Unlocated.

    "Small head," 1784, London.
    Unlocated.

    Replica, "small," 1784, London.
    Unlocated.

SIR GRENVILLE TEMPLE, 9th baronet (1768–1829), British, eldest child of Sir John Temple.

    Bust, *ca.* 1784(?), London.
    Massachusetts Historical Society.

    Same as the above(?), 1844 auction sale no. 15.
    Unlocated.

GRENVILLE TEMPLE (see below).

SIR JOHN TEMPLE, 8th baronet (baptized 1732–d. 1798), first British Consul-General at New York.

    Three-quarter length, 1784, London (Royal Academy, London, 1784, no. 68).
    Canajoharie Library and Art Gallery, Canajoharie, N.Y. (Fig. 59)

SIR JOHN TEMPLE AND FAMILY; his wife, Lady (Elizabeth Bowdoin) Temple, their son, Grenville, and infant daughter, Augusta.

    Full-length group, small, 1784, London.
    George Temple Bowdoin, "Nevis," Oyster Bay, N.Y. (Fig. 60)
    Study in pen and wash, not used for full-length group, 1784, London.
    Yale, no. 1946.476. (Fig. 61)

LADY (ELIZABETH BOWDOIN) TEMPLE (1759–1809).

    "Small head," 1784, London.
    Copied by Gilbert Stuart; see Lawrence Park, *Gilbert Stuart* (New York, 1926), no. 824.
    Unlocated.

MRS. NATHANIEL TERRY (see CATHERINE WADSWORTH).

COL. WILLIAM THOMPSON (1736–81), Thompson's Pennsylvania Regt.

    No. 5 in *Quebec,* posthumous. (See Figs. 152 and 153)

CHARLES THOMSON (1729–1824), Member of Congress from Pennsylvania.
    No. 42 in *Declaration, ca.* 1790 at or near Philadelphia. (See Figs. 158 and 159)
    No. 2 in *Resignation.* (See Figs. 203 and 204)

CAPT. TENCH TILGHMAN (1744–86), Military Secretary to Gen. Washington.
    No. 8 in *Trenton,* posthumous. (See Figs. 164 and 165)

CAPT. ROBERT TIPPING (1760–1823), British, 72d Regt. of Foot (Royal Manchester Volunteers).
    No. 10 in *Gibraltar,* 1785–87, London. (See Figs. 198 and 199)

DANIEL D. TOMPKINS (1774–1825), Governor of New York, Vice President of the United States.
    Full-length, 1808, New York.
    City Hall, New York. (Fig. 62)

NATHANIEL TRACY (1751–96), merchant of Newburyport, Mass., and London.
    Full-length, 1784, London.
    Unlocated.

PATRICK TRACY (1711–89), merchant and shipowner of Newburyport, Mass.
    Full-length, head copied from an unknown source, 1784, London; figure and background 1786.
    National Gallery of Art, Washington, D.C., gift of Patrick T. Jackson, Jr., no. NGA 1926.

LIEUT. COL. THOMAS TRIGGE, British, 12th Regt. of Foot.
    No. 5 in *Gibraltar,* 1784–87, London. (See Figs. 198 and 199)

LIEUT. COL. ROBERT TROUP (1757–1832), aide-de-camp to Gen. Gates.
    No. 20 in *Saratoga, ca.* 1790, New York(?). (See Figs. 184 and 185)

ABIGAIL TRUMBULL (1781–1861) (see CHILDREN OF DAVID TRUMBULL and MRS. PETER LANMAN).

DAVID TRUMBULL (1751–1822), Norwich, Conn., the artist's brother, third son of Jonathan Trumbull, Sr., merchant, Assistant Commissary of the Continental Army.
    "Small whole-length, standing in a landscape," begun 1774, finished 1777, Lebanon, Conn.; *Autobiography,* no. 24.
    Unlocated.
    Bust, *ca.* 1792, Connecticut.
    Mrs. Clifton M. Bockstoce, Hartford, Conn.

Miniature, *ca.* 1792, Connecticut.
Unlocated.

Mrs. David (Sarah Backus) Trumbull (1769–1846).
Miniature, probably same date.
Unlocated.

Children of David Trumbull and Mrs. David (Sarah Backus) Trumbull (married 1778), Sarah, Abigail, Joseph, John, and Jonathan George Washington.
Pencil drawing, 1790, Connecticut.
Mrs. Clifton M. Bockstoce, Hartford, Conn.

Faith Trumbull (later Mrs. Daniel Wadsworth) (1769–1846), the artist's niece, eldest daughter of Jonathan Trumbull, Jr.
Miniature, 1791, Hartford, Conn., signed and dated on back.
Yale, Trumbull Collection, no. 1832.36. (Fig. 115)

Pencil sketch, slightly later, possibly at the time of her marriage in 1794.
Yale, gift of Mrs. George H. Gray, no. 1939.282.

See also group portrait of the family of Jonathan Trumbull, Jr. (Fig. 79)

Harriet Trumbull (see Mrs. Benjamin Silliman).

John Trumbull (1756–1843), Revolutionary officer, aide-de-camp to Gen. Washington, "Patriot-Artist," diplomat, amateur architect, incorporator and fourth President of the American Academy of the Fine Arts.
Small bust, oval, 1774, Lebanon, Conn.; *Autobiography,* no. 26.
John McClellan, Woodstock, Conn. (Fig. 63)

Half-length, 1777, Lebanon, Conn., signed and dated on back; *Autobiography,* no. 29.
Museum of Fine Arts, Boston (bequest of George Nixon Black), no. 29.791. (Fig. 64)

On oval copper plate, 1779, Boston; *Autobiography,* no. 62.
Unlocated.

Half-length (also known as *Portrait of an Artist* and *Portrait of a Gentleman*), 1801, London, dated.
Wadsworth Atheneum, Hartford (bequest of Daniel Wadsworth, 1848), no. 1848.6. (Fig. 65)

Half-length, *ca.* 1812, London.
Marshall Hill Clyde, Jr., Geneva, Switzerland. (Fig. 66)

Bust, on wood, 1833, New York (badly damaged by fire, repainted in part) (engraved by Daggett, Hinman & Co. of New Haven, *ca.* 1840).
Connecticut State Library, Hartford, deposited at Yale, no. 927.1929.

"In a blue coat and white vest."
Unlocated.

"Belonging to D. Lanamar [David Lanman], of Brooklyn, L.I.," in 1867.
Unlocated.

In Prison, half-length, head by Gilbert Stuart, remainder by Trumbull, 1781, London.
Pilgrim Hall, Plymouth, Mass.

Mrs. John (Sarah Hope Harvey) Trumbull (1774–1824, married 1800 at London).
Bust, *ca.* 1800, London.
Spencer R. McCulloch, Kirkwood, Mo.

"15 x 12, a fine painting" (1844 auction sale, no. 18).
Unlocated.

"Small size" (1844 auction sale, no. 24).
Unlocated.

Half-length, *ca.* 1800, London.
Mrs. Charles H. Higgins, New York. (Fig. 67)

Half-length (formerly attributed to Samuel Lovett Waldo), 1804–08(?), New York(?).
Yale, gift of Mrs. Pat Woodward, no. 1929.1.

Half-length, identical with the above, possibly the original (and the above a later replica), painted between 1800 and 1804, London.
The Henry Francis du Pont Winterthur Museum, Winterthur, Del., no. 60.150. (Fig. 69)

With a spaniel, half-length, *ca.* 1812, London.
Marshall Hill Clyde, Jr., Geneva, Switzerland. (Fig. 68)

As "Sensibility," half-length, *ca.* 1816(?), New York.
Mrs. Elizabeth Lawrence Anderson, Saranac Lake, N.Y.

In lace cap, bust, 1816–24, New York.
Lieut. Col. Trumbull Warren, Corwhin Acres, Puslinch, Ontario, Canada.

Identical with the above but with right hand at breast, on wood.
Mrs. H. Bull Richardson, New York.

Identical with the above, but a miniature.
Unlocated.

Study for *Innocence,* full-length, seated, pencil, *ca.* 1816, New York.
Yale, no. 1947.479.

In a lace cap, as "Innocence," with a dove, half-length, 1816–24, New York.
Yale, Trumbull Collection, no. 1838.1. (Fig. 70)

On her deathbed, 1824, New York.
Joseph Lanman Richards, New London, Conn. (Fig. 71)

JOHN TRUMBULL (1750–1831), second cousin of the artist, poet, jurist, "Hartford Wit,"
author of *M'fingal.*

Bust, 1793, Hartford, signed and dated.
Detroit Institute of Arts, no. 38.13. (Fig. 72)

Miniature, 1794, Hartford, signed and dated on back.
Yale, Trumbull Collection, no. 1832.69. (Fig. 113)

JOHN M. TRUMBULL (1784–1859), the artist's nephew, second son of David Trumbull.
Half-length, with a spaniel, *ca.* 1800, London. (Note: The "M," standing for noth-
ing at all, was added later to distinguish him from the other John Trum-
bulls.)
Heyward Isham, Washington, D.C., on loan to The Corcoran Gallery of Art,
Washington, D.C., no. L.62.3. (Fig. 73)

JONATHAN TRUMBULL, SR. (1710–85), the artist's father, Colonial and Revolutionary
Governor of Connecticut.
1774, Lebanon, Conn.
John Trumbull Band, Toronto, Canada.

Bust, in oval frame with symbolic figures, 1774 or 1775, Lebanon, Conn.
Trumbull College, Yale, gift of Lt. Gov. Jonathan Trumbull, no. 1797.1. (Fig. 74)

1783, Lebanon, Conn.
Unlocated.

Miniature, posthumous, after the 1783 portrait, in 1793, signed and dated on back.
Yale, Trumbull Collection, no. 1832.66. (Fig. 113)

Bust, replica of the above, *ca.* 1820, New York(?).
Wadsworth Atheneum, Hartford, no. 1848.7.

Three-quarter length, posthumous, 1820, New York; from the Woodstock double
portrait, inscribed and signed on back.
Trumbull College, Yale, gift of the artist, no. 1821.1. (Fig. 78)

Portrait of Jonathan Trumbull, Governor of Connecticut, During the Revolution
(American Academy Cat., 1820, no. 51), probably one of the above.
Unlocated.

JONATHAN AND MRS. JONATHAN (FAITH ROBINSON) TRUMBULL, SR.

> Large double portrait, "heads in oval spaces, surrounded by ornamental work, from Houbraken's heads [the Dutch engraver, Jacob Houbraken, 1698–1780], Justice and Piety, etc.," 1774, Lebanon, Conn.; *Autobiography*, no. 22 (1st Silliman sale, no. 344).
> Wadsworth Atheneum, Hartford, no. 1950.835.

> Replica of the above, heads in ovals with symbolic figures, 1775, Lebanon, Conn., inscribed on back, signed in front.
> Connecticut Historical Society, no. 103.

> Double portrait, "size of life—my father dressed in a blue damask night gown," seated at a table; Lebanon, Conn., signed and dated on back; *Autobiography*, no. 33.
> Connecticut Historical Society, no. 72. (Fig. 75; see also Fig. 76)

> Small double portrait, busts, the governor standing in front of his (deceased) wife, 1783, Lebanon, Conn.
> Vose Galleries, Boston, Mass. (stolen in 1958).

> Same as above, on wood, also 1783, Lebanon, Conn.
> Trumbull College, Yale, gift of Mrs. Malcolm E. Anderson, no. 1958.51. (Fig. 77)

> Same as above, on wood, same year.
> Mrs. Clifton M. Bockstoce, Hartford, Conn.

MRS. JONATHAN (FAITH ROBINSON) TRUMBULL, SR. (1718–80), daughter of Rev. John Robinson of Duxbury, Mass.

> 1779, Lebanon, Conn.
> Unlocated.

> Wash drawing, posthumous, 1783, Lebanon, Conn., used in the double portrait of that year (1st Silliman sale, no. 54), signed and dated on back.
> Mrs. Richard Ely Danielson, Groton, Mass.

> Miniature, 1793, Lebanon, Conn., "copied from one done—from life in 1779," signed and dated on back.
> Yale, Trumbull Collection, no. 1832.37. (Fig. 115)

JONATHAN TRUMBULL, JR. (1740–1809), the artist's brother, second son of Jonathan Trumbull, Sr., Military Secretary to Gen. Washington, Governor of Connecticut.

> Miniature, 1792, Philadelphia, signed and dated on back.
> Yale, Trumbull Collection, no. 1832.65. (Fig. 113)

> (?) Miniature replica of above.
> Mrs. William Williams Mathewson, Washington, D.C.

Half-length, *ca.* 1806(?), in Connecticut.
Mrs. Clifton M. Bockstoce, Hartford, Conn.

No. 22 in *Yorktown*, 1786 or 1787, London, as lieut. col. (See Figs. 187 and 188)

JONATHAN, MRS. JONATHAN (EUNICE BACKUS) TRUMBULL, JR., and THEIR ELDEST DAUGHTER, FAITH TRUMBULL (who became the wife of Daniel Wadsworth, founder of the Wadsworth Atheneum, Hartford, Conn.).
Drawing, 1777, Lebanon, Conn. (1st Silliman sale, no. 55).
Unlocated.

Group portrait, 1777, Lebanon, Conn.; *Autobiography*, no. 28.
Yale, gift of Miss Henrietta Hubbard, no. 1920.2. (Fig. 79; see also Fig. 80)

MRS. JONATHAN (EUNICE BACKUS) TRUMBULL, JR. (1749–1826).
Miniature, 1793, Connecticut.
Yale, gift of Miss Maria Trumbull Dana, no. 1958.34. (Fig. 125)

JONATHAN GEORGE WASHINGTON TRUMBULL (1787–1853), fire insurance underwriter of Norwich, Conn.
Bust, on academy board, 1828, Norwich, Conn.
Miss Elizabeth M. Trumbull, Norwich Town, Conn.

MRS. JONATHAN G. W. (JANE ELIZA LATHROP) TRUMBULL (1795–1843).
Half-length, but a companion portrait, also on academy board, 1828, Norwich, Conn.
Same as above.

JOSEPH TRUMBULL (1737–78), the artist's brother, oldest son of Gov. Jonathan Trumbull, Sr., first Commissary General of the Continental Forces.
Full-length, posthumous, "from memory," 1778, Boston, Mass.; *Autobiography*, no. 52.
Probably the version owned by Mrs. Clifton M. Bockstoce, Hartford, Conn. (Fig. 81)

Replica, 1778, Lebanon, Conn.; *Autobiography*, no. 56.
Pilgrim Hall, Plymouth, Mass., on indefinite loan to Connecticut Historical Society.

Drawing, posthumous, 1783, Lebanon, Conn.
Signed and dated (1st Silliman sale, no. 53).
Estate of Hall Park McCullough, Bennington, Vt. (Fig. 136)

MRS. JOSEPH (AMELIA DYER) TRUMBULL (married 1777), later Mrs. Hezekiah Wyllys (married 1785).

Half-length, 1777 or 1778, Lebanon, Conn., partially repainted (by another hand: Ralph Earl?).
Connecticut Historical Society, no. 3.1955.0.

JOSEPH TRUMBULL (1782–1861), later Governor of Connecticut (see CHILDREN OF DAVID TRUMBULL).

MARY TRUMBULL (see MRS. WILLIAM WILLIAMS).

SARAH TRUMBULL (1779–1839), later Mrs. William T. Williams (see CHILDREN OF DAVID TRUMBULL).

THOMAS GIBBONS TRUMBULL (1811–48), son of John M. Trumbull and his first wife, Anne Gibbons.
Bust, *ca.* 1839, New York.
Mrs. Allan Traine Trumbull, Englewood, N.J.

2D LIEUT. CHARLES TURNBULL (d. 1795), Proctor's Battalion Pennsylvania Artillery.
No. 2 in *Princeton, ca.* 1790(?). (See Figs. 169 and 170)

TUSKATCHE MICO (properly Fus-Hatchee Miko) of the Bird Tail, King of the Cusitahs (Kasihta).
Pencil sketch, 1790, New York (1st Silliman sale, no. 65).
Yale, no. 1947.497. (Fig. 130)

ROYALL TYLER (1757–1826), jurist, playwright.
"Head, with both hands," 1779, Boston, Mass.; *Autobiography,* no. 67.
Unlocated.

JOHN TYRRELL (also spelled Terrill and Terrell) (1776–1857), son of the American Loyalist, William Terrill, secretary to his uncle, Sir George Nugent, Governor of Jamaica, in 1804.
Bust with hands, 1806, New York.
Rear Admiral William Sherbrooke Popham, USN ret., Charleston, S.C.

V

MAJ. CHARLES VALLOTTON, British, 56th Regt. of Foot.
No. 8 in *Gibraltar,* 1784–87, London. (See Figs. 198 and 199)

CORNELIUS VAN DER GEEST (see under GEEST).

SIR ANTHONY VAN DYCK (1599–1641), Flemish painter.
"Head, copied from a picture in possession of Gov. Hancock"; *Autobiography,* no. 50.
Unlocated.

MARIE VAN RANST (see MRS. GEORGE CODWISE).

STEPHEN VAN RENSSELAER (1764–1839), patroon, Revolutionary officer, Member of Congress from New York.
> Half-length, 1806, New York.
> Yale, Trumbull Collection, no. 1832.14. (Fig. 82)

PETER VAN SCHAACK(?) (1747–1832), Loyalist, lawyer and scholar from Kinderhook, N.Y.
> 1824(?), Kinderhook, N.Y.(?); see engraved frontispiece by Joseph Napoleon Gimbrede, in Henry C. van Schaack, *Life of Peter van Schaack, LL.D.* (New York, D. Appleton & Co., 1842).
> Unlocated.

RICHARD VARICK (1753–1831), Revolutionary officer, Mayor of New York.
> Half-length, 1805, New York.
> City Hall, New York. (Fig. 83)

> "Portrait of a Gentleman, Lent by Richard Varrick, Esq." (American Academy Cat., 1817, no. 129), probably the above.
> Unlocated.

> Same.
> The Misses Maria and Amy Reid Knox, Chappaqua, N.Y., in 1949.

JOHN VERNET (1764–1827), West Indian merchant of Norwich, Conn.
> Bust, 1806, Norwich.
> Mrs. W. V. Ingham, Kingston, Pa., in 1949.

JOHN AND MRS. (ANNE BROWN) VERNET.
> Pencil drawing, "7 pieces . . . including a Portrait of Mr. and Mrs. Vernet" (2d Silliman sale, no. 839).
> Unlocated.

JOHN AND MRS. JOHN (ANNE BROWN) VERNET, AND THEIR TWO CHILDREN, JOHN GILL AND PETER CROISE VERNET.
> Group portrait, 1806, Norwich, Conn.
> Yale, gift of Yale University Art Gallery Associates, no. 1943.1. (Fig. 84)

MRS. WILLIAM GORDON VER PLANCK (see MARY ELIZABETH HOPKINS).

ELIZABETH VIGÉE-LEBRUN (1755–1842), French portrait painter, and her daughter.
> Pen sketch after self-portrait painted in 1786 at Paris, now in the Louvre (1st Silliman sale, no. 133 or 135).
> Yale, no. 1947.493.

LIEUT. GEN. ANTOINE CHARLES DU HOUX, BARON DE VIOMÉNIL (1728–92), French.
No. 11 in *Yorktown*, 1787, Paris. (See Figs. 187 and 188)

MARÉCHAL-DE-CAMP CHARLES JOSEPH HYACINTHE DU HOUX, MARQUIS DE VIOMÉNIL (1734–1827), French.
No. 6 in *Yorktown*, 1787, Paris. (See Figs. 187 and 188)

CAPT. BARON VON HELMSTADT (died from wounds after the Sortie, 1781), Walloon Guards.
No. 18 in *Gibraltar*, posthumous. (See Figs. 198 and 199)

BARON VON STEUBEN (see STEUBEN).

W

CATHERINE WADSWORTH (later Mrs. Nathaniel Terry) (1774–1841), daughter of Jeremiah Wadsworth of Hartford, Conn.
Miniature, 1792, Philadelphia, signed and dated on back.
Yale, Trumbull Collection, no. 1832.38. (Fig. 115)
Replica, miniature, 1792, Philadelphia.
Faneuil Adams, South Duxbury, Mass.

MRS. DANIEL WADSWORTH (see FAITH TRUMBULL).

HARRIET WADSWORTH (1769–93), daughter of Jeremiah Wadsworth, beloved by the artist, died at 24 in Bermuda.
Miniature, 1793, from memory, posthumous, signed and dated on back.
Yale, Trumbull Collection, no. 1832.35. (Fig. 115)
Miniature, probably painted in 1793 for Daniel Wadsworth.
Mrs. Paul van Horn (Catherine Wadsworth Whyte) Aikman, Alhambra, Calif.
(Fig. 126)

JAMES WADSWORTH (1768–1844), landed proprietor, pioneer in public school education.
Bust, 1820s.
William Perkins Wadsworth, "The Homestead," Geneseo, N.Y.

JEREMIAH WADSWORTH (1743–1804), Commissary General of the Continental Army (following Joseph Trumbull), merchant, banker, Member of Congress from Connecticut.
Small miniature (2½ inches high) on copper, 1790 or 1792, Philadelphia.
Mrs. Paul van Horn (Catherine Wadsworth Whyte) Aikman, Alhambra, Calif.

JEREMIAH WADSWORTH AND HIS SON, DANIEL WADSWORTH (1771–1849), merchant, banker, art patron, founder of the Wadsworth Atheneum.

> Double portrait full-length, 1784, London (the "bent tin" portrait, the last in the "early Copley manner"; see *Autobiography*, p. 86).
>
> Faneuil Adams, South Duxbury, Mass., on loan to the Wadsworth Atheneum, Hartford, no. 725. (Fig. 85)
>
> Enlarged replica (of the bust only, figure of young Daniel Wadsworth omitted); from the above, 1838–39, New Haven.
>
> James Jeremiah Wadsworth, Washington, D.C.

GEN. WILLIAM WADSWORTH (1761–1833), farmer.

> Bust, 1820s.
>
> William Perkins Wadsworth, "The Homestead," Geneseo, N.Y.

REV. JONATHAN MAYHEW WAINWRIGHT (1792–1854), Episcopal minister, later Bishop of the Diocese of New York.

> Half-length, *ca.* 1822, New York, probably the same as "Portrait of a Clergyman" (American Academy Cat., 1822, no. 33).
>
> New Britain Museum of American Art, New Britain, Conn. (Fig. 86)

MRS. JONATHAN MAYHEW (AMELIA MARIA PHELPS) WAINWRIGHT (married 1818).

> Half-length, seated, 1822, New York.
>
> The Corcoran Gallery of Art, Washington, D.C., no. 55–22. (Fig. 87)

MISS WALDO.

> "Small portrait," 1783, London.
>
> Unlocated.
>
> Replica, 1784, Boston.
>
> Unlocated.

LIEUT. COL. BENJAMIN WALKER (1753–1818), Revolutionary officer, naval officer of the Port of New York (note to Dr. David Hosack, 9 May 1828).

> Bust(?), for no. 23 in *Resignation*.
>
> Unlocated.
>
> No. 23 in *Resignation*, from the above. (See Figs. 203 and 204)

GEORGE WALTON (1741–1804), Senator from Georgia.

> No. 27 in *Declaration*, from a miniature by Charles Willson Peale (now at Yale). (See Figs. 158 and 159)

CAPT. SAMUEL WARD (1756–1832), 1st Rhode Island Regt.
No. 9 in *Quebec,* not from life. (See Figs. 152 and 153)

MAJ. GEN. JOSEPH WARREN (1741–75) (killed at Bunker's Hill), Massachusetts Militia.
Pencil sketch, posthumous, 1785, London, for no. 1 in *Bunker's Hill.*
Yale, gift of Mrs. Robert F. Jefferys, no. 1952.3.1a.

No. 1 in *Bunker's Hill,* posthumous (probably after John Singleton Copley's 1772–74 portrait, now in the Museum of Fine Arts, Boston, no. 95.1366). (See Figs. 145 and 146)

GEN. GEORGE WASHINGTON (1732–99), Commander-in-Chief (Washington notes in his diary that he sat for Trumbull five times in February, three in March, and four in July 1790), first President of the United States.

EARLY TYPE

"Half-length," copied after Charles Willson Peale's 1776 portrait for John Hancock, now in the Brooklyn Museum, no. 34.1178 (Fig. 88); *Autobiography,* no. 47; 1778, Boston, Mass., cut down at undetermined date, leaving head alone.
Yale, no. 1870.2. (Fig. 89)
"Half-length from memory," 1778, Lebanon, Conn.; *Autobiography,* no. 57.
Unlocated.

DE NEUFVILLE TYPE

Full-length, with his bodyservant, Billy Lee, holding dark brown horse, flag of alternate white and red stripes (no blue canton) flying at West Point. 1780, London, from memory.
Given by the artist to L. de Neufville of the international banking house of John de Neufville & Son, Amsterdam, Holland; there for a century.
Bequest of Charles Allen Munn to the Metropolitan Museum of Art, no. 24.109.88. (Fig. 90)
(Engraved in mezzotint by Valentine Green, 1739–1813, London, 1781 [Fig. 91] and again, bust only, in 1783).
(Bust used on U.S. postage stamp no. 712, 7¢, black, 1932; Morgan and Fielding, no. 1).

WRIGHT PORTRAIT

Half-length, head painted in 1784 by Joseph Wright, completed by Trumbull in 1787(?), Paris.
Painted for Thomas Jefferson.
Israel Thorndike to the Massachusetts Historical Society.

Martha Washington Type

Full-length, small; leaning against the saddle of a white horse—"the Background represents the encampment of the American Army at Verplanck's point on the North River in 1782;—and the reception of the French Army on their return from Virginia, after the capture of York Town—Stoney Point, & part of the Highlands, and a glimpse of the North River, at the place where the Troops of France crossed are seen in the distance" (Trumbull's note with the picture); 1790, New York, signed and dated, presented by the artist to Martha Washington (Washington, "Diary," 8 July 1790).

Eliza Parke Custis Law, to Gen. Edmund Law Rogers, to Mrs. Wilfred P. Mustard, to Edmund L. R. Smith, "Reunion," Lutherville, Md. (Morgan and Fielding, no. 4).

The Henry Francis du Pont Winterthur Museum, Winterthur, Del. (Figs. 92 and 93)

Same, life size, 1790, New York, signed and dated; "a large Portrait for this City (New York) which I am now finishing—the figure is near seven feet high compos'd with a Horse, & the background the evacuation of this Place by the British at the Peace—the Harbour & Fleet with a Part of the fortifications & Ruins of the Town" (Trumbull to Benjamin West, 30 August 1790).

Painted for City Hall, New York (Morgan and Fielding, no. 5). (Fig. 94)

Yale Type

At Trenton, pencil, on same sheet as sketch for *Washington Resigning His Commission* (1st Silliman sale, no. 8).

Unlocated.

At Trenton, full-length, life-size, with soldier holding white horse, 1792, Philadelphia, painted for the City of Charleston, S.C. (see *Autobiography*, pp. 166–67), once the property of the Society of the Cincinnati of Connecticut, purchased by Yale College in 1806: "Voted, that the Treasurer [of Yale College] be authorized to purchase a picture of General Washington, now in possession of Col. John Trumbull, out of the money deposited in his hands by the Cincinnati" (for $500); engraved by Asher B. Durand, 1834, and William E. Tucker.

Yale, gift of the Society of the Cincinnati, no. 1806.1. (Figs. 95 and 96)

(Bust used on U.S. postage stamps no. 39, 90¢, blue, 1860; and no. 72, 90¢, blue, 1861; no. 703, 2¢, carmine rose and black, 1931; no. 711, 6¢, red-orange, 1932; no. 785, 1¢ green, 1936). (Morgan and Fielding, no. 6).

Replica, 90 by 60 inches or approximately the same size as the above. 1792/3,
    Philadelphia, or 1794, London.

The Hon. John Crichton-Stuart, 6th Marquess of Bute, "Dumfries House," Ayr-
    shire, Scotland.

"Small whole length of Washington—picture out—sent to Mr. Poggi, to print from
    . . . left at Mr. West's, Newman Street, London . . . 1797," presumably for the
    stipple by Thomas Cheesman, engraved in 1795 and published in 1796.

Unlocated.

Replica, small, with brown horse.

Bequest of Grace Wilkes to the Metropolitan Museum of Art, no. 22.45.9.

(?) Replica, with gray horse.

Robert Gilmor, Baltimore; until 1848 to Maj. Henry Gilmor, to Dr. Michel A.
    Abrams, to Thomas Edward Hanley, Bradford, Pa.

CHARLESTON TYPE

Full-length, life-size, right arm resting on cane, white horse in background, no
    attendant, 1792, Philadelphia.

Painted for the City Hall, Charleston, S.C. (Morgan and Fielding, no. 7).

CIVILIAN TYPE

"Portrait of President Washington—head, the size of life. Painted in Philadelphia,
    May 1793" (American Academy Cat., 1831, no. 13).

From the artist for the Trumbull Gallery, New Haven; Yale, Trumbull Collec-
    tion, no. 1832.10 (Fig. 97) (Morgan and Fielding, no. 8).

Same.

Gift in 1794 from Andrew Craigie to Harvard, no. H54 (Morgan and Fielding, no.
    9).

Same, later replica.

Property of John Jay.

Now owned by the children of the late Mrs. William J. Iselin; on loan to "Bedford
    House," Katonah, N.Y.

TYPE UNKNOWN

"Full length Portrait of General Washington" (American Academy Cat., 1816, no.
    43), probably one of the "Yale Type" replicas.

Unlocated.

"Head of WASHINGTON . . . left at Mr. West's, Newman Street, London . . . 1797."
Possibly one of the two "Civilian-Type" busts listed above.

Unlocated.

Miniature, *ca.* 1793.

Purchased in 1878 from the heirs of Laurence Lewis (husband of Eleanor Parke Custis of "Mt. Vernon") by the Patent Office, transferred in 1883 to the United States National Museum, Washington, D.C. (Morgan and Fielding, no. 11).

Miniature (once belonged to Rufus King).
Unlocated.

(In historical pictures: Washington's "Diary," 1 March 1790, New York, "Exercised on horsebak this forenoon attended by Mr. Trumbull who wanted to see me mounted.")

No. 9 in *Trenton,* on horseback (studies made for this and the three following, 1790, New York) (Morgan and Fielding, no. 1). (See Figs. 164 and 165)

No. 5 in *Princeton,* on horseback, same (Morgan and Fielding, no. 2). (See Figs. 169 and 170)

No. 17 in *Yorktown,* on horseback, same (Morgan and Fielding, no. 3). (See Figs. 187 and 188)

No. 22 in *Resignation,* standing, full-length, same. (See Figs. 203 and 204)

Apotheosis of Washington, drawing (a baroque-like sketch in the manner of Benjamin West's later *Apotheosis of Nelson* of 1807), *ca.* 1784, London.
Avery Architectural Library, Columbia University, New York.

MRS. GEORGE WASHINGTON (MARTHA DANDRIDGE, MRS. DANIEL PARKE CUSTIS) (1732–1802).

Miniature, 1792, Philadelphia, signed and dated on back.
From the artist for the Trumbull Gallery at New Haven, Conn.
Yale, Trumbull Collection, no. 1832.57. (Fig. 114)

Miniature, *ca.* 1793; same history as the companion miniature of George Washington (see above).
United States National Museum, Washington, D.C.

No. 30 in *Resignation,* from the above. (See Figs. 203 and 204)

CAPT. WILLIAM (AUGUSTINE) WASHINGTON (1752–1810), 3d Virginia Regt.
No. 16 in *Trenton, ca.* 1789. (See Figs. 164 and 165)

(?) WATERS.
Bust(?), 1790, Philadelphia.
Unlocated.

Replica, larger than the original.
Unlocated.

ELIZABETH WATSON (see MRS. THOMAS RUSSELL).

JAMES WATSON (1750–1806), Revolutionary officer, New York merchant, Senator from New York.

> Bust, *ca.* 1789, New York(?).
> Munson-Williams-Proctor Institute, Utica, N.Y. (Fig. 98)
>
> Replica, 1827, New York.
> John Booth Hopkins, on loan to Mr. and Mrs. James Scribner Hopkins, South
>   Yarmouth, Mass.

ROBERT WATTS, JR. (1784–1850), of New York, philanthropist.
> Bust, 1815, New York.
> Mr. and Mrs. Hugh C. Wallace, New York.

BRIG. GEN. ANTHONY WAYNE (1745–96), Revolutionary officer.
> Pencil sketch, either 1790, Philadelphia, or 1791/2, New York.
> Fordham. (Fig. 137)
>
> No. 25 in *Yorktown,* from the above. (See Figs. 187 and 188)

BRIG. GEN. SAMUEL BLACHLEY WEBB (1753–1807), Revolutionary officer, aide-de-camp to Gen. Washington.
> Bust known as *Portrait of a Revolutionary Officer,* 1844–70, and as *Gen. E. Hun-*
>   *tington*(?) 1871 to 1941, *ca.* 1790.
> New-York Historical Society, no. 1858.73. (Fig. 99)

BRIG. GEN. GEORGE WEEDON (*ca.* 1730–93), Revolutionary officer.
> Pencil sketch, 1791, Fredericksburg, Va.
> Yale, gift of Mrs. Winchester Bennett, no. 1930.65.
>
> No. 15 in *Trenton,* from the above, as col., 3d Virginia Regt. (See Figs. 164 and
>   165)

ARTHUR WELLESLEY, DUKE OF WELLINGTON (1769–1852), British general and states-man.
> Bust, from a marble bust of 1813 or 1814 by the English sculptor, Joseph Nolle-
>   kens; *ca.* 1814, London.
> Yale, Trumbull Collection, no. 1840.10 (Fig. 100). (Color chart for portrait, Yale,
>   no. 1947.503.)
> Same, with slight differences (not a replica), from same bust, before 1815, London.
> Thomas Hyde Clarke, Cooperstown, N.Y.
>
> Half-length, after Sir Thomas Lawrence, before 1815, London.
> Wadsworth Atheneum, Hartford, no. 1848.23.

Portrait of the Duke of Wellington (American Academy Cat., 1816, no. 42), probably one of the above.
Unlocated.

BENJAMIN WEST'S BODY SERVANT (see JAMES DYER).

BRIG. GEN. WILLIAM WHIPPLE (1730–85), New Hampshire Militia.
No. 2 in *Declaration*, posthumous, "from memory." (See Figs. 158 and 159)
No. 25 in *Saratoga*, same. (See Figs. 184 and 185)

MARY WHITE (see MRS. ROBERT MORRIS).

BRIG. GEN. ANTHONY WALTON WHITE (1750–1803), Revolutionary officer.
Pencil sketch, before 1795 (1st Silliman sale, no. 52).
Unlocated.

COL. EDWARD WIGGLESWORTH (1741/2–1826), 13th Massachusetts Regt.
No. 1 in *Trenton, ca.* 1790, Massachusetts(?). (See Figs. 164 and 165)

WILKES, said to be "Thomas Wilks," possibly John Wilkes, lawyer, Treasurer of the American Academy of the Fine Arts, of which Trumbull was long president.
Portrait, or simply, *Portrait of an Unknown Gentleman*, probably 1804–08, New York.
Thomas Gilcrease Institute of American History and Art, Tulsa, Okla., no. 3218. (Fig. 101)

LIEUT. COL. JAMES WILKINSON (1757–1825), Deputy Adjutant General, Northern Dept.
"Small," 1778, Boston, Mass.; *Autobiography*, no. 40.
Unlocated.
No. 13 in *Saratoga*. (See Figs. 184 and 185)

MARINUS WILLETT (1740–1830), Revolutionary officer, Mayor of New York.
Bust, 1808, New York.
City Hall, New York. (Fig. 102)

ELISHA WILLIAMS, probably Col. Elisha Williams (1717/8–84), of Wethersfield, Conn., Connecticut Militia, member of the Connecticut General Assembly, son of Rev. Elisha Williams (1694–1755), Congregational clergyman and Rector of Yale College; or, posthumously, after John Smibert's portrait of *ca.* 1736, now lost, of the Rector of Yale, which might have been at the house of his half-brother, Rev. Solomon Williams of Lebanon, the father of William Williams, the artist's brother-in-law; or, less likely, of Rev. Elisha Scott Williams, 1757–1845, of East Hartford, Conn., and Boston, Mass., Congregational minister, army chaplain at the Battle of Trenton.

"Head the size of life," 1777, Lebanon, Conn.; *Autobiography,* no. 32. Unlocated.

BRIG. GEN. OTHO HOLLAND WILLIAMS (1749–94), Revolutionary officer.
Miniature, 1790, Philadelphia.
Richard Neville White, Buffalo, N.Y. (see Fig. 105, copy by George W. Flagg)
No. 26 in *Resignation,* from the above. (See Figs. 203 and 204)

WILLIAM WILLIAMS (1731–1811), the artist's brother-in-law, Signer, statesman.
Bust, 1778, Lebanon, Conn.; *Autobiography,* no. 53.
John McClellan, Woodstock, Conn.
No. 40 in *Declaration,* probably 1792, Lebanon, Conn. (See Figs. 158 and 159)

MRS. WILLIAM (MARY TRUMBULL) WILLIAMS (1745–1831), the artist's sister.
1778, Lebanon, Conn.; *Autobiography,* no. 54.
John McClellan, Woodstock, Conn.

DR. HUGH WILLIAMSON (1735–1819), scientist, physician, patriot, Revolutionary surgeon general of North Carolina troops, Member of Congress from North Carolina, author.
Bust, *ca.* 1805, New York, engraved by Asher B. Durand.
William Hamilton Swan, Hampton Bays, N.Y., on loan to North Carolina Museum of Art, Raleigh, N.C.
No. 4 in *Resignation, ca.* 1790, Philadelphia(?). (See Figs. 203 and 204)

THOMAS WILLING (1731–1821).
No. 18 in *Declaration, ca.* 1790, Philadelphia(?) or later, and not from life, but from description furnished by Thomas Jefferson. (See Figs. 158 and 159)

JAMES WILSON (1742–98).
No. 28 in *Declaration, ca.* 1790, Philadelphia. (See Figs. 158 and 159)

FRANCIS BAYARD WINTHROP (1754–1817), New York man of property.
Bust, *ca.* 1808, New York.
Robert Winthrop, "Groton Place," Westbury, N.Y., on loan to Winthrop House, Harvard University.

MRS. FRANCIS BAYARD (PHOEBE TAYLOR) WINTHROP (married 1790, d. 1841), second wife.
Same as above.

CAPT. ABRAHAM WITHAM, British, Royal Regt. of Artillery.
No. 9 in *Gibraltar,* 1784–87, London. (See Figs. 198 and 199)

JOHN WITHERSPOON (1723–94), Presbyterian clergyman, sixth President of the College of New Jersey (Princeton University).

    No. 38 in *Declaration*, before 1794. (See Figs. 158 and 159)

ELIZABETH STOUGHTON WOLCOTT (see MRS. WILLIAM GRACIE).

OLIVER WOLCOTT, SR. (1726–97), Governor of Connecticut.

    No. 41 in *Declaration*, before 1794. (See Figs. 158 and 159)

OLIVER WOLCOTT, JR. (1760–1833), Secretary of the Treasury, Governor of Connecticut.

    Miniature, on heavy paper, *ca.* 1790, Philadelphia.
    Yale, gift of Nicholas Roosevelt, no. 1966.62. (Fig. 127)

    Half-length, 1806, New York.
    Oliver W. Roosevelt, Jr., Birmingham, Ala., on permanent loan to the Birmingham Museum of Art.

MRS. OLIVER (ELIZABETH STOUGHTON) WOLCOTT, JR. (1767–1805).

    Half-length, *ca.* 1804, New York.
    Same as above.

    Probably a posthumous replica, before 1808, New York.
    Mrs. Goran F. (Elizabeth Wolcott Elkins) Holmquist, N.Y.

MAJ. GEN. JAMES WOLFE (1727–59), British officer.

    "Head—from an engraving—," 1770 or earlier, Lebanon, Conn.; *Autobiography*, no. 1.
    Unlocated.

"MR. WOODFORDE" (unidentifiable; note to Dr. David Hosack, 9 May 1828).
    Unlocated.

REV. RALPH WORSLEY (1766–1848), British, minister of the church of St. Mary-le-Bow, London (officiated at the marriage of the artist and Sarah Hope Harvey, 1 October 1800).

    Portrait, probably painted at that time (erroneously listed as "Ralph Worley" in note to Dr. David Hosack, New York, 9 May 1828).
    Unlocated.

ELIZA B. WRIGHT (see MRS. ROBERT BALL HUGHES).

MRS. HEZEKIAH WYLLYS (see MRS. JOSEPH TRUMBULL).

GEORGE WYTHE (1726–1806), Signer, statesman, professor of law, Chancellor of Virginia.

Pencil sketch, endorsed on back "Geo. Wythe, 25th April '91," 1791, Virginia (1st Silliman sale, no. 51).
Unlocated.

No. 1 in *Declaration*, from the above. (See Figs. 158 and 159)

UNIDENTIFIED MEN

"Six small portraits of eminent men, Newton, Locke, etc."
1772–73, Cambridge, Mass.; *Autobiography*, nos. 10–15.
Unlocated.

Portrait of a French Officer.
Pencil, 1786 or 1787 in France (1st Silliman sale, no. 43).
Unlocated.

Invalid Soldier.
Pencil, 1786 in France (1st Silliman sale, no. 122).
Yale, no. 1947.492. (Fig. 245)

Invalid Soldier. "Near Amiens 1 August 1786."
Pencil and ink (*Autobiography*, Pl. 4; "Soldier, Old, Blind and Poor begging—Picardy, 1st August 1786").
The Five Daughters of Mrs. Winchester Bennett, New Haven, Conn.

Soldier of the King's Horse Guards.
Sketch, 1785, London.
Unlocated.

Portrait of a Soldier in the Horse Grenadiers.
Probably after the above (Royal Academy, London, 1785, no. 432).
Unlocated.

Unknown Gentleman.
Miniature head three-quarters to the left, possibly late 1790s at Philadelphia.
Unlocated. (Fig. 128)

Portrait of a Gentleman.
Probably a duplicate of a portrait listed (Royal Academy, London, 1785, no. 72).
Unlocated.

Portrait of a Gentleman.
Probably a duplication (Royal Academy, 1785, no. 94).
Unlocated.

Portrait of a Gentleman.
> Probably a duplication (Royal Academy, 1809, no. 356).
> Unlocated.

Portrait of a Young Man(?).
> Half-length; 1804–08, New York(?).
> Museum of the City of New York, no. 41.425.

Portrait of an American Military Officer.
> Pencil sketch, *ca.* 1790.
> Yale, gift of Mrs. Winchester Bennett, no. 1931.69.

Portrait of an Unknown Man.
> Half-length, *ca.* 1805(?), New York(?).
> Mrs. C. Oliver Iselin, "Hopelands," Aiken, S.C.

Miniature of an Unknown Man(?).
> Mrs. Howard Townsend, Clearwater, Fla.

Portrait of a Gentleman (see American Academy Cats., 1816, no. 6; 1817, no. 117; 1821, nos. 36, 39, and 41; 1824, nos. 84 and 88; 1825, nos. 23, 26, 29, and 52; 1827, no. 107), undoubtedly duplications, possibly all accounted for in lists above.
> Lost(?).

Portrait of a Gentleman (see JOHN TRUMBULL, painter).

Portrait of an Artist (see JOHN TRUMBULL, painter).

Portrait of a Revolutionary Officer (see BRIG. GEN. SAMUEL BLACHLEY WEBB).

Portrait of the Uncle of J. Lenox ("cash from J. Lenox for his uncle's portrait 150," see DAVID SPROAT).

UNIDENTIFIED WOMEN

The Pearl Necklace, from Paris Bordone.
> Exhibited at the Boston Athenaeum, 1829 (no. 62 under works by "Living Artists"), a copy after the Venetian, Paris Bordone (1495–1570), probably made at London during the War of 1812, possibly after the Earl of Dudley's picture, now called *The Mirror.*
> Unlocated.

Portrait of a Lady in a Turban.
> Pencil sketch (1st Silliman sale, no. 130).
> Farnsworth Library and Museum, Rockland, Me.

Portraits: "3 female heads."
>Before 1815, London.
>Unlocated.

Portrait of a Lady (see American Academy Cats., 1816, nos. 15, 20, and 25; 1820, nos. 42 and 46; 1822, nos. 30 and 32; 1824, nos. 106 and 108; and 1827, no. 109). Undoubtedly duplications, possibly all accounted for in lists above.
>Unlocated.

Portraits of two Ladies (possibly the Misses Murray). (American Academy Cat., 1816, no. 58).
>Unlocated.

Portrait of a Lady.
>1800, London (American Academy Cat., 1831, no. 16).
>Unlocated.

Portrait of a Lady.
>Possibly the above (Royal Academy, London, 1811, no. 457).
>Unlocated.

Portrait of a West India Lady.
>1804, New York.
>Unlocated.

Portrait of a Lady.
>Before 1826 (National Academy of Design, 1826, no. 53), possibly one of the above.
>Unlocated.

Portrait of a Lady.
>1827, New York (American Academy Cat., 1831, no. 35), possibly one of the above.
>Unlocated.

Portrait of a Lady (see Mrs. THOMAS SULLY).

Portrait of a Matron Lady (see Mrs. ALEXANDER HOSACK).

Portrait of a "Lady in White."
>Bust with left hand, possibly 1804–08, probably *ca.* 1820s, New York(?).
>Victor D. Spark, New York. (Fig. 103)

Unidentified Lady, middle-aged, dressed in the mode of the 1790s, wearing house cap with blue ribbon, possibly a member of the Terry, Brinley, or Wadsworth family of Hartford.
>John Brinley Muir, Philadelphia, Pa.

UNKNOWN

Charlestonians.
> ("I have painted or drawn about 20 heads since I have been here," Charleston,
> S.C., 7 April 1791, of which only a few can be identified.
> Unlocated.

"3 portraits."
> Before 1815, London.
> Unlocated.

"Copy of Vandyk."
> Before 1815, London (see CORNELIUS VAN DER GEEST).
> New-York Historical Society.

Two "portraits."
> Unlocated; once owned by Mrs. Edward B. Huntington, Norwich, Conn.

Two "portraits."
> Mr. A. Bradhurst Field, Sloatsburg, N.Y.

HISTORICAL SUBJECTS
(Listed in chronological order of events represented)
Ancient

Brutus (Tarquin's foe) *Condemning His Sons.*
"Original design," oil(?), 1777, Lebanon, Conn.; *Autobiography*, no. 23.
Unlocated.

Brutus and His Friends at the Death of Lucretia.
After an engraving by Domenico Cunego, after Gavin Hamilton, and "partly original."
"3f .. 4 in by v .. 2," 1777, Lebanon, Conn.; *Autobiography*, no. 30.
Yale, gift of Jonathan Trumbull Lanman, no. 1942.111. (Fig. 138)

The Rape of Lucrece (Lucretia)(?).
Possibly the above; once belonged to the David Trumbull Lanman family.
Unlocated.

Cincinnatus (Roman consul and general).
India-ink wash drawing, 1784, London (1st Silliman sale, no. 121).
Unlocated.

The Deputation from the Senate Presenting to Cincinnatus the Command of the Roman Armies.
"Four small figures on a half-length cloth," 1784, London (Royal Academy, London, 1784, no. 153).
Unlocated.

The Death of Paulus Aemilius (Roman consul) *at the Battle of Cannae.*
Small oil, "my first attempt at composition," 1774, Lebanon, Conn., signed and dated on back; *Autobiography*, no. 21 (American Academy Cat., 1831, no. 10).
Yale, Trumbull Collection, no. 1832.100. (Fig. 139)
Title erroneous: "studies for two female figures" (1st Silliman sale, no. 116; see *Priam*).
Ink sketch, 1785, London (1st Silliman sale, no. 103).
Unlocated.
A finished oil after 1785(?).
Unlocated.

The Continence of Scipio (Scipio Africanus).

> After John Smibert's copy (now in the Walker Art Gallery, Bowdoin College, Brunswick, Me., no. 1813.10, after Nicolas Poussin), 1778, Boston; *Autobiography,* no. 45.
> Owned in 1858 by Prof. Benjamin Silliman.
> Unlocated.

Brutus (Caesar's assassin) *Brandishing a Dagger.*

> Described by Prof. Benjamin Silliman (1858) as "a spirited female figure brandishing a naked dagger aloft. It was painted in oil colors on a door panel inside a closet [at the artist's home at Lebanon, Conn.] and may be there still."
> Possibly 1771, but before 1774; the earliest surviving work in oils.
> Wadsworth Atheneum, Hartford, no. 1844.9.

The Dead Body of Brutus.

> After the painting by Jacques Louis David (now belonging to Jules David, Paris).
> Pen sketch, 1786, Paris (1st Silliman sale, no. 133 or no. 135).
> Yale, no. 1947.493a.

"A Variation from a Picture of *Cleopatra,* by Titian."

> "The original was beautifully colored, and represented a beautiful woman, but with arms that might have belonged to a blacksmith" (no such composition known, possibly after Titian's *Lucretia,* at Hampton Court).
> Ca. 1812, London, or a copy of a copy made at New Haven or at New York, late 1830s (Apollo Assn. Cat., Oct. 1838, no. 16; Jan. 1839, no. 14; and May 1839, no. 170).
> Unlocated.

The Blind Belisarius (general in the Eastern Roman Empire).

> After an engraving by Robert Strange of 1757(?), after Salvator Rosa (cat. no. Le Blanc, 25) with "several figures of Roman soldiers, ruins, etc., added on a half-length cloth."
> 1778, Lebanon, Conn.; *Autobiography,* no. 63.
> Wadsworth Atheneum, Hartford, no. 1962.158. (Fig. 140)

Modern

Battle of La Hogue (English and Dutch victory over the French fleet in 1692).

> Copy by Trumbull in 1785 after Benjamin West's original of 1778 (now at the National Gallery of Art, Washington, D.C., no. NGA 1535), "retouched and harmonized by Mr. West," who enlarged and completed the picture and again retouched it in 1806; all at London.
> Metropolitan Museum of Art, New York, no. 64.57. (Fig. 143)

Peter the Great at the Capture of Narva, 1704.

> Drawing in India ink, before 1811 (1844 auction sale, no. 10).
> Unlocated.

> Small oil, before 1811, London.
> Unlocated.

> Large oil, 1812, London (British Institute, London, 1813, no. 34. American Academy Cats., 1817, no. 120; 1819, no. 39; 1820, no. 61; 1821, no. 30; 1822, no. 4; 1823, no. 6; and 1831, no. 29).
> Yale, Trumbull Collection, no. 1832.88. (Fig. 141)

Contemporary

The Death of General Warren at the Battle of Bunker's Hill, 17 June 1775.

> Sketches, pencil on one sheet of paper, 1785, London (1st Silliman sale, no. 2).
> The Historical Society of Pennsylvania.

> Sketches, in sepia and pencil on one sheet of paper, 1785, London (1st Silliman sale, no. 3).
> Same as above.

> Sketch, ink drawing, said to be Gen. Montgomery lying on the ground with sword in hand (illustrated by John Durand, *John Trumbull* [Boston, 1881], p. 14), possibly an early study for Gen. Warren.
> Unlocated.

> Sketch in sepia, line and wash, without Peter Salem, 1785, London (1st Silliman sale, no. 1) (illustrated by Durand, frontispiece).
> Mrs. Norman Holmes Pearson, New Haven, Conn.

> Detail, Lieut. Grosvenor and his Negro servant, Peter Salem, oil on wood, 1785, London.
> Yale, Mabel Brady Garvan Collection, no. 1932.302.

> Small oil for the engraving, "finished March 1786," London, signed and dated (American Academy Cats., 1816, no. 47; 1824, no. 58; and 1831, no. 1).
> Yale, Trumbull Collection, no. 1832.1. (Figs. 145–151; see also Fig. 142)

> Late replica, small oil.
> Howland Shaw Warren, Nahant, Mass.

> Replica, large oil, figures half life-size, 1832–34, New York.
> Wadsworth Atheneum, Hartford, no. 1844.1.

The Death of General Montgomery in the Attack on Quebec, 31 December 1775.

> Sketches(?), 1785, London.
> Unlocated.

Sketch in sepia and wash, 1785, London (1st Silliman sale, no. 4).
Fordham.

For the central group, ink, 1785, London.
Yale, gift of Yale University Art Gallery Associates, no. 1938.276.

Tracing in ink of the central group.
Mrs. Thomas Denison Hewitt, Greenwich, Conn.

Small oil for the engraving, "finished June 1786," London (American Academy
      Cats., 1816, no. 39; 1824, no. 55; and 1831, no. 2).
Yale, Trumbull Collection, no. 1832.2. (Figs. 152–56; see also Fig. 144)

Replica, large oil, figures half life-size, 1832–34, New York.
Wadsworth Atheneum, Hartford, no. 1844.2.

The Declaration of Independence, Philadelphia, 4 July 1776 (often referred to, incorrectly, as the "*Signing* of the Declaration of Independence").

Preliminary sketch, "first idea of Declaration of Independence, Paris, Sept. 1786,"
      pencil sketch by Trumbull and ink sketch by Thomas Jefferson, "done by
      Mr. Jefferson . . . to convey an idea of the Room, in which congress sat . . ."
      (1st Silliman sale, no. 6).
Yale, gift of Ernest A. Bigelow, no. 1926.8. (Fig. 157)

Sketch, in India-ink wash, "America, Lebanon, 2d January, 1790" (1st Silliman
      sale, no. 5).
Unlocated.

Pencil, of interior of Independence Hall, 1790, Philadelphia (1st Silliman sale, no.
      7).
The Historical Society of Pennsylvania.

Ink, floor plan, Independence Hall, and of group, 1790, Philadelphia.
Same as above.

Small oil for engraving (by Asher B. Durand in 1823) 1786 to before 1797, London
      (used on the reverse of the $100 national currency note, 1863 and 1864, and
      on U.S. postage stamp no. 120, 24¢, green and violet, 1869).
Yale, Trumbull Collection, no. 1832.3. (Figs. 158–61)

Replica, large oil, figures life-size, 1818, New York (used on U.S. postage stamp,
      no. 120, 24¢, green and violet, 1869).
Rotunda of the Capitol, Washington, D.C. (Fig. 163; see also Fig. 162)

Replica, large oil, figures half life-size, 1832, New York.
Wadsworth Atheneum, Hartford, no. 1844.3.

Evacuation of New York, September 1776.
Proposed only, miniatures at Yale to have been used.

Capture of the Hessians at Trenton, 26 December 1776.

Sketch, India ink, "Lebanon, Dec. 1789" (1st Silliman sale, no. 25).
Unlocated.

Pencil (1st Silliman sale, no. 26).
Unlocated.

Pencil (1st Silliman sale, no. 27).
Unlocated.

Trenton Bridge, pencil (1st Silliman sale, no. 28).
Yale, no. 1941.78.

Small oil for the engraving, 1786 to before 1797, London (American Academy Cat., 1831, no. 4).
Yale, Trumbull Collection, no. 1832.5. (Figs. 164–68)

Replica, large oil, figures half life-size, 1830, New York (American Academy Cat., 1831, no. 9).
Wadsworth Atheneum, Hartford, no. 1844.4.

The Death of General Mercer at the Battle of Princeton, 3 January 1777.

Sketches, in ink and in pencil, study for Mercer, nude, arising from fallen horse, British soldiers, etc. (1st Silliman sale, no. 18).
Yale, gift of Yale University Art Gallery Associates, no. 1938.277.

Sketch, ink and wash, Mercer, clothed, on ground, his horse fallen, British soldiers, Washington mounted (1st Silliman sale, no. 17).
Princeton. (Fig. 181)

Outline in ink, for the entire picture, Mercer to left (no. 1 in *Princeton*) (1st Silliman sale, no. 11).
Same as above. (Fig. 175)

Outline in pencil and ink, composition changed, incomplete, Mercer in center (no. 2 in *Princeton*) (1st Silliman sale, no. 12).
Same as above. (Fig. 176)

Outline in ink, composition changed (no. 3 in *Princeton*) (1st Silliman sale, no. 13).
Same as above. (Fig. 177)

Ink and wash, same composition (no. 4 in *Princeton*), signed and dated, 11 May 1786 (1st Silliman sale, no. 14).
Same as above. (Fig. 178)

Outline in pencil and ink, composition changed (no. 5 in *Princeton*) (1st Silliman sale, no. 15).
Same as above. (Fig. 179)

Ink and wash, composition changed, signed and dated, 18 May 1786 (1st Silliman
    sale, no. 16).
Same as above. (Fig. 180)
(All of the above done in 1786, London.)
Preliminary study, composition slightly changed, small, but too large for engraver,
    unfinished, in oil, 1786–87, London.
Yale, Trumbull Collection, no. 1832.6a. (Fig. 174)

Sketch, in pencil, "The College & Village of Princeton as seen from the Field on
    which the Battle was fought on the 2nd Jan. 1777," signed and dated, 10 De-
    cember 1790, "drawn on the spot," Princeton (1st Silliman sale, no. 19).
Estate of Hall Park McCullough, Bennington, Vt. (Fig. 183)

In wash, 2⅞ by 4⅝ inches, same (1st Silliman sale, no. 20).
Unlocated.

Small oil for the engraving, 1787 to before 1797, London (American Academy
    Cat., 1831, no. 5).
Yale, Trumbull Collection, no. 1832.6. (Figs. 169–73)

Replica, large oil, figures half life-size, 1830–31, New York.
Wadsworth Atheneum, Hartford, no. 1844.5.

The Murder of Jane McCrea, at Fort Edward, New York, 26 July 1777.
    Proposed only, miniatures at Yale and following sketches to have been used.
    Preliminary sketch in outline, ink, *ca.* 1790 (1st Silliman sale, no. 33).
    Fordham.

    Sketches of details, pencil on blue paper, *ca.* 1790 (1st Silliman sale, no. 34).
    Fordham.

    Sketch, *ca.* 1790, in sepia (1st Silliman sale, no. 32).
    The Bennington Museum, Bennington, Vt.

Death of General Fraser at Bemis's Heights, near Saratoga, New York, 7 October 1777
(Simon Fraser, British brigadier).
    Proposed only.
    "Small sketch in Indian ink on paper . . . first attempt at the composition of a mili-
        tary scene, taken from the War of the Revolution," 1785, London.
    Unlocated.

The Surrender of General Burgoyne at Saratoga, New York, 16 October 1777.
    "Finished sketch in outline, partly filled in with India ink," August 1791, Leba-
        non, Conn. (1st Silliman sale, no. 21).
    Unlocated.

Sketch, pencil (1st Silliman sale, no. 22).
Yale, gift of Yale University Art Gallery Associates, no. 1938.288.

Pencil (1st Silliman sale, no. 23).
Fordham.

Sepia wash, September 1791 (1st Silliman sale, no. 24).
Fordham.

Small oil for the engraving, *ca.* 1816, New York (American Academy Cat., 1831, no. 6).
Yale, Trumbull Collection, no. 1832.7. (Figs. 184 and 185)

Replica, large, figures life-size, 1817–21, New York (used on U.S. postage stamp, no. 644, 2¢, carmine rose, 1927).
Rotunda of the Capitol, Washington, D.C. (Fig. 186)

The Siege of Savannah, 6 September–18 October 1779.
Proposed only, miniatures at Yale to have been used.

The Attack on Charleston, South Carolina, 9 and 10 May 1780.
Proposed only, miniatures at Yale to have been used.

Shipwreck.
"A small composition," 1780–81, London.
Unlocated.

Arrest of Colonel Trumbull in London, 19 November 1780.
India-ink wash sketch (1st Silliman sale, no. 61).
Unlocated.

Prisoners Starving (scene on a prison ship).
Wash drawing, *ca.* 1780, London (1st Silliman sale, no. 126).
Fordham.

The Battle of Eutaw Springs, South Carolina, 8 September 1781.
Proposed only, miniatures at Yale to have been used.

Sketch (noted in Prof. Benjamin Silliman's papers).
Unlocated.

Surrender of Lord Cornwallis at Yorktown, 19 October 1781.
"Various studies," 1786–87, London, possibly some or all the following.
Unlocated.

Study for the following, 2⅜ by 4 inches, pen and sepia wash, 1787, London (1st Silliman sale, no. 29).
Hugh Kindersley Foster, Needham, Mass.

Study, with Gen. Lincoln's back to beholder, on white horse, American flag of alternate stripes of red, white, and blue, usual blue canton, oil, 14 by 21 inches, 1787, London, incomplete.
Detroit Institute of Arts, no. 48.217.

Study, with Gen. Lincoln on white horse, facing beholder, oil, 14 by 21 inches, 1787, London, incomplete.
Detroit Institute of Arts, no. 48.216.

"Study for the Surrender of York Town, size 10 by 20 inches finished in 1787, . . . given to Mr. Jefferson," oil, exhibited at the Boston Athenaeum in 1828, no. 310.
Unlocated.

"Yorktown, in Virginia—as seen from the point the British army entered between the lines of the allied troops . . . ," a panorama in sepia on three cards, 23 April 1791, Yorktown (1st Silliman sale, no. 30).
Fordham.

Study for horses, pencil on two cards (1st Silliman sale, no. 31).
Yale, gift of Yale University Art Gallery Associates, nos. 1938.287 and 1938.289.

Study for the figure of Col. Deux-Ponts, 1787, Paris, "Soldier . . . explanations for a military uniform . . ." (2d Silliman sale, no. 828).
Yale, gift of Yale University Art Gallery Associates, no. 1938.275.

Preliminary picture, oil, 15 by 21¾ inches, *ca.* 1794, London.
Unlocated.

Small oil for engraving, 20 by 30 inches, finished before 1797, London (American Academy Cat., 1831, no. 7).
Yale, Trumbull Collection, no. 1832.4. (Figs. 187–94)

Replica, large oil, figures life-size, 1817–20, New York.
Rotunda of the Capitol, Washington, D.C. (Fig. 195; see also Figs. 196 and 207)

The Sortie Made by the Garrison of Gibraltar, 27 November 1781.
Sketch, "Gen. Elliot at Gibraltar, May 20, 1786," London (1st Silliman sale, no. 105, and 3d Silliman sale, no. 884).
Connecticut Historical Society.

Bound volume containing many sketches in ink or wash, 1786, London, including the "head of the dying Spaniard" for which Sir Thomas Lawrence posed.
Boston Athenaeum. (Fig. 200)

Small sketch, ink and wash, 1786, London.
Princeton.

Oil, "say fourteen by twenty-one inches" (sight size?), 1784–87, London, given to
  Benjamin West by the artist; most probably the version, 15⅛ by 22⅛ inches
  (stretcher size).
The Corcoran Gallery of Art, Washington, D.C., no. 66.18.

Replica, 20 by 30 inches, finished 1788, London, "intended for the Engraver"
  (probably the version exhibited at the American Academy, 1828, no. 45, and
  at the Apollo Assn., 1841, no. 65).
Cincinnati Art Museum, Cincinnati, Ohio, no. 1922.104. (Fig. 197)

Replica, 72 by 108 inches, finished April 1789, London, "Engraved by Mr. Sharp."
Museum of Fine Arts, Boston (deposited by Boston Athenaeum), Ath. 10. (Fig.
  198; see also Fig. 201)

Replica, 117 by 126 inches, probably between 1808 and 1812 (British Institution,
  London, 1812, no. 26).
Unlocated.

Replica, 35½ by 54 inches, *ca.* 1840, probably after the William Sharp, 1799, engraving.
Yale, gift of Herbert L. Pratt, no. 1935.198. (Fig. 202; see also Fig. 201)

Replica, 37½ by 58½ inches, *ca.* 1840, probably also after same engraving (3d
  Silliman sale, no. 884).
Caldwell Colt Robinson, Newport, R.I., on loan to the Lyman Allyn Museum,
  New London, Conn.

(?) Replica, 36 by 44 inches.
Unlocated.

(?) Replica, 26 by 36 inches.
Unlocated.

"Small Gibraltar . . . left at Mr. West's, Newman Street, London . . . 1797"; prob-
  ably one of the above.
Key to the picture, pen and ink drawing.
Yale, gift of Herbert L. Pratt, no. 1932.123. (Fig. 199)

The Preliminary Treaty, Paris, 30 November 1782, or possibly *The Treaty of Paris,*
3 September 1783.
  Proposed only, miniatures at Yale to have been used.
  Sketch, Franklin seated at a table surrounded by six unidentifiable persons (prob-
    ably John Adams, John Jay, Henry Laurens, the American Secretary William
    Temple Franklin, the British Commissioner Richard Oswald, and the British
    Secretary Caleb Whitefoord), domed building seen through open window,
    possibly the recently completed Panthéon at Paris; ink, shaded (composition

close to Benjamin West's unfinished *American Peace Commissioners,* begun in 1783); *ca.* 1786, London (1st Silliman sale, no. 129).

The Historical Society of Pennsylvania.

The Presentation of the Peace Treaty in the House of Lords, 19 February 1783(?).

Ink sketch in outline, on same sheet of paper as the above.

General Washington Resigning His Commission, Annapolis, Maryland, 23 December 1783.

Sketch, pencil, *ca.* 1816 (1st Silliman sale, no. 8).

Unlocated.

Pen, *ca.* 1816 (1st Silliman sale, no. 9).

Unlocated.

Of the interior architecture of the State House, pencil, *ca.* 1816 (1st Silliman sale, no. 10).

Yale, gift of Yale University Art Gallery Associates, no. 1938.286.

Small oil, *ca.* 1817–22, New York (American Academy Cat., 1831, no. 8).

Yale, Trumbull Collection, no. 1832.8. (Figs. 203 and 204)

Replica, large oil, figures life-size, 1824, New York.

Rotunda of the Capitol, Washington, D.C. (Fig. 205; see also 206 and 207)

Unidentified American Battle Scene.

Preliminary pen-and-ink sketch, possibly for the *Battle of Trenton.*

Fordham.

MISCELLANEOUS

Lunardi's Balloon (Vincenzo Lunardi, 1759–1806, Italian balloonist), ascent from the Artillery Ground.

"Never finished," 1784, London.

Unlocated.

The Arch at Trenton, New Jersey, 21 April 1789.

Proposed only, miniatures at Yale to have been used.

The Inauguration of President Washington, New York, 30 April 1789.

Proposed only, miniatures at Yale to have been used.

Taking of the Bastille, Paris, 14 July 1789.

Proposed only.

Louis XVI's Visit to Paris, 17 July 1789.

Proposed only.

The Defense of Baltimore, mid-September 1814.
> Proposed in 1817 for the City of Baltimore.

The Defense of Fort McHenry.
> Same.

MYTHOLOGICAL

Priam Returning with the Body of Hector.
> Ink drawing, 1784, London, signed and dated.
> Jonathan Trumbull Isham, New Canaan, Conn.

> Figure studies, ink sketch, 1784, London, signed and dated.
> Fordham.

> Ink sketch of two female figures, endorsed on back "Jno Trumbull, London, 20 Decr. 1784."
> Fordham.

> Study, ink, 1785, London, signed and dated (1st Silliman sale, no. 128) (illustrated by John Durand, *John Trumbull*, p. 1).
> Mrs. Percy Chubb, Chester, N.J.

> Oil, 1785, London (Royal Academy, London, 1786, no. 132).
> Museum of Fine Arts, Boston (deposited by Boston Athenaeum), Ath. 389. (Fig. 208)

The Dying Mother and Infant.
> "An abortive attempt at the celebrated Greek story, the mother, mortally wounded, repelling the child from her bosom lest he drink her blood," 1779, Boston; *Autobiography*, no. 68.
> Unlocated.

The Education of Achilles by the Centaur Chiron.
> Pen sketch, after Jean-Baptiste Regnault (now in the Louvre); 1786, Paris (1st Silliman sale, no. 133 or 135).
> Yale, no. 1947.493b.

Also classical studies in sketchbook in Yale University Library.

LITERARY SUBJECTS

Britannia.
> "In India ink," 1772–73, Cambridge, Mass.; *Autobiography*, no. 16.
> Unlocated.

Contemplation.
> Oil.
> Unlocated.

Mother and Child, after Vigée-LeBrun(?).
> Pen sketch, 1786, Paris (1st Silliman sale, no. 133 or 135), study for the following.
> Yale, no. 1947.493c. (Fig. 210)

Maternal Affection, Tenderness, or *Love.*
> From the above and the 1786 Fordham drawing, *Madonna and Child with Saints,* 1809, London (American Academy Cats., 1825, no. 61; 1826, no. 8; 1827, no. 105; 1828, no. 65; and 1831, no. 23).
> Probably the version at Yale, Trumbull Collection, no. 1832.86. (Fig. 209)

Maternal Affection, or *Mother and Child.*
> Probably a replica of the above, 1826, New York (American Academy Cats., 1826, no. 107; 1827, no. 130; and 1831, no. 34).
> Unlocated.

Other allegorical subjects contained in sketchbook at Yale University Library.

The Death of Hotspur, from Shakespeare's *Henry IV,* Part 1.
> Pen drawing in brown ink, 1786, London, signed and dated.
> Vassar College, Poughkeepsie, N.Y. (Fig. 211)

Subject from *Ossian.*
> "Small picture" (12 by 14 inches), 1792, London.
> The Toledo Museum of Art, Toledo, Ohio, no. 58.27. (Fig. 212)

Lamderg and Gelchossa, from Macpherson's *Ossian,* 5th book of *Fingal.*
> Large oil, 1809, London (British Institution, London, 1810, no. 93; American Academy Cats., 1816, no. 16; 1818, no. 120; 1819, no. 12; 1820, no. 41; 1821, no. 66; 1822, no. 43; 1823, no. 20; 1824, no. 49; and 1831, no. 24).
> Yale, Trumbull Collection, no. 1832.85. (Fig. 213)

The Earl of Angus Conferring Knighthood on de Wilton, from Scott's *Marmion.*
> Ink sketch after 1808 and before 1810, London (1st Silliman sale, no. 63).
> Fordham.
>
> Small oil, *ca.* 1810, London.
> Unlocated.
>
> Large oil, signed and dated, 1810, London (British Institution, London, 1811, no. 147; American Academy Cats., 1816, no. 37; 1817, no. 115; 1818, no. 168;

1819, no. 50; 1820, no. 60; 1821, no. 63; 1822, no. 40; 1823, no. 31; 1824, no. 59; and 1831, no. 25).

Yale, Trumbull Collection, no. 1832.82. (Fig. 214)

Lady of the Lake, from Scott's *Lady of the Lake,* published in 1810.

Large oil, 1811, London (this or following, Royal Academy, London, 1811, no. 237).

Mrs. Cyrus L. Fulton, Lancaster, Ohio.

A smaller version, probably 1811, London (American Academy Cats., 1816, no. 10; 1824, no. 95; and 1831, no. 28; Pennsylvania Academy Cat., 1818, no. 50; and Cat. of Paintings in the Wadsworth Gallery, Hartford, 1863, no. 1848.3).

Unlocated.

The Grief of Andromache Over the Body of Hector (incorrectly considered "The Dead Body of Brutus").

After the painting by Jacques Louis David of 1783 (now in the École des Beaux-Arts, Paris).

Pen sketch, 1786, Paris (1st Silliman sale?).

Yale, no. 1947.493a. (Fig. 215)

RELIGIOUS SUBJECTS

OLD TESTAMENT

The Deluge (Genesis).
> Ink sketch, 1781, London (1st Silliman sale, no. 125).
> Fordham.

The Last Family Who Perished in the Deluge (Genesis).
> Large oil, from the above, 1838–39, New Haven, Conn.
> Yale, Trumbull Collection, no. 1840.6. (Fig. 216)

Abraham's Servant Meeting Rebekah at the Well Surrounded by Her Damsels.
> "Copied in oil from an engraving after the picture by Noel Coypel, in the Library
> of Harvard College, the same size as the engraving" (*Rebecca at the Well with
> Six Maidens, Receiving Gifts from the Servant of Abraham,* by Pierre Imbert
> Drevet after Antoine Coypel—cat. nos. Le Blanc 3, Andresen 2).
> 1773, Cambridge, Mass,; *Autobiography,* no. 20.
> C. D. Haskell, Laurel, Nebr.

Joshua Attended by Death at the Battle of Ai or *The Conquest of Canaan.*
> Ink sketch, 1786, London, signed and dated.
> Fordham.

> Large oil, from the above, 1839–40, New Haven.
> Yale, Trumbull Collection, no. 1840.5. (Fig. 217)

Elisha Restoring the Shunammite's Son (II Kings).
> Oil on "half-length cloth . . . copied from a print done from Mr. West's picture in
> the possession of Lord Grosvenor," 1777, Lebanon, Conn.; *Autobiography,*
> no. 31.
> Wadsworth Atheneum, Hartford, no. 1956.622. (Fig. 218)

Susannah and the Elders or *The Chastity of Susannah* (Apocrypha).
> Oil, 1811, London (American Academy Cats., 1831, no. 27, and 1833, no. 41;
> Apollo Assn. Cats., 1838, no. 20, and 1839, no. 18; 1844 auction sale, no. 3).
> Unlocated.

New Testament

Madonna.
> A "copy," 1778, Lebanon, Conn.; *Autobiography,* no. 58.
> Unlocated.

Madonna della Sedia.
> After Benjamin West's copy after Raphael, 1780, London (American Academy
> > Cat,. 1831, no. 11).
> Stolen from the Yale Gallery, *ca.* 1880.

Holy Family.
> After a copy after Correggio, oil, 1784, London, for Benjamin West.
> Unlocated.

Holy Family.
> "From a picture by Rubens at Antwerp, 1786" (Trumbull attribution mistaken),
> > ink sketch (1st Silliman sale, no. 134).
> Yale, no. 1947.495.

Madonna and Child with Saints Joseph and John.
> Ink drawing, *ca.* 1786, London (this drawing used for *Holy Family* and *Maternal
> > Tenderness;* both at Yale [Figs. 209 and 219]).
> Fordham.

Madonna and Child.
> After Correggio, pencil drawing, after 1800, London (1st Silliman sale, no. 62).
> Yale, no. 1947.481.

Madonna and Child.
> On "half-length cloth" (American Academy Cat., 1824, no. 8), probably one of the
> > above or below.
> Unlocated.

> Same (American Academy Cat., 1824, no. 107).
> Unlocated.

Madonna and Child with the Cross.
> Oil on wood, signed, *ca.* 1830, New York.
> Dominican Sisters of the Sick Poor, Ossining, N.Y.

Madonna and Child with St. John the Baptist.
> After a copy after Raphael's *Madonna au Corset Rouge,* oil, 1801, London (Amer-

ican Academy Cats., 1817, no. 137; 1819, no. 23; 1820, no. 31; 1821, no. 85; 1822, no. 78; 1823, no. 77; 1824, no. 10; and 1831, no. 18).
Yale, Trumbull Collection, no. 1832.98. (Fig. 220)

Holy Family (Madonna and Child with Saints Joseph, John the Baptist, Elizabeth, and Zacharias).
Adapted from the above, large oil, composed 1802 at London and finished 1806 at New York (Royal Academy, 1809; British Institution, London, 1810, no. 134; American Academy Cat., 1817, no. 36, and 1831, no. 20).
Yale, Trumbull Collection, no. 1832.83.

Holy Family, St. John, and Angel.
A copy from an unknown source.
Wadsworth Atheneum, Hartford, no. 1863.9.

Holy Family and St. John.
After a copy after Rubens, oil, begun 1801 at London and finished 1806 at New York.
Wadsworth Atheneum, Hartford, no. 1856.5.

Madonna and Child, Holy Family, or "Copy of Vandyk."
After the *Madonna and Infant Saviour* by Sir Anthony Van Dyck, once owned by the artist and sold by him in 1797, now in the Dulwich College Gallery, London; before 1815, London (American Academy Cat., 1819, no. 53, and 1844 auction sale, no. 1).
Unlocated.

Holy Family.
Six small individual pictures, probably near replicas (American Academy Cats., 1826, nos. 49, 50, and 105; 1827, nos. 51, 98, 100, 101, and 128; 1828, no. 66; and 1831, no. 48), probably all painted between 1826 and 1827, New York.
One of the above private collection, New Haven, Conn., destroyed, the other five unlocated.

Holy Family, "with a group of Angels in the Sky."
"Small picture," offered by the artist to the American Academy "as a Specimen of my Talents" in 1826, probably one of the above.
Unlocated.

Holy Family with St. John and His Parents (Madonna and Child with Saints Zacharias, Elizabeth, and John the Baptist).
Late 1820s or early 1830s, New York.
Connecticut Historical Society, no. 102.

Holy Family (Madonna and Child with Saints Joseph, Elizabeth, and John the Baptist).
 Small oil, canvas on wood, possibly one of the above.
 Mrs. Charles H. Higgins, New York.

Holy Family (Madonna and Child with Saints Joseph, Elizabeth, and John the Baptist).
 Large oil, 1839–40, New Haven, from a drawing of *ca.* 1786.
 Yale, Trumbull Collection, no. 1840.4. (Fig. 219)

Also, Holy Family, in sketchbook in Yale University Library.

Infant Saviour with St. John the Baptist Dressing the Lamb with Flowers.
 1801, London (American Academy Cats., 1816, no. 13; 1824, no. 53; and 1831, no.
  19).
 Wadsworth Atheneum, Hartford, no. 1899.13. (Fig. 221)
 Oil on composition board, 1830s, New York, "copy of favorite picture painted in
  England, long since."
 Yale, Trumbull Collection, no. 1832.84.

Our Saviour and Little Children, or *Suffer Little Children.*
 Small-scale study, based on Correggio, 1821, London (Royal Academy, London,
  1812, no. 331, exhibited by "Colonel Trumbull, President of the Academy of
  Arts, New York." British Institution, London, 1813, no. 80; American Acad-
  emy Cat., 1817, no. 37; and Boston Athenaeum, 1828).
 Unlocated.
 Large oil, 1812, London (American Academy Cats., 1816, no. 44; 1817, no. 123;
  1818, no. 114; 1819, no. 52; 1820, no. 58; 1821, no. 60; 1822, no. 37; 1823, no.
  26; 1824, no. 54; and 1831, no. 30).
 Yale, Trumbull Collection, no. 1832.87. (Fig. 223)

Christ and the Woman Taken in Adultery, or *The Woman Accused by the Scribes and
the Pharisees.*
 Pencil sketch, 1811, London.
 Connecticut Historical Society.
 "Small," 1811, London (American Academy Cat., 1817, no. 35; Boston Athe-
  naeum, 1828).
 Unlocated.
 Large oil, 1811, London (British Institution, London, 1812, no. 84; American
  Academy Cats., 1816, no. 41; 1819, no. 51; 1820, no. 59; 1821, no. 57; 1822,
  no. 34; 1823, no. 39; and 1831, no. 26).
 Yale, Trumbull Collection, no. 1832.80. (Fig. 224)

Christ Crowned with Thorns.
> A copy after a copy of the original Titian in the Alte Pinakothek, Munich, with a marble bust of the Emperor Tiberius added; *ca.* 1840, New Haven.
> Wadsworth Atheneum, Hartford, no. 1848.22.

Christ Under the Cross or *Our Saviour Bearing the Cross and Sinking Under Its Weight.*
> After Peter Paul Rubens, oil on wood, 1826, New York (American Academy Cat., 1827, no. 106).
> Yale, Trumbull Collection, no. 1832.99.

Elevation of the Cross.
> After Rubens.
> Unlocated; once owned by the Wadsworth Atheneum, Hartford, no. 1855.22.

The Crucifixion of Our Saviour.
> Oil(?), 1771, Lebanon, Conn.; *Autobiography,* no. 5.
> Unlocated.

The Crucifixion.
> "In water colors, from a print by Rubens," 1772–73, Cambridge, Mass.; *Autobiography,* no. 8.
> Unlocated.
>
> "Small single figure," oil(?), 1777, Lebanon, Conn.; *Autobiography,* no. 25.
> Unlocated.

The Deposition.
> Pencil drawing, 1784, London, possibly used for the following.
> Yale, no. 1947.476a.

Preparation for the Entombment of the Saviour, or *The Lamentation for the Dead Christ.*
> After Annibale Cerracci, oil on wood, 1826, New York (American Academy Cats., 1827, no. 108; and 1831, no. 33).
> Yale, Trumbull Collection, no. 1832.97. (Fig. 226)

Doubting Thomas, or *The Unbelief of Thomas* (John).
> Projected, 1834, New York (possibly never executed).
> Unlocated.

The Transfiguration.
> Copy after a copy after Raphael, oil on wood, signed and dated, 1839, New Haven.
> Yale, Trumbull Collection, no. 1840.8.

St. John and the Lamb.

"From memory of an exquisite picture by Murillo in possession of the Emperor of
Russia" (original in the National Gallery of Ireland, Dublin, ex coll. Count
Besborodko, Chancellor of Catherine II of Russia).

Oil, 1800, London.

Yale, Trumbull Collection, no. 1832.81. (Fig. 222)

The Good Samaritan.

Ink and wash drawing, 1786(?), London(?).

Fordham.

St. Paul Preaching at Athens.

Drawing in India ink after an engraving, 1774, Lebanon, Conn. (1st Silliman sale,
no. 102); *Autobiography,* no. 46.

Fordham.

"Drawing in India ink," 1778, Boston, Mass.

Unlocated.

"I Was in Prison and Ye Came Unto Me" (Matthew).

Large oil, 1834 and after, New York.

Yale, Trumbull Collection, no. 1840.7. (Fig. 227)

Study for central figure, crayon (1st Silliman sale, no. 104).

Yale, no. 1947.505. (Fig. 228)

Post-Biblical

St. Jerome(?).

Pencil sketch, 1786, London.

Fordham.

St. Jerome of Parma.

After Benjamin West's copy after Correggio.

Large oil, 1780, London (American Academy Cat., 1831, no. 12).

Yale, Trumbull Collection, no. 1832.94. (Fig. 225)

St. Jerome.

Referred to by the artist as "The Sapagniolet," a copy after *Lo Spagnoletto* (José
Ribera, *ca.* 1590–*ca.* 1652); offered by the artist to the American Academy "as
a Specimen of my Talents" in 1826.

Wadsworth Atheneum, Hartford, no. 1855.29.

The Last Communion of St. Jerome.

After a copy after Domenichino, large oil, 1839, New Haven, signed and dated.

Yale, Trumbull Collection, no. 1840.9.

Pencil sketch, 1786, London.
Fordham.

Doctors of the Church.
Eight India-ink wash drawings, June 1783, Lebanon, Conn. (1st Silliman sale, nos. 106–13).
Two at Fordham; one with C. V. Whitney, Lexington, Ky.; one with William B. Bean, Paterson, N.J.; two at Yale, nos. 1947.475 and 1947.480; two unlocated.

The Religion of Nature, or "Nature's God."
India-ink wash sketch, 1782, Lebanon, Conn. (1st Silliman sale, no. 123).
Fordham.
"Small single figure," oil, "on Kit-Kat cloth," from the above, 1784, London.
Unlocated.

A Nun by Candlelight.
A "copy," probably after John Singleton Copley's *Nun With Candle* or some European painting, 1778, Boston, Mass.; *Autobiography,* no. 44.
Unlocated.

A Monk at His Devotions by Lamplight (also described as "a Religious at his devotions by candlelight").
A "copy," source unknown, 1778, Lebanon, Conn.; *Autobiography,* no. 55.
Unlocated.

LANDSCAPES

Early Copies

Fireworks in London, on the Occasion of the Peace of Aix-la-Chapelle, in 1748.
   "Copied in India ink, from an engraving," 1770, Lebanon, Conn. (see engravings
      noted in *Rariosa* [London, 1902], collected by John Eliot Hodgkin, 3, 71, nos.
      113–24); *Autobiography,* no. 2.
   Unlocated.

View of Part of the City of Rome.
   Pen and watercolor, 1770 or 1771, Lebanon, Conn. (the earliest surviving work of
      the artist in any medium); *Autobiography,* no. 3, described as "in the Family"
      (1st Silliman sale, no. 363).
   At Trumbull College, Yale, gift of Maria Trumbull Dana, no. 1928.26. (Fig. 229)

The Virginia Water in Windsor Park.
   After a print, 1771, Lebanon, Conn.; *Autobiography,* no. 4.
   Unlocated.

Ruins of the Temple of the Sun, Palmyra.
   "From an engraving in the *Gentleman's Magazine,*" 24 (1754), opp. p. 109. 1771,
      Lebanon, Conn.; *Autobiography,* no. 7.
   Unlocated.

Eruption of Mount Vesuvius (in 1767).
   "Small water colors, on vellum; copied from the Italian picture in the philosophi-
      cal lecture room" at Harvard (this picture, a gift in 1772, has disappeared),
      1772–73, Cambridge, Mass.; *Autobiography,* no. 17.
   Unlocated.
   "The same in oil, size of original" (earliest landscape in oils), 1772–73, Cambridge,
      Mass.; *Autobiography,* no. 18.
   Unlocated.

Classical Landscape.
   "From a print after Salvator Rosa" (actually quite unlike that 17th-century Italian
      artist's style), 1778, Boston; *Autobiography,* no. 48.
   Mrs. Joseph E. Corrigan on loan to Jonathan Trumbull House, Lebanon, Conn.

Romantic Landscape.
> Somewhat in the manner of the 17th-century French artists Gaspar Dughet and
> Claude Lorraine; "composition as companion" for the above, 1778, Lebanon,
> Conn.; *Autobiography*, no. 64.
> Mrs. Alexander M. White, Oyster Bay, N.Y.

Britain

Shakespeare Cliff, Dover.
> Ink and wash, 1781, on shipboard (1st Silliman sale, no. 117).
> Yale, no. 1947.474. (Fig. 230)

Fitfill and Swinberg Heads, Shetland.
> Ink and wash, 1781, on shipboard (1st Silliman sale, no. 120).
> Yale, no. 1947.482.

Fair Island between Shetland and the Orkneys.
> Ink and wash, 1781, on shipboard (1st Silliman sale, no. 120).
> Yale, no. 1947.483.

Swinberg Head, Shetland.
> Ink and wash, 1781, on shipboard (1st Silliman sale, no. 120).
> Yale, no. 1947.484.

The Southernmost Land of Shetland.
> Ink and wash, 1781, on shipboard (1st Silliman sale, no. 120).
> Yale, no. 1947.485.

View from Caermarthin to the East.
> Watercolor, "Oct. 1803, finished at Bath Nov." (1st Silliman sale, no. 70).
> Unlocated.

Landscape from Claverton Stone Quarries Near Bath.
> Watercolor, 1803 or 1813 (American Academy Cat., 1816, no. 26).
> Unlocated.

Ragland Castle in Monmouth.
> Watercolor, 1803, or 1813, "finished at Bath" (1st Silliman sale, no. 71).
> I. Sheldon Tilney, Palm Beach, Fla.

View of Prior Park Near Bath.
> Watercolor(?), "sketched at Bath, from nature, 1813—finished in America, 1829"
> (American Academy Cats., 1616, no. 21, and 1831, no. 31).
> Unlocated.

Landscape—Near Bath.
>   Four items (1844 auction sale, nos. 6, 7, 8, and 9), possibly the four landscapes
>   above.
>   Unlocated.

Worthing in Sussex.
>   Watercolor, 1803 (1st Silliman sale, no. 73).
>   I. Sheldon Tilney, Palm Beach, Fla.

Worthing in Sussex, "looking to the north."
>   Watercolor, 1803 (1st Silliman sale, no. 74).
>   Same as above.

The Miller's Cottage Near Worthing.
>   Watercolor, "finished at Bath, 1804" (1st Silliman sale, no. 75).
>   Same as above.

Caerphilly Castle in South Wales.
>   Watercolor, 1803 (1st Silliman sale, no. 72).
>   Same as above.

Landscape, View Near Bath, England.
>   Probably one of the above (American Academy Cat., 1824, no. 74).
>   Unlocated.

Landscape, View in England.
>   Probably one of the above (American Academy Cat., 1824, no. 76).
>   Unlocated.

Scene in Wales.
>   Watercolor, 1803 (2d Silliman sale, no. 922).
>   Unlocated.

>   Two sketches.
>   Mrs. Norman Holmes Pearson, New Haven, Conn.

Views near Bath 1813.
>   Six sketches, pencil and wash.
>   Mrs. Norman Holmes Pearson, New Haven, Conn.

Germany

Turckheim ... Approaching the Valley of the Rhine.
>   Pencil, 1786; *Autobiography,* pl. 8.
>   The Five Daughters of Mrs. Winchester Bennett, New Haven, Conn.

Frankenstein . . . Black Forest in the Distance.
    Pencil, 1786; *Autobiography,* pl. 9.
    Mrs. Norman Holmes Pearson, New Haven, Conn.

Elvent, Below Mainz.
    Pencil, 1786; *Autobiography,* pl. 13.
    Unlocated.

Entrance of the Highlands of the Rhine.
    Pencil, 1786; *Autobiography,* pl. 14.
    Mrs. Norman Holmes Pearson, New Haven, Conn.

Near Bingen.
    Pencil, 1786; *Autobiography,* pl. 15.
    The Five Daughters of Mrs. Winchester Bennett, New Haven, Conn.

Bingen.
    Pencil, 1786; *Autobiography,* pl. 16.
    Unlocated.

Old Electoral Palace at Mainz.
    Pencil, 1786; *Autobiography,* pl. 10.
    Mrs. Norman Holmes Pearson, New Haven, Conn.

Bacherach.
    Pencil, 1786; *Autobiography,* pl. 17.
    Unlocated.

"Sketches in France and Germany 1786. J.T."
    Pencil and pen and ink.
    The Five Daughters of Mrs. Winchester Bennett, New Haven, Conn.

France

Place Louis XV, Paris.
    Pencil, 1786; *Autobiography,* pl. 6.
    Mrs. Norman Holmes Pearson, New Haven, Conn.

Paris, as Seen from the House of the Abbé Chalut.
    Pencil, 1786; *Autobiography,* pl. 7.
    Mrs. Norman Holmes Pearson, New Haven, Conn.

Spain

View Toward the Bar of Bilbao.
    Ink and wash, 1781, on shipboard (1st Silliman sale, no. 119).
    Yale, no. 1947.488. (Fig. 231)

Castro, Near Bilbao.

> Ink and wash, 1781, on shipboard (1st Silliman sale, no. 120).
> Yale, no. 1947.486.
>
> Different view, same (1st Silliman sale, no. 120).
> Yale, no. 1947.487.

Port of Vivari.

> Ink and wash, 1781, on shipboard (1st Silliman sale, no. 120).
> Yale, no. 1947.490.

Fishing Cove and Town of Vivari.

> Ink and wash, 1781, on shipboard (1st Silliman sale, no. 118).
> Unlocated.

The Asturian Mountains.

> Ink and wash, 1781, on shipboard (1st Silliman sale, no. 120).
> Yale, no. 1947.489.

United States and Canada

CONNECTICUT

View of the West Mountain Near Hartford.

> Sepia wash, 1791 (2d Silliman sale, no. 840).
> Yale, gift of Yale University Art Gallery Associates, no. 1938.290.
>
> Oil(?) (American Academy Cat., 1817, no. 168), probably the following.
> Unlocated.

Landscape View Near Hartford.

> (American Academy Cat., 1924, no. 45), probably the following.
> Unlocated.

Monte Video (Daniel Wadsworth's country seat), Talcott Mountain, Avon, Conn.

> Oil, 1791(?).
> Yale, bequest of Miss Marian Cruger Coffin, no. 1957.24. (Fig. 234)

The Great Falls of the Connecticut River at Walpole, "a view of the first timber cantilever bridge erected in this country."

> India ink, 1791 (1st Silliman sale, no. 60).
> Fordham. (Fig. 233)

Norwich, Near the Paper Mills.

> Pencil, 1806.
> Yale, gift of Mrs. Robert Scoville, no. 1935.3.3.

Pencil, 1806.

Same as above, no. 1935.3.5.

Norwich Falls, or *The Falls of the Yantic at Norwich.*
Four pencil drawings, 1804.
Same as above, nos. 1935.3.2, .8, .10, and .11.
From the Grounds of Mr. Vernet (see *Portraits*).
Pencil, 1806.
Same as above, no. 1935.3.7.
Oil, 1806.
Slater Memorial Museum, Norwich, Conn.
Oil, 1806.
(The above two oils, Pennsylvania Academy Cat., 1818, nos. 35 and 41; American Academy Cats., 1817, nos. 64 and 67; 1824, nos. 7 and 11; and 1831, nos. 21 and 22.)
Yale, Mabel Brady Garvan Collection, no. 1947.186. (Fig. 235)
Oil, 1806(?) ("my three pictures of Norwich Falls" sold to Jonathan G. W. Trumbull of Norwich in 1835 for $500); possibly some or all of the above.
Unlocated.

NEW JERSEY

Sketches of Passaic Falls (on the Passaic River near Newark).
"Two drawings in India ink" (1844 auction sale, no. 11); possibly either or both of the following.
Unlocated.

Falls of the Passaick.
Watercolor, 1804 (1st Silliman sale, no. 69).
Unlocated.

Pencil, 1804.
Unlocated.

NEW YORK

Dr. Hosack's Greenhouses, Hyde Park.
Pencil, 1806.
Yale, gift of Mrs. Robert Scoville, no. 1935.3.6.

Fort at Stony Point on the Hudson River (between West Point and Nyack).
India ink, 1782 (1st Silliman sale, no. 56).
Unlocated.

Haverstraw Bay, View Toward Sugar Loaf Hill in the Highlands of the North River (between Stony Point and Ossining).
    India ink, 1782 (1st Silliman sale, no. 57).
    Unlocated.

View of the Mountain Called the Clove from the North River above Fishkill.
    India ink, 1783 (1st Silliman sale, no. 58).
    Unlocated.

The Cohoes Falls, Near Albany, on the Mohawk River.
    India-ink wash, 1791 (1st Silliman sale, no. 59; and 2d, no. 921).
    Addison Gallery, Andover, Mass., no. 1940.27. (Fig. 232)

Canajoharie Bridge.
    Pencil, 1807.
    Yale, gift of Mrs. Robert Scoville, no. 1935.3.12.

Looking Down Stream.
    Pencil, 1807.
    Same as above, no. 1935.3.13.

Indian Lorette.
    Pencil, 1807.
    Same as above, no. 1935.3.30.

Lake George.
    Pencil, 1808.
    Same as above, no. 1935.3.21.
    Pencil, 1808.
    Same as above, no. 1935.3.22.

Regence Rock(?).
    Pencil, 1808.
    Same as above, no. 1935.3.23.

Black Mountain.
    Pencil, 1808.
    Same as above, no. 1935.3.25.

Niagara Falls.
    Eight pencil sketches, probably 1806.
    Same as above, nos. 1935.3.14 to .19; .27 and .28.
    "Sketch in India ink" (1844 auction sale, no. 12).
    Unlocated.

"Small," probably painted in 1808, taken to London, and returned in 1815.
Unlocated.

"Two small cloths with outlines of Falls," same as the above.
Unlocated.

From an upper bank on the British side, oil, *ca.* 1807 (American Academy Cat.,
　　　1824, no. 109).
Wadsworth Atheneum, Hartford, no. 1848.5. (Fig. 237)

From below the great cascade on the British side.
Oil, *ca.* 1807 (American Academy Cat., 1824, no. 111).
Wadsworth Atheneum, Hartford, no. 1848.4. (Fig. 236)

From two miles below Chippawa.
Oil, panorama, 2½ by 14½ feet, 1808 (American Academy Cats., 1816, no. 18;
　　　1822, no. 51; and 1823, no. 52).
New-York Historical Society. (Fig. 239)

From under Table Rock.
Oil, panorama, pendent to the above, 1808 (American Academy Cats., 1816, no.
　　　14; and 1822, no. 49).
New-York Historical Society. (Fig. 238)

(?) Albany Institute of History and Art, Albany, N.Y., no. 1945.83.

"More Recent Sketches," paperbound sketchbook, landscape studies of Norwich Falls,
Lake George, and Niagara Falls, 1804–08 (mostly listed above).
　　　Yale, gift of Mrs. Robert Scoville, no. 1935.3.

ONTARIO

Entrance of the Mountain at Queenston Through Which Flows the St. Lawrence.
　　　Pencil, 1808.
　　　Yale, gift of Mrs. Robert Scoville, no. 1935.3.29.

QUEBEC

La Chaudière (river that flows into the St. Lawrence above Quebec).
　　　Pencil, 1807.
　　　Yale, gift of Mrs. Robert Scoville, no. 1935.3.31.

Montmorency Falls (on the St. Lawrence River).
　　　Pencil, 1807.
　　　Same as above, no. 1935.3.35.

UNIDENTIFIED

Landscape.

Oil(?) (American Academy Cat., 1817, no. 65), probably one of the above.
Unlocated.

Landscape with One Figure.

Oil(?), 1783.
Unlocated.

Rock-Bound Lake.

India-ink wash, in America *ca.* 1806 (1st Silliman sale, no. 76).
Fordham.

Seven Pencil Sketches, *ca.* 1804–08.

Yale, gift of Mrs. Robert Scoville, nos. 1935.3.9, .20, .24, .26, .32, .33, and .34.

ROMANTIC

The Tempest.

India-ink wash, 1784, London (1st Silliman sale, no. 125).
Mrs. Percy Chubb, Chester, N.J.

Landscape With Figures.

1820s, New York(?).
Mrs. Clifton N. Bockstoce, Hartford, Conn.

Landscape With a Horseman.

Same as above.

"Composition, suggested from no. 102" by "an Unknown Artist, lent by Mrs. Rogers"
(American Academy Cat., 1825, no. 99), a landscape(?), possibly one of the above.
Unlocated.

Mountainous Landscape.

Small pen-and-wash sketch, probably after prints after Italian (or French?) paint-
ing, 1783, probably Boston.
Given to Theodore Dwight, Sr. (or Jr.?), in the late 1820s.
Bequest of Stephen B. Luce to Harvard, Fogg Art Museum, no. 1962.109.

Landscape With Dead Tree.

Small pen-and-wash sketch, probably after prints after Italian (or French?) painting, 1783, probably at Boston.
Same as above, no. 1962.108.

FIGURE STUDIES

FROM THE ANTIQUE

(All 1784, London, from casts in the Royal Academy School.)

A Faun.
>Crayon (1st Silliman sale, no. 95).
>Cooper Union, New York.

The Dancing Faun.
>Crayon (1st Silliman sale, no. 99).
>Unlocated.

Bacchanalian Figure.
>Crayon (1st Silliman sale, no. 96).
>Unlocated.

Apollo.
>Crayon (1st Silliman sale, no. 97).
>Fordham.

Venus de' Medici.
>Crayon (1st Silliman sale, no. 98).
>Yale, no. 1947.491.

Germanicus.
>Pencil (1st Silliman sale, no. 101).
>Fordham.

>Two studies, pencil (1st Silliman sale, no. 101).
>Yale, gift of Yale University Art Gallery Associates, nos. 1938.279. and .280.

Further studies in sketchbook in Yale University Library.

LIFE DRAWINGS

Male Torso.
>Four studies, crayon, 1780 in the Tothill-fields Prison, London (1st Silliman sale, no. 100).
>Fordham.

The following, 1784, London:

Male Figure.
>Full-length, crayon (1st Silliman sale, no. 78).
>Fordham.

Male Figures.
>Two drawings (1st Silliman sale, nos. 80 and 82).
>Mrs. Percy Chubb, Chester, N.J.

Male Figures.
>Crayon on blue-gray paper (1st Silliman sale, nos. 84, 88, 89, 91, and 94).
>Unlocated.

>Same (1st Silliman sale, nos. 86 and 87).
>Yale, gift of Gifford A. Cochran, nos. 1949.66 and .67. (Figs. 243 and 244)

Two Men.
>Crayon on white paper (1st Silliman sale, no. 93).
>Joseph Wright Alsop, Washington, D.C.

Reclining Female.
>Full-length, crayon (1st Silliman sale, no. 77).
>Yale, gift of Yale University Art Gallery Associates, no. 1938.273. (Fig. 242)

Reclining Female.
>Crayon, full-length (1st Silliman sale, no. 83).
>Yale, gift of Yale University Art Gallery Associates, no. 1938.274.

Female Figure.
>Crayon (1st Silliman sale, no. 81).
>Fordham.

Female Figures.
>Two drawings (1st Silliman sale, nos. 79 and 85).
>Mrs. Percy Chubb, Chester, N.J.

Female Figure.
>Crayon on blue-gray paper (1st Silliman sale, no. 90).
>Unlocated.

Female Figure.
>Full-length, crayon (1st Silliman sale, no. 92).
>Fordham.

Other life studies in sketchbook in Yale University Library; the Five Daughters of Mrs. Winchester Bennett; and Mrs. Norman Holmes Pearson, New Haven, Conn.

Draped Figures

Two Men.
> Both rear view, wash drawings, studies for drapery; signed and dated; 1783, London (Royal Academy School?).
> Paul A. Frederick, Milwaukee, Wis. (Figs. 240 and 241)

Sleeping Man, in Five Attitudes.
> 1778, Lebanon, Conn.(?).
> Yale, gift of Mr. and Mrs. Luke Vincent Lockwood, no. 1939.279.

Peasant Girl Leading a Donkey.
> 1786, Europe.
> Unlocated.

Monument in White Marble, Made by Ceracchi.
> Sketch (2d Silliman sale, no. 920).
> Unlocated.

"Various Subjects."
> 6 sketches (1st Silliman sale, no. 132).
> Unlocated.

> "Small and large" sketches (1st Silliman sale, no. 133).
> Unlocated.

> 15 sketches (1st Silliman sale, no. 135).
> Unlocated.

> 17 sketches (1st Silliman sale, no. 136).
> Unlocated.

Further miscellaneous sketches in sketchbooks in Yale University Library.

Lady Dressing, a Copy After Murillo.
> None exists, possibly after a French painter (1844 auction sale, no. 2).
> Unlocated.

MISCELLANEOUS SUBJECTS

HERALDRY

Arms of the Trumbull Family.
> "First attempt in oil colors—age 15," 1771, Lebanon, Conn.; *Autobiography*, no. 6.
> Unlocated.
>
> (?) Copy(?), in watercolor.
> Mrs. Harold K. English, New Haven, Conn.

MEDALS

Insignia of the Society of the Cincinnati and Design of the medal.
> Obverse and reverse (2d Silliman sale, no. 808).
> Unlocated.

Three Indian Peace Medals, known as the "Washington Season Medals."
> "Slight sketches," 1796, London.
> Unlocated.
>
> *Obverse:* (1) cattle raising; (2) agriculture—man sowing wheat; and (3) domestic tranquillity and employment—woman spinning.
>
> *Reverse:* same for all three: "Second Presidency of George Washington, MDCCXCVI." Dies cut by C. H. Kuchler, medals struck in both silver and copper by Bolton & Watt of Birmingham, England, size 45 mm.
> Yale University Library. (Fig. 246)

Seal for the City of Hartford, Conn. (with Col. Samuel Wyllys), 1785.

MAPS

The Colony of Connecticut.
> Pencil, unfinished, rococo cartouche in ink, signed and dated, 1774, Lebanon, Conn.; prepared for the artist's father, Jonathan Trumbull, Governor of Connecticut.
> Massachusetts Historical Society. (Fig. 247)

Connecticut and Part of the Colony (Susquehannah).
> Ink, colored boundaries, signed and dated, 1775, Lebanon, Conn.; prepared for the artist's father.
> Massachusetts Historical Society. (Fig. 248)

Boston and Surrounding Military Posts, "part of the lines of Charlestown where the enemy carried on their approaches."

> In brown ink (2d Silliman sale, no. 810).
> Unlocated.

"Boston, With the British and American Military Positions as They Were in September, 1775, drawn by John Trumbull."

> 2d Silliman sale, no. 814.
> Unlocated.

> Not endorsed (2d Silliman sale, no. 815).
> Unlocated.

"Boston & the Surrounding Country, & Posts of the American Troops, Sept. 1775."

> Engraved; plate 2 (opp. p. 23) in the *Autobiography* (original copper plate, 2d Silliman sale, no. 945).
> Unlocated. (Fig. 249)

Fortifications and Disposition of Troops at Ticonderoga, New York.

> "I found time to draw three copies, one to be submitted to Gen. Gates, one to Gen. Schuyler, and one to Congress," *Autobiography,* p. 33.
> None located, though probably among the following.

> Military map contained in letter of 15 July 1776 to his brother, Joseph Trumbull, the Commissary General of the Continental Forces.
> Joseph Trumbull Collection, Connecticut State Library, Hartford. (Fig. 251)

> "I have lately obtained, from among the papers of my father, a drawing of the post made by me in the month of August and sent to him; an accurate copy of this is given in the annexed plate" (engraved map, "Ticonderoga & its Dependencies, August 1776 J.T.," opp. p. 33 in the *Autobiography*).
> Unlocated. (Note: Original copper plate for this was in the 2d Silliman sale, no. 946; also unlocated.)

> *Mount Independence at Ticonderoga.*
> Pen and watercolor (2d Silliman sale, no. 809).
> Unlocated.

> *"Plan of Tyconderoga, Mount Independence, etc."*
> Ink, 11 August 1776 (2d Silliman sale, no. 811).
> Unlocated.

> Ink and watercolor, undated, probably one of the above.
> Estate of Hall Park McCullough, Bennington, Vt. (Fig. 250)

Chart of New London Harbor Indicating Fire Capability from Four Fortified Positions, April 1776.

> Jonathan Trumbull Papers, Connecticut State Library, Hartford. (Fig. 252)

ARCHITECTURAL PROJECTS

An Anglo-Palladian Villa.

> Perspective view of exterior and plan, pen and ink, 1777, Boston, possibly the artist's earliest architectural studies (in the Davis papers).
>
> Alexander J. Davis Collection, New-York Historical Society. (Fig. 253)

Seven Drawings.

> Four in pencil, three in brown ink, 1781 at Tothill-fields Bridewell Prison, and others later, all architectural in subject.
>
> The Cooper Union, New York, 1963.47.1, .2, .3, .4, .5, and 1964.1212.2. (See Fig. 257)

Plan for the Development of Yale College, Including a Proposed Layout of the College Grounds.

> Drawn in 1792 at Philadelphia for James Hillhouse, Treasurer of Yale College, 1782–1832, and Member of Congress, 1791–1810.
>
> Yale University Library. (Fig. 254)

Designs(?) for the New First Presbyterian Church, Philadelphia(?) (to replace "Old Buttonwood," erected in 1704 and enlarged in 1729).

> If by Trumbull, 1792, Philadelphia (see Stephen's *Philadelphia Directory* for 1796, "The first Presbyterian Church by Mr. Trumbul," the new church begun in 1793, in use by 1796, congregation removed in 1821).
>
> Unlocated. (See Fig. 260)

"Drawings by Col. John Trumbull, Esq. . . . All of Architectural Subjects, while in London, Washington, N.Y. and N. Haven. Put up in this volume by himself . . . This vol. was presented to Alex'r J. Davis, Arc't. The pupil and friend of Trumbull." (See Figs. 255 and 256)

> A large scrapbook, caption in Davis' hand, subjects in pen and ink, some with wash and watercolors added, 1777 (see above) to 1830.
>
> Alexander J. Davis Collection, New-York Historical Society.

"20 Architectural Studies" (1st Silliman sale, no. 137), possibly the following.

> Unlocated.

Elevations and Plans for a Number of Residences.
> 1790 to 1794, Lebanon, Conn.
> Yale, gift of Yale University Art Gallery Associates, nos. 1938.282–285.
> At London(?).
> Yale, nos. 1947.498–500. (See Fig. 258)

Plans for the Meetinghouse at Lebanon, Conn.
> 1804.
> Unlocated.

Various Sketches for the Dome of the Capitol at Washington.
> 1818, New York (see *Autobiography*, pp. 266 and 268 ff.; two plans for the base-
> ment of the Rotunda in the Davis papers).
> Unlocated.

Plans for the American Academy of Fine Arts, 8½ Barclay Street, New York.
> 1830, New York (in the Davis papers, see above).

Plans for the Trumbull Gallery, Yale College.
> 1831, With the limited assistance of Ithiel Town of Town and Davis, architects,
> New York (see "Designs . . . Pinacotheca for Col. Trumbull's Paintings,"
> Yale, no. 1947.506).
> Unlocated.

> Drawing of entrance façade, pen and wash; though endorsed "Drawn by Geo.
> Gill" (contractor for the building, who made some of the working drawings,
> for which he received ten dollars), stylistically Trumbull.
> Yale University Library.

Buildings Erected

Meetinghouse, Lebanon, Conn.
> Built 1804 to 1806. Interior remodeled (balcony turned into a second floor) in
> 1875; largely destroyed in the great hurricane of 1938; fully restored by the
> late J. Frederick Kelly and his brother, Henry Schraub Kelly, both of New
> Haven. Completed in 1954. (Figs. 261 and 262)

American Academy of the Fine Arts, 8½ Barclay Street, near Broadway, in the rear of
Dr. David Hosack's residence on Vesey Street, New York.
> Built in 1831, partly destroyed by fire in 1837 and again in 1839; Academy dis-
> solved in 1841.

Trumbull Gallery, Old Yale Campus, New Haven.

Built 1831–32, collections removed in 1867, building remodeled in 1868 for the office of the College Treasurer; demolished in 1901. (see Fig. 276)

OTHER PROJECTS

Design for a Mahogany Sarcophagus.

"Containing the remains of the unfortunate André . . . in the shape of a Ladies work case about 2 feet high and 1½ wide . . . designed by Col. Trumbull . . . ," *Letters from John Pintard to His Daughter, 1816–1833* (4 vols., New-York Historical Society, New York, 1940), *2, 75*, letter of 18 August 1821.

Presumably enclosed in Major John André's tomb, designed by P. M. van Gelder, in Westminster Abbey, London.

"Early Sketches and Drawings."

Parchment-bound sketchbook containing studies in perspective, architecture, the draped figure and physiognomy, in ink, pencil and wash, late 1770s and early 1780s (mostly listed above).

Yale, gift of Mrs. Robert Scoville, no. 1935.3.

"Composition, suggested from no. 102" by "an Unknown Artist, lent by Mrs. Rogers."

So listed by Trumbull (American Academy Cat., 1825, no. 99), unidentified. Unlocated.

APPENDIX

Decoration from the cover of the catalog of the 7th *Annual Exhibition of the Pennsylvania Academy of the Fine Arts* (Philadelphia, 1818), at which Trumbull exhibited three pictures.

TRUMBULL'S PAINTING PROCEDURE

The Colonel was a sound and careful craftsman, following traditional usage and procedure. He was as much of a conservative in technical matters as in those of the spirit. His pictures were thinly and cleanly painted, most of them on well-made English linen cloth "whose strength and texture is very similar to that used for the topgallant sails of a ship of war" (*Autobiography*, p. 282). In a few instances, at the beginning of his career, he used copper. He employed wood panels only occasionally but throughout his life—for some fifteen portraits, a half dozen or so religious compositions, and a landscape or two. All his miniatures, except two or three, are painted (invariably in oils) on thin pieces of mahogany, and, except in a few instances, cut in oval shape. "Academy board" was employed only for three or four portraits. His pigments, oils, and varnishes were largely supplied by his "colourman Brown of Holborn opposite the new buildings near Broad Street and St. Giles," London, the well-known Thomas Brown (see William T. Whitley, *Art in England, 1821–1837* [New York, Macmillan, 1930], p. 44), and canvases from James Poole, High Holborn. He also patronized various artists' colormen in Paris, when opportunity afforded, and in his later years one E. Déchaux of 709 Broadway, New York. His material was the best obtainable.

He mixed his dry, powdered colors with the oil vehicle (sun-thickened or boiled linseed oil) on a stone slab, following the usual eighteenth-century manner. He neatly set his palette fresh each morning, as can be seen in his self-portrait (1777) (Fig. 64) at the Museum of Fine Arts, Boston. The pigments in this carefully laid-out palette are "divided into seven classes" according to Hogarth (*Analysis of Beauty*, p. 116 of the original 1753 edition), though there are three registers in place of the more complicated Hogarthian five. It will be noted that the wooden palette of the twenty-one-year-old artist rests upon a leather-bound volume labeled "Hogarth." In the self-portrait, painted about 1812 at London, now privately owned in Switzerland (Fig. 66), the palette "has six colors: flake white, Naples yellow, Venetian red, vermilion, raw umber, and blue black. In the middle of the palette we find the light yellowish flesh tints (Naples yellow and plenty of flake white) and the light reddish flesh tint (Venetian red and plenty of flake white). He uses five hog's hair brushes of a medium size; the palette is the modern shape (with a deep curve near the thumb hole)." (For this information I am indebted to Fritz Schmid of Zurich.) There is a palette shown in the portrait of Trumbull painted about 1820 by Samuel Lovett Waldo (Fig. 270), at the Yale University Art Gallery (no. 1910.2). The colors, as restricted as those in the Geneva portrait, are freshly laid out with a palette knife. The wooden palette, which rests on a volume, as in the Boston self-portrait, is partly cut off by the edge of the picture. Six soft, round brushes protrude from the thumb hole. The hilt of his military sword is visible beneath the palette—a romantic allusion—for "he gave his SWORD and his PENCIL to his Country."

(Since Thomas Sully derived much from Trumbull, his posthumous *Hints to Young Painters and the Process of Portrait-Painting* [Philadelphia, J. M. Stoddard & Co., 1873] should be consulted. He illustrates a palette somewhat similar to that used by Trumbull, stating that "the principal colors from which these tints are made are white, yellow ochre . . . ultramarine or permanent blue, vermilion, Indian red, raw umber, ivory-black and burnt umber." But Trumbull used no blue. Fritz Schmid comments, "as mostly in eighteenth century palettes—Vien, Duplessis, Drouais—we find no blue on Trumbull's palette.")

His brushes, referred to by the then current, now archaic, word "pencils," were soft, round, and pointed. These veritable "pencils" were quite different from the hard, flat brushes made of stiff pigs' bristles now generally employed in painting with prepared oil colors in tubes.

The artist applied his pigment, thinly and evenly, on prepared canvas or panel, grounded with warm ocher of about middle value (a like ground can be seen in the unfinished "Athenaeum" Washington by Gilbert Stuart in the Museum of Fine Arts, Boston). Uninfluenced by the not altogether happy changes wrought by the industrial revolution, Trumbull, the careful craftsman, endowed his work with lasting qualities.

An interesting technical document on the care of paintings (in the Library of Congress, Division of Manuscripts), printed in his *Autobiography* (pp. 281–86), was addressed to the Speaker of the House on the occasion of the restoration made by the artist of his four murals in the Capitol. These had been delivered and installed before the building was finished and, consequently, suffered from dampness and mold.

"To produce fine Colouring," a record of a conversation with his old master, Benjamin West, dated 8 June 1784 (in Trumbull College, Yale University) is also revealing:

Nature has but three primitive Colours. Yellow, Red & Blue, from which all others arise by Composition—Yellow & red produce Orange, Yellow & Blue, Green—& Red with Blue, Purple;—Yellow, Red, & Blue, produce Black, which is a privation of Colour by Darkness,—& Yellow, Orange Red, Purple, Blue & Green produce White, which is a privation of Colour by Light:—

In Colouring, Opposite Colours are as much as possible to be placed near to each other, as Red to Green—Blue to Orange, or Yellow to Purple:—for by this means the whole of Colour is comprehended,—the Green, which arises from the two primitives Blue & Yellow, becomes opposed by the other primitive Red—& so of the others, by which that kind of Union is produc'd which gives the Effect of Air or Atmosphere:—this Opposition is the fundamental principle from which Harmony & Brilliance of Colour results, but, owing to the imperfection of the substances which are used in Art to produce Colour, it becomes frequently impracticable with body colour.—& glazing is necessary to produce it in the highest perfection—for how the three primitive colours may be absolutely blended in one & the same piece of Drapery. &c. as a Red Drapery, may be Glaz'd with Green, a Blue, with Orange & a Purple with Yellow:—from which will arise an astonishing degree of Union, & Brilliance—and this rule being founded in Nature can never be departed from, without impropriety.—as suppose that in a painting, a Blue drapery is found to be too powerfull & glittering for the other parts, & you wish it to be lower'd, this cannot be done by glazing with Blue, for that will but encrease the glitter. It cannot be glaz'd with Black without producing a Mudiness—Red will produce a purple & Yellow gives a Green:—but Orange in which are contain'd the two remaining Primitives, will at once reduce the Colour to the depth requir'd & at the same time give the most pleasing Modesty & Union of Tone:—in like manner suppose a Yellow is to be glaz'd to a more quiet tone—Red will evidently give an Orange hue—& Blue will bring on a Green,—but the Purple in which Red & Blue the two remaining primitives are united, will at once reduce the Glitter of the Yellow & give Modesty united with Clearness:—

And the same principle is true throughout all possible combinations of Colour:—Black may be glaz'd with White, & the reverse, & Browns, Olives, Slates, &c, &c, are all to be aided by their opposites:—this is the principle on which the fine colouring of the Venetian School was produc'd, & whoever practices in strict conformity to it, need not apprehend going wrong: however from want of practice, he may fail for some time of absolute Brilliance.—

N.B. the substances which in oil painting approach most nearly to the Atmospheric Colours of Nature, are Prussian Blue—Red Lake, & Yellow Lake.—No other Colour'd substances now in use possessing so much of Transparency as these: Asphaltum is also most wonderfully usefull when great Depth is requir'd, united with clearness:—other Oil with which these substances are to be mix'd may be a composition of drying Oil with a small proportion of Mastic Varnish & oil of turpentine:—the Picture should first be thoroughly dry—& if it has stood two or three Years the better.—remembering before you glaze to wash the surface with clean hot water, to take away a degree of greasiness which it will construct.

The subject of painter's palettes has been recently treated by Fritz Schmid in *The Practice of Painting* (London, Faber & Faber, 1948). He advises the author that Trumbull's notes on "fine Colouring" are "partly cited from" Jacques Christophe Le Blon, *Coloritto, or the Harmony of Colouring in Painting* (Paris, 1756), and from Moses Harris, *The Natural System of Colours* (London, 1766?). See also F. Schmid, "The Color Circles by Moses Harris," *The Art Bulletin, 30* (1948), 227–30. Mr. Schmid further writes,

The only contemporary note on the painting methods of Benjamin West I found in an English repository dated 1808 (Anon., "A Compendium of Colours," *The Artist's Repository of the Fine Arts* [London, 1808], III, 216): "According to Mr. West, when you intend to re-paint, re-touch, or glaze your picture, let it first be tolerably dry, then give the whole, or the part which you intend to paint, a coat of varnish a day or two before, after which you may mix some of the same varnish with the colours you put on, which will make them bear out with great force and clearness, insomuch that there will not be the least occasion for varnishing those parts when the whole is finished, only covering the other parts that appear dull or sunk in."

Trumbull used a scaled palette, according to contemporary practice. (See Denman Waldo Ross, *The Painter's Palette* [Boston, Houghton Mifflin, 1919] and Arthur Pope, *The Language of Drawing and Painting* [Cambridge, Harvard, 1949].) In the Yale collections there are three interesting charts showing what colors were used on certain portraits. These notations are as follows (without reproducing the colors):

For the portrait of the Duke of Wellington (Fig. 100), which Trumbull did after the marble bust carved by his British friend, Joseph Nollekens, in September 1813 at London:

1. Flake white & Naples yellow.
2. Venetian Red to No. 1.
3. Naples yellow to No. 2.
4. Flake white & Venetian Red.
5. Venetian Red to No. 4.
6. Venetian red to No. 5.
7. Indian red to No. 6.
8. Naples Yellow & Venetian Red.
9. Venetian Red.
10. Indian red.
11. Indian red & blue black.
12. Madder Lake.
13. Blue black.

No. 11 was the general Shadow & half tint. Where this proved too purplish, blue black alone was used for the lightest half tint.

Colours ground in Linseed Oil with Resin.

The picture varnished with Canada Balsam diluted with Eth¹—turp.

Memo—in the second head of Wellington the Tint No. 11. was composed of *Purple* Red & blue black & is finer.

For the late replica of the portrait of Mrs. Rufus King, painted in 1820 at New York, after the original of 1800 executed at London when her husband was serving as American Minister to Great Britain (Fig. 36):

This picture was painted with only four Colours: viz. White Oxford Ochre Venetian red & calcined Sea Coal—except that in the darkest tint under the Nose, Mouth, Ear and Chin, the tint No. 9 was employed viz. Sea Coal calcined & Antwerp light Red. The result is to my Eye singularly harmonious, J.T.

1. White with Oxford yellow.
2. White with Venetian Red.
3. White with Oxford yellow.
4. White with Venetian Red.
5. White with Oxford ochre.
6. White with Venetian.
7. Venetian Red.
8. Venetian Red with calcined Sea Coal.
9. Antwerp light Red with do.
10. Antwerp light Red.
11. Calcined Sea Coal.
12. Calcined Sea Coal & White—the general half tint.

For the portrait of the young bride, Mrs. Frederick Prime (Mary Rutherford Jay, granddaughter of John Jay), who was painted in 1829 at Norwich, Conn.:

1. Flake White & Naples yellow.
2. Do. & Venetian Red.
3. Do. & Naples yellow.
4. Do. & Venetian Red.
5. Do. & Do.
6. Do. & Do.
7. Venetian Red.

8. Venetian Red & blue black.
9. Venetian Red & blue black.
10. Blue black.
11. 3 & 9 } half tint of flesh.
12. 3 & 9 }
13. Umber (raw) & white } Hair
14. Raw Umber }

Portrait of Miss Jay (Mrs. Fredc. Prime) November 1829
Nut Oil & Sandarach.

There is much additional material of like interest—a small painting box, complete with colors and palette, with "J. Trumbull, Lebanon, 1777," painted on the underside of the lid, in the National Collection of Fine Arts, Smithsonian Institution, Washington, D.C. Joseph Lanman Richards of New London, Conn., has a traveling paint box of mahogany, of English make, which came from Abigail Trumbull Lanman (b. 1806), the artist's favorite niece and one of the heirs to his estate. It contains four squarish glass jars for oils and turpentine and twelve small jars for dry colors. At the Yale Gallery there is a mahogany, table-high painting cabinet, on top of which is a locked, hinged cover, opening to left and right, resting on a set of five deep drawers. The top contains a large porphyry slab for mixing colors and rows of receptacles to hold squarish jars of powdered pigment. The glass jars still contain the actual colors procured by the painter and little paper packages neatly labeled in his hand. His brushes, both soft sable hair and bristle, and his pestles are in side pockets just as he left them. The "Patriot-Artist's" long maulstick was, symbolically, the first object to be brought into the present Gallery building (Yale's fourth), the lineal successor of the original Trumbull Gallery of 1831. This act of piety was performed in 1928 by the Associate Director at that time—the present author.

VIEW OF THE U.S. CAPITOL AT WASHINGTON

From Noah Webster's *History of the United States*
(New Haven, 1832)

Trumbull painted four large decorations for the Rotunda of
the Capitol, finishing them in 1824. (See Figs. 163, 186, 195–
196, 205–207)

TRUMBULL'S PRICES

It is interesting to note what the artist received for his work. Prices will, of course, have
to be multiplied many times to equal today's purchasing power. The following are
typical:

1774, "Portraits of my Father & Mother—half-length Cloth sold to Colo. Jedh. Huntington—for Seven Guineas"; now owned by Wadsworth Atheneum, Hartford.

1777, "Portrait of Majr. Genl. Jabez Huntington of the Militia, wholelength half the
size of life—was paid for it (paper) fifteen Gns"; now owned by the Connecticut
State Library, Hartford, Conn. (Fig. 31)

1777, "Portraits of my brother Jonathan, his Wife & daughter, in one piece, 4 feet by
3 . . 2 . . . . paper £42 l.m." (i.e. lawful money); now in the Yale University Art
Gallery. (Fig. 79)

1784, "Small portraits of Colo. Wadsworth & Son—15 Guineas"; now owned by Faneuil
Adams, South Duxbury, Mass. (Fig. 85)

1784, "Whole length of Mr. P. Tracy (father of Nat) leaning on an Anchor—head copied—recd 20 Guineas"; now owned by National Gallery of Art, Washington, D.C.

1789, "The Sortie from Gibraltar, size 6 feet high by 9. long.—finished in April 1789—

Exhibited at Spring Gardens May 1789—& Engraved by Mr. Sharp. For this picture I was offered & refused 1200 Guineas. . . . It is now in the hands of Saml. Williams Esqr. 13 Finsbury Square, with the hope of being Sold—1818.'' The picture was eventually sold to the Boston Athenaeum in 1828 for $2,000 and is now on loan at the Museum of Fine Arts, Boston. (Fig. 198)

1803, "The Same Subject [Sortie from Gibraltar], portraits from life—intended for the Engraver, 20 by 30 Inches.—finished 1788. and Sold in 1803 to Sr. Francis Baring for Five hundred Guineas"; now in the Cincinnati Art Museum. (Fig. 197)

1817 to 1824, Received from the United States Treasury for the four large pictures in the Rotunda of the Capitol at Washington a total of $32,000. (Figs. 163, 186, 195, 205)

1828, Two small panoramas of the Niagara Falls sold to Daniel Wadsworth, $200 each, now in the Wadsworth Atheneum, Hartford. (Figs. 236 and 237)

1828, Portrait prices are best summed up in a letter from Trumbull to Joseph Elgar, Commissioner of Public Buildings, Washington, D.C., 10 December 1828 (HM 23051, reproduced by permission of The Huntington Library, San Marino, Calif.):

My price was then, and has always been, as follows

For the Head alone	100. Dollars.
Head with the hands	150.
Half length	250.
Whole length	500.

These prices are 50 pr Ct. below those obtained by Stuart—and are not ¼ of what is received by Sr. Thos. Lawrence—instead of Dollars He has Guineas.

COMPARATIVE NOTE

When Sir Thomas Lawrence first arrived in London in 1786 his bust portraits fetched 25 to 30 guineas. By 1822 he was receiving 600 gn. for his full-lengths and 1500 gn. in 1828. His income in 1807 was about £3000 and three times that amount in 1815. (See Sir Walter Armstrong, *Lawrence* [London, Methuen, 1913].)

It is surprisingly difficult to find what Gilbert Stuart charged for portraits, owing to his recklessness in financial matters. After West introduced him to London society, he induced him to raise his price from 5 gn. to 30 gn. Entries in Thomas Jefferson's account books show he paid Stuart $100 each for portraits. The Samuel King Williams portrait, 1824, cost $100. Stuart referred to his many replicas of his celebrated "Athenaeum" head of Washington as his "hundred dollar bills." (Information from Frick Art Reference Library, New York.)

Charles Willson Peale, who was fifteen years Trumbull's senior, received such prices as these:

Just before the Revolution:

Gov. Robert Eden	full-length	£22–10–0
Samuel Chase (of whom Trumbull made a drawing)		
	three-quarter-length	£10– 1–0
Charles Carroll of Carrollton (who appears in Trumbull's *Declaration* and *Resignation*)		
	half-length	£ 7– 7–0

In 1780:

Baron von Steuben (who appears in Trumbull's *Yorktown*)		
	half-length	10 guineas
	replica	6 guineas

In 1789:

Mrs. Francis Charlton and Child		
	half-length	£26– 5–0
"Head of Washington for Dutch Consul"		£12–15–0
(Yale, bequest of John Hill Morgan, no. 1943.64.)		

(Figures supplied by Charles Coleman Sellers, author of *Charles Willson Peale*).

From Henry W. Harrison, *The Battle-Fields of the Republic from Lexington to the City of Mexico* (Philadelphia, Henry Carey Baird, 1857).

TRUMBULL'S VARIATIONS OF THE AMERICAN FLAG*

The national flag was adopted by the Continental Congress on 14 June 1777, the resolution reading, "That the flag of the thirteen United States be thirteen stripes, alternate red and white; that the union be thirteen stars, white in a blue field, representing a new constellation." Though this flag was probably first displayed at the Battle of Bennington, 16 August 1777, many variations seem to have been used, which makes the Trumbull paintings peculiarly interesting. It should be remembered that during the War of 1812 the flag bore fifteen stripes and as many stars; on 4 July 1818 the original thirteen stripes were restored and a star for each state; in the Mexican War there were twenty-nine stars; in the Civil War thirty-five; forty-five in the Spanish-American War; forty-eight in World Wars I and II; and fifty in the Vietnam War.

In the 1784 portrait, *Jeremiah Wadsworth and His Son Daniel,* privately owned in South Duxbury, Mass. (Fig. 85), Trumbull displays on a ship in the distance the flag of the East India Company, known the world over, of alternate red and white stripes with no field or "canton." How far this flag suggested itself to the Founding Fathers is an insoluble problem. The first naval jack bore the thirteen alternate red and white stripes with the rattlesnake motive and the "Don't tread on me." In the background of the portrait of General Washington (Fig. 90), and now in the Metropolitan Museum of Art, a flag of thirteen alternate white and red stripes with the white at the top and bottom, without the blue canton, flies over West Point. In the large *Gen. Washington at*

Trenton, at Yale, painted in 1792 (Fig. 95), the flag has the white stripe outermost, and the canton has thirteen stars in a circle, "the new constellation." The stars of the constellation are set forth in a series of rows, and the stripes are white (at the top) and red in the flag in the Yale version of the *Battle of Trenton* (Fig. 164), fought on 26 December 1776. In the early sketch (also at Yale) (Fig. 174) for the *Battle of Princeton* (Fig. 169), which took place on 3 January 1777, the *cantonless* flag bears thirteen alternate stripes of white, red, and *blue,* with white at the top; and the finished picture, also at Yale, has the usual red (this time at the top) and white stripes with thirteen stars in a square. The same type of flag, but with *six*-pointed stars, is employed in the *Surrender at Saratoga* (Fig. 184), which occurred on 16 October 1777. In the unfinished picture now at the Detroit Institute of Arts, of the final surrender of the British forces at York-town on 19 October 1781, a windblown flag bears the usual blue field or canton with thirteen white *six*-pointed stars in a circle, but the stripes are alternate red, white, and *blue,* with red at the top and bottom. In a more advanced study for *Yorktown,* the stripes are alternate white and red, the white stripe again at the bottom and twice the width of the red. In the finished *Yorktown* at Yale (Fig. 187), the flag has fourteen red and white stripes with white, again, at the bottom. The flag in two of the pictures in the Rotunda of the Capitol (Figs. 186 and 195), executed by the aged colonel between 1816 and 1824, have *eight*-pointed stars. Congress never specified how many points the stars should have. It should be noted, too, that the portraits of Gen. Washington, at Mount Vernon, and *Washington at Princeton,* at Yale, by Charles Willson Peale who was fifteen years Trumbull's senior, have *six*-pointed stars.

Why all these variations? Was Trumbull's memory or his information faulty? All the pictures, with the exception of *Gen. Washington at Trenton* and those in the Rotunda of the national Capitol, were executed at London, far from the scenes of action. As the Colonel was so scrupulous about matters of military accoutrements, one wonders how far the evidence of Washington's aide should be accepted.

* The author regrets to find certain discrepancies in his "Trumbull's *Yorktown* and the Evolution of the National Flag," *The Art Quarterly,* Autumn 1948, which are herein corrected.

See Frank Earle Schermerhorn, *American and French Flags of The Revolution, 1775–1783* (Philadelphia, Pennsylvania Society of Sons of the Revolution, 1948).

TRUMBULL'S *THE BATTLE OF PRINCETON**

The study of the creative process, whether of poet or painter, is revealing and reward-ing. Rare is the occasion when this absorbingly interesting pursuit can be followed, step by step, from inception to conclusion. Fortunate is the library possessing the work of an author from manuscript, through early printings with their varying textual changes, to final edition. Such can almost be accomplished at the Princeton University Library with Colonel John Trumbull's celebrated painting *The Battle of Princeton* (Fig. 169). There the most complete series of the patriot-artist's sketches for this his-torical composition is to be found (Figs. 175–181). Let us look first at the author and then at his work.

Trumbull was peculiarly endowed by nature and circumstance for the painting of the principal events which gave rise to the founding of this nation. . . . It was due to his ability as an amateur cartographer that the brilliant and versatile youth came to serve General Washington as an aide, with the rank of brigade major, and later General Gates as colonel—this before reaching the age of one-and-twenty. During the Rhode Island campaign, the hypersensitive young Colonel, believing himself slighted in the matter of date of rank, dramatically resigned his commission and set out to become a professional painter.

This, during the height of the Revolution, was not easily accomplished. He estab-lished himself in Boston and proceeded to copy the best provincial portraits and im-ported European pictures he could find. He also painted, in a hard, unrelenting man-ner, portraits of family and friends. But it soon became evident that self-teaching would not suffice. The ex-Colonel wangled a safe-conduct to England and, armed with proper introductions, became the pupil of the transplanted Philadelphian, Benjamin West. Dispossessed Loyalists in London were furious. The would-be painter shortly landed in prison, as a reprisal, so he believed, for the hanging of the popular Major André. Eventually he was deported but was back again immediately after the peace in 1783. After three years of intensive study, his master, West, historical painter to George III, undoubtedly suggested that his gifted pupil paint the stirring scenes he had witnessed, or could envision, during his recent military experience among the top "brass" of the American Revolutionary army. Jefferson, then on a visit to London from his post in Paris, was highly enthusiastic, encouraging, and full of practical suggestions. It was

* From *The Princeton University Library Chronicle, 12,* Autumn 1950.

under these circumstances that Trumbull undertook his "national history" series, as he called it. He started in painting *Bunker's Hill* (Fig. 145), under the eye of his benevolent master, and finished it by March 1786. Then in the heat of creative excitement he began to produce sketches for *The Death of General Mercer at the Battle of Princeton*, but put them aside to paint another dramatic incident of similar character, *The Death of General Montgomery at the Attack on Quebec* (Fig. 152), both of which were strongly reminiscent of West's great success, *The Death of General Wolfe at Quebec*, of 1771 (Fig. 142). This was in June; by September the thirty-year-old painter was well embarked on *The Declaration of Independence* (Fig. 158). *The Battle of Princeton*, however, was constantly in mind, as the eleven known sketches for it, all of the year 1786, indicate. It is interesting to arrange these in their probable sequence in order to reveal the workings of the artist's mind.

The central idea was, of course, Mercer's dramatic death from repeated bayoneting. The earliest conception (now at Yale) is a pen-and-ink study of the general, in the nude, partially astride his fallen horse, attempting to deal a slashing blow with his sword and, at the same time, vainly warding off a bayonet thrust with his left hand. The steed's head is upturned and its glance directed at two British grenadiers as if in dumb supplication—a decidedly distracting, sentimental note which was not eliminated until the final picture. This was followed by a pen-and-wash sketch (the property of Princeton University) portraying the wounded General, now clothed, beaten to his knees, with Washington and his staff officers, all mounted, in the middle distance. The six Princeton sketches come next, all expanding and elaborating the central theme. In the first of these (Fig. 175) the Mercer incident is moved to the right corner, balanced on the left by a bayoneting action; Lieutenant Charles Turnbull of Proctor's Battalion, Pennsylvania Artillery, backed against a cannon, waves a sword and manfully grasps a British bayonet with his bare hand. Washington and his staff, set off by the smoke of battle, occupy a dominating position in the center of the composition. The dead and dying and military gear strewn about the foreground suggest the horror and confusion of the conflict; Nassau Hall, seen in the far distance, indicates the locale.

That this conception was unsatisfactory to the artist, or more probably to his mentor, West, is illustrated by the next sketch (Fig. 176), also in outline, but unfinished. Mercer, rightly, takes the center of the stage, his importance being further enhanced by leafless trees—marking the season, the dead of winter. Artilleryman Turnbull is pushed off to the right, balanced by Washington and his entourage to the left. Again the artist was not content, for in the next Princeton sketch (Fig. 177), highly finished in outline, the actors are shifted, Turnbull is again at the left, balanced by Washington on the right, with Mercer and the winter windblown trees in the center. These readjustments were then rendered in a pen-and-wash color-value sketch (Fig. 178). The inconspicuous placing of Washington in the corner of this last composition must have troubled the former aide-de-camp, for in the following study (Fig. 179), unfinished in outline, the Commander-in-Chief is back again in the center and Turnbull, at the left, is balanced on the right by two soldiers who walk out of the picture. This compositional error is rectified in the last of the Princeton sketches (Fig. 180)—a file of British infantrymen, with their bayoneted muskets on high, bravely marches in from the right toward the center; the readjustment was complete. The group comprising the fallen Mercer and his savage antagonists in the immediate foreground, with Washington and staff, plus the leafless trees, in the middle distance, form a Raphaelesque isosceles triangle according to the best academic tradition. Still the artist was not satisfied; the classical equilibrium was perfect, but static and ill-adapted to express the turmoil of battle. With this defect in mind, he began an oil (twenty-five by thirty-six inches, now at Yale), moving the central trees, with their branches now shot away, to the side and throwing the composition into a violent, baroque-like opposition of diagonals (Fig. 174). This improved arrangement also contained serious faults—Mercer's long-necked white horse was far too prominent and, worst of all, actuality was imperfectly expressed in this London studio creation, which was left unfinished. Ten years had elapsed since the battle had been fought and won. The artist could readily improvise generalizations from a rich store of memories, but such did not wholly suffice. Particularization of actors and stage was manifestly necessary to give the ring of reality. Portraits for this and other scenes he had to have. The artist was obliged to return to America.

He visited the battle ground in December 1790 and made a pencil sketch (now owned by the estate of Hall Park McCullough) of "The college and village of Princeton as seen from the field on which the battle was fought on the 2nd Jan. 1777." This was worked up into a color-value sketch (now lost) in pen-and-wash. The chief problem of portraiture (Hugh Mercer had died of his seven bayonet wounds the day following the battle) was solved by making studies of the deceased general's sons at the family home in Fredericksburg, Virginia, in April, 1791. There are penciled portraits of John Mercer, the eldest boy, at the Metropolitan Museum of Art and at Fordham University. A third study, this of one of John's younger brothers, formerly misidentified as "Major André" (whom Trumbull could never have seen), is also at Fordham. Armed with these and other particulars, the artist returned to London in 1794.

There he ultimately finished, by 1797, a second canvas (twenty by thirty inches, also at Yale), begun in 1787, but the lapse of a decade proved disastrous. There was no longer the fire and gusto of the early Princeton sketches. Though the composition was perfected—and the disturbing element of Mercer's charger corrected—it remained a dull, spiritless performance (Fig. 169).

When the artist was seventy-five, and living a rather neglected life in New York, he repeated this last, listless picture at a greatly increased scale (six by nine feet), making the figures half the size of life. Trumbull, it should be remembered, had but one good eye and his larger pictures, in consequence, suffer from his monocular vision. This last, monotonous rendition of the battle was purchased in 1844, the year after the Colonel's death, by his nephew-in-law, Daniel Wadsworth of Hartford, and is now in the Wadsworth Atheneum, Hartford.

It will be seen that *The Battle of Princeton* commanded, though intermittently, the soldier-artist's attention for forty-five years—over half his life's span. It is appropriate that Princeton should have this series of spirited, small-scale studies of the battle by the chief visual recorder of the Revolution.[1]

1. Colonel Trumbull gave the six sketches now at Princeton to his nephew-in-law, Professor Benjamin Silliman, the Yale scientist, in the late 1830s. They were inherited by his son, of the same name and also a Yale professor, and then by the latter's son, a third Benjamin Silliman. They were sold at auction in 1896 at Philadelphia (Stan V. Henkels, no. 770, items 11 to 16). The last of the Princeton sketches was illustrated (opposite p. 2) in the sales catalogue. They were purchased by Junius Spencer Morgan '88 and by him given to the Library in 1904.

Three of the Princeton sketches, all in outline, were illustrated in John Durand's "John Trumbull," *The American Art Review,* II, 2d div. (1881); the first opposite p. 184, the third opposite p. 188, and the fifth opposite p. 190. The same illustrations were reproduced, but not in this order, in a reprint of the articles, Boston, Estes and Lauriat, 1881.

COLONEL TRUMBULL AND A NEWLY-FOUND PORTRAIT OF DR. FRANKLIN*

John Trumbull was a dual personality: proud and punctilious, eminently practical but romantically inclined; considerate and irascible; a socially conscious member of one of Connecticut's leading families—and he married a socially unacceptable woman; a Patriot and revolutionist who yearned to live like the landed British gentry; in fine, he was a man continuously frustrated by conflicting emotions and ideals. His boyhood ambition was to become a painter and work under the great Copley at Boston, but in this he was thwarted by his father, Governor Jonathan Trumbull, who would have none of it. Instead the old gentleman packed him off to Harvard to acquire a classical education. . . . He joined the Continental Forces, marched off to Boston and, literally, "drew" himself to Washington's attention by his newly-acquired ability as a cartographer, becoming, in short order, one of the general's aides. . . . He then proceeded, dramatically, to lay aside his "cockade and sword"—to become an artist. Even in this decision he vacillated, possessed as he was by Yankee mercantile blood, for he toyed with the idea of entering commerce. (Business ventures, uniformly unsuccessful, were to color much of his life.) None the less, he went to Boston, hired the painting rooms of the late John Smibert and applied himself as best he could. As there was no one to teach him he took to copying that early artist's copies of old masters,[1] painting from prints, from portraits by others and, when he could get friends to pose, from life. Saturated as we are today by illustrated magazines, newspapers and picture books of all kinds, it is difficult for us to appreciate the difficulties of the Colonial artist. The young, visually starved painter craved illustrative information.

As Smibert had been dead for twenty-six years when Trumbull took over his studio, one might surmise that little of that master's work survived on the premises. There was, however, an interesting collection of paintings and prints in the great stone Hancock House on Beacon Hill.[2] John Hancock, richest of the New England patriots, who

* From *The Art Quarterly*, Winter 1961.

1. The best known is from Smibert's copy of Van Dyck's *Cardinal Bentivoglio*, which Trumbull gave to Harvard College in 1791. During this period he made thirty paintings after prints. (Fig. 5)

2. Erected in 1737–40, demolished in 1863. See Walter Kendall Watkins, "The Hancock House and its Builder," *Old Time New England*, *17* (July 1926), 3–19 (well illustrated), and Hugh Morrison, *Early American Architecture*, New York, Oxford University Press, 1952, pp. 480–85.

then lived in his uncle's palazzo, seems to have borne no rancor for the young ex-Army officer's previous highhanded conduct. He not only opened his doors to him but, hearing that the struggling artist was ill, called at his lodgings and insisted that he be removed to his house immediately, where he could be more carefully attended. Among the pictures Trumbull painted in Hancock's elegant and sophisticated mansion was a half-length copy (Fig. 89) of a full-length portrait of General Washington by Charles Willson Peale, which Hancock had commissioned in 1776 (Fig. 88).[3] There was also a "Head of Rubens" and "Head of Vandyck, copied from pictures in possession of Gov. Hancock." The artist also noted that in 1778 he painted the "Head of Dr. Franklin— a fur cap—from a French print." As the engraving by Augustin de Saint-Aubin, after Charles Nicholas Cochin,[4] was the only print issued in France prior to the year 1778 depicting Franklin in a fur cap, it is obvious this is the one young Trumbull used in 1778. May we not assume, at the same time, that the young painter used the particular impression of the print in the Hancock House? Certainly, one might expect to find there this most recent portrait of the newly appointed American minister to the court of Louis XVI.

In December 1959 a small portrait painted on a wooden panel (6¼ by 5¼ inches) of Franklin in a fur cap turned up in the New York market (Fig. 19). Although little of its provenance was known it was said to have come from the celebrated Holden Collection of Americana, as the bookplate of the bibliophile Edwin B. Holden,[5] pasted on the back of the panel, would indicate. The owners of the little portrait, the Kennedy Galleries, Inc., inquired of me if it were possibly that listed by Trumbull in his *Autobiography*. Although I harbored some doubt, it was purchased by Yale University Art Gallery from funds bequeathed by the late John Hill Morgan,[6] who would have welcomed and enjoyed the problem of authentication. Further study and careful com-

---

3. The Peale portrait is now in the Brooklyn Museum; Trumbull's copy, cut down to head size at some undetermined date, is at Yale.

4. The original copperplate of this engraving, still in remarkably good condition, together with four impressions from it, came from the Edwin B. Holden Collection, sold at the American Art Galleries, New York, sale no. 10143, April 1910, item no. 1230. Purchased by the late William Smith Mason, they were subsequently given to the Yale University Library for the Mason-Franklin Collection. See George Simpson Eddy, "A Ramble Through the Mason-Franklin Collection," *Yale University Library Gazette*, X (April 1936), 65–90. The inscription on the print reads: "Benjamin Franklin. Né à Boston, dans la nouvelle Angleterre le 17 Janvier 1706. Designé par C. N. Cochin Chevalier de l'Ordre du Roi, en 1777, et Gravé par Aug. de St. Aubin Graveur de la Bibliothèque du Roi. Se vend à Paris chés C. N. Cochin aux Galeries du Louvre; et chés Aug. de St. Aubin, rue des Mathurins."

Included in the catalogue of the Holden Collection under the heading "Portraits Painted by John Trumbull, From the Ed. Frossard Collection," are seventeen spurious items, nos. 7525 through 7541; they include: 7526. Franklin (Benjamin), miniature on ivory in old metal frame, with certificate from Ed. Frossard. 7527. ——— Miniature at the age of 83 years, on ivory in old frame, with certificate from Ed. Frossard. 7540. Franklin (Benjamin). Wash drawing on deer skin. Framed.

5. The picture was not included in the Holden Collection auction of 1910.

6. New York lawyer, connoisseur and collector of early American paintings and miniatures.

parison with known works of the same period[7] have led me to believe that it is the one described by, and from the hand of, the young Colonel.

The little portrait is meticulously and thinly painted. Trumbull early achieved a beauty of surface. He prepared his colors afresh each day, using sable rather than pig bristle brushes. His method, even at this early stage in his development, was sound, in contrast to much of the inadequate and defective technique of the present. The face of Franklin is rendered in a ruddy red, the cap a soft gray, the coat brownish and the background neutral. It is his characteristic hard-as-nails, early Copley style, a manner which he dramatically abandoned a few years later when studying in the London studio of Benjamin West after a humiliating observation by Sir Joshua Reynolds.[8]

Trumbull first met Franklin, a friend of his family, at Paris in June 1780. It was from him that the aspiring artist obtained a letter of introduction to Benjamin West, under whose friendly surveillance he obtained his knowledge of formal composition and the art and craft of painting. He saw Franklin again at Philadelphia in 1790 and painted his portrait there, this time from life directly in the *Declaration of Independence,* the original version of which came to Yale from the artist in 1831 (Figs. 158 and 159).

The newly discovered little portrait is a sensitive, homespun interpretation of the suave French, Louis XVI original. Though its aesthetic merit is small, it is of considerable historic and associative value. It is appropriate that it should be at Yale, where the Franklin Papers are being edited, where Trumbull's own collection is housed, and where his mortal remains lie beneath his portrait of his master, General Washington. The stone over his grave describes him as "Patriot and Artist"[9]—two sides of a complicated character.

7. Especially the following, the numbers corresponding to those set forth in the *Autobiography:* 26 *Self-Portrait,* painted in 1774 (the year following his graduation from Harvard), Lebanon; John McClellan, Woodstock, Conn. 27 *Maj. Gen. Jabez Huntington,* 1777, Lebanon (based on a print by Salvator Rosa); Connecticut State Library. 28 *Jonathan Trumbull Junior, His Wife and Child,* 1777, Lebanon (very much in the Copley manner); Yale University Art Gallery. 29 *Self-Portrait,* 1777, Lebanon (Copley manner); Museum of Fine Arts, Boston. 35 *Mrs. Joseph Trumbull,* 1777, Lebanon; Connecticut Historical Society. 36 *Jabez Huntington, Junior,* 1777, Lebanon; Yale University Art Gallery. 39 *Benjamin Franklin*—the picture in question—1778, Boston; Yale University Art Gallery. 47 *George Washington,* after C. W. Peale, 1778, Boston; Yale University Art Gallery.

Meyric R. Rogers, former Curator of the Garvan and Related Collections of American Art at the Yale University Art Gallery, states that the panel is of oak and that the chamfered edges are in the eighteenth-century manner.

8. "That coat is bad, sir, very bad; it is not cloth—it is tin, bent tin." *Autobiography,* pp. 85–87.

9. The title, "Patriot-Artist," which has been attached to Trumbull ever since his death in 1843, was due to his nephew-in-law, Benjamin Silliman, the celebrated Yale scientist. See Silliman *Note Book,* 1858, p. 35 of the typescript copy.

THE JOHN TRUMBULLS AND
MME. VIGÉE-LEBRUN*

On the walls of the Detroit Institute of Arts hangs an American portrait, somewhat in the manner of the French painter Mme. Vigée-Lebrun, *John Trumbull,* by John Trumbull (Fig. 72). The tale of these three—of the two contemporary Connecticut cousins and of the influence the lovely French lady exerted on one, is worth telling.

The subject of the portrait is John Trumbull, 1750–1831, Yale 1767, son of the Reverend John Trumbull, Yale 1735, a Congregational minister and Fellow of the College. The painter was John Trumbull, 1756–1843, Harvard 1773, son of Governor Jonathan Trumbull, Harvard 1727, of Lebanon, Connecticut, first cousin of the Reverend John Trumbull of Westbury, Connecticut. The second cousins are constantly confused.

Both the John Trumbulls were brilliant and precocious boys. John, subsequently poet and jurist, was ready to enter Yale at the age of seven and a half, but was honorably rusticated until he was thirteen before being admitted. Ultimately this John became a tutor at Yale, the author of the celebrated comic epic poem *M'Fingal,* reprinted more than thirty times between 1782 and 1840, literary leader of the "Hartford Wits," and judge of the Supreme Court of Errors of Connecticut. He spent the last six years of his life at Detroit. Like his cousin John, he was a strong Federalist.

John, the future "patriot-artist," who wanted to study painting at Boston under Copley, was sent instead to Cambridge by his practical-minded father with the hope that he might become a lawyer. The fifteen-year-old boy entered Harvard in the middle of his junior year, graduating a year and a half later the youngest member of his class. He has the distinction of being the first college graduate in British America to become a professional painter.

Besides receiving a sound classical education, John, the future painter, derived three lasting extracurricular benefits from his Harvard experience. He obtained some acquaintance with the fine arts, as there were books on the subject in the College Library. (The charge list of books he withdrew still exists.) Hogarth's *Analysis of Beauty* became a sort of bible, and his imagination was set aflame by newly arrived bound volumes of Piranesi's prints. The portraits by the great Copley hanging in the college halls

* From *The Art Quarterly,* Summer 1952.

were to be studied and copied. Besides this slight introduction to the arts he acquired some fluency in French from a family of displaced Acadians. Finally, he made friends who were destined to become influential—and most helpful—in the new Republic. Friends, French, and the fine arts were, eventually, of far greater consequence than all his classical learning.

As the young Trumbull, after participating in the Revolutionary War with the rank of colonel, became the pupil of Benjamin West at London, it is all too easy to consider that his style in painting was exclusively derived from his master and modeled on that of the current British school. The Colonel was, however, during his long stay in England and on trips to the Continent, deeply moved by European painting, especially by Rubens, whose work he admired above all others. The classical battle pieces by Charles Lebrun excited emulation. His contemporary, David, whose cold classical compositions he held in high esteem, became a firm and very useful friend. It was, however, Mme. Vigée-Lebrun to whom he felt most sympathetic. Trumbull first met that good-looking and talented lady in 1786 at Paris, whither he had gone on Jefferson's invitation. He had an eye for beautiful women—one can hardly blame an artist for that. With David, Mme. Vigée, and others, language offered no barrier to the French-speaking Colonel. He participated in the delightful soirées at Mme. Vigée's salon at 67 rue de Cléry. The influence the contemporary French artists exerted upon the impressionable Yankee was direct, powerful and personal. West is present in his work but so are the French, especially Mme. Vigée-Lebrun.

There exists an extraordinary parallelism in the lives, fortunes, and works of this charming Frenchwoman and the sensitive New Englander. They must have been born under the same star. Let us examine this curious coincidence of celestial similarity.

Their lives were exactly contemporary. They were born less than a year apart. Both passed long years in exile; Trumbull's was voluntary, Vigée's an escape to Italy and Russia during the Revolution. The aesthetic antecedents of the pair of expatriates were much akin. We may presume that both were nurtured on such common sources as Roger de Piles and Du Fresnoy. Both had the same reverence for Rubens.

Mme. Vigée-Lebrun's dependence upon the lusty Fleming is manifest if we compare, for instance, her early success *Peace and Plenty,* of 1783, with Rubens' *Venus and Adonis,* or her self-portrait in the straw hat, now in the Louvre, with his *Helena Fourment* in Leningrad. It is the same with Trumbull; "for color, composition and expression," he wrote in 1786, "nothing can excel Rubens." There is a relationship, though separated by more than a century and a half, not only between some of the portraits but between Rubens' battle compositions and Trumbull's baroque-like *Bunker's Hill* (Fig. 145). "Lebrun is one of the most charming women I ever saw," Trumbull wrote in 1788. "Her pictures have great merit, particularly the portrait of herself and her daughter, which is not yet finished; in composition of this picture there is simplicity and sweetness worthy of the artist, and a brilliance of coloring quite charming." Both drew inspiration from the same Rubenesque source.

Again both the Connecticut Yankee and the Frenchwoman knew and painted the "V.I.P.'s" of their respective countries. They were both documentary recorders at critical periods in history; they were both intimately related to their times. To carry the similarity of their lives still further, both wrote long and interesting autobiographies in their old age; Vigée's *Memoirs* appearing in three volumes from 1835 to 1837 and Trumbull's, begun in 1835, in 1841.

As to their diversities, Mme. Vigée-Lebrun was a liberal-minded Catholic, Trumbull a Connecticut Congregationalist. The lady, Parisian born and bred, was of a joyous nature; the military man, austere and combative, was a small-town New Englander. Vigée was the daughter of an obscure artist, Trumbull the son of a celebrated statesman. The girl went to a convent school, the boy to Harvard. The woman was happiest when painting her own sex, the Colonel was a man's man. Vigée painted some six hundred and sixty portraits, fifteen compositions, and about two hundred landscapes; the "patriot-artist" about half that number. Vigée was exclusively an artist, Trumbull, unhappily for his art, indulged in a variety of other activities—soldiering, commerce, diplomacy, architecture, land speculation, and so on. Vigée depicted an old social order on the way out, Trumbull recorded the birth of a new one. Both, however, had a great and tragic bond in common. Their respective marriages were singularly unfortunate.

The wife of the proud and pompous Trumbull was an obscure English woman whom he married at London. A visiting nephew, John M. Trumbull, wrote to his family in 1800: "Mrs. Trumbull had neither Father, Mother, Sister, Uncle, Aunt, and may almost say Friend but her husband. I have not yet found her name before married; will inform you when I do." She was Sarah Hope Harvey, possessed of little besides a pretty face and fine figure. She continuously embarrassed her punctilious husband by the effects of her too frequent use of punch. Vigée, on her part, married secretly the picture-dealer Jean-Baptiste Pierre Lebrun (1748–1813), grandnephew of the painter Charles Lebrun. This is her candid estimate of her husband: "Not that M. Lebrun was a bad man; his character showed a mixture of gentleness and vivacity; he was obliging towards everybody—in a word, likeable enough; but his unbridled passion for women of bad morals, joined with his fondness for gambling, brought about the ruins of his fortune as well as mine, which was entirely in his keeping. Indeed, when I left Paris in 1789, I had not much as twenty francs of income, though I had earned more than a million. He had squandered the lot." She kept her artistic identity, however, by hyphenating her maiden and married names.

Curiously enough there also exists a bond between Trumbull and Mme. Vigée-Lebrun's disreputable, art-dealing husband. The two men entered into a speculation;

the latter purchased Old Masters during the evil days of the Terror, which were to be sold in the peaceful and profitable market of London. The venture, however, did not work out too well. The crates containing the pictures, Trumbull recorded, were landed on the banks of the Thames on the eve of the Prince of Wales' birthday; there was an exceptional high tide the next day, and while the lightermen were making merry the cases floated off. As the underwriters would not be held, the poor painter was forced to pass "the remainder of the season repairing—the damage . . . in the extensive rooms of [his] friend, Mr. West." The lot was sold at Christie's on February 16, 1797. The *Times* for the 20th stated that "the sale of Mr. Trumbull's collection of pictures . . . sold extremely well. The highest price pictures were bought by Mr. West supposed to be for the King." The event was even reported in the *Connecticut Journal* of New Haven, though not until April 26, thus: "the sale of Mr. Trumbull's pictures . . . has greatly excited the attention of connoisseurs and with good reason. They have chiefly been collected during the unhappy troubles and distresses in France. . . . Mr. Trumbull's collection of 91 pictures produced the comfortable sum of £8217–17–0." The partnership was of limited duration and nearly disastrous. Vigée's influence on the Yankee's style was lasting and beneficial.

The constantly confused John Trumbulls were kin; the two artists were kith. To conclude the curious case of parallelism between the gay Parisian painter and the dour Colonel both died at the identical age of eighty-seven. Truly those two were born under the same star.

TOM PAINE'S PORTRAIT*

The tale of the recent discovery of the portrait (Fig. 123) of the celebrated propagandist, Thomas Paine, painted by Colonel Trumbull for Thomas Jefferson—a picture which dropped out of sight over a century ago—is worth telling in some detail.

The little portrait was first and last publicly exhibited in Boston two years after Jefferson's death, appearing in *A Catalogue of the Second Exhibition in the Athenaeum Gallery Consisting of Specimens by American Artists . . . May 1828,* under the notice, "The following are a part of the Collection formed by the late PRESIDENT JEFFERSON . . . [and] are for sale . . . [Item] 316—Thomas Paine,—an original on wood,—Trumbull." It then faded into oblivion. . . .

The editor of *The Papers of Thomas Jefferson,* Julian P. Boyd of Princeton, was responsible for the first clue to the lost portrait. In March 1955 he brought to my attention both sides of correspondence which established the date of the sitting and re-affirmed the connection of the three principals, Paine, Trumbull, and Jefferson. The first letter (now in the Pierpont Morgan Library) was written by the Colonel from London to Jefferson in Paris, 19 December 1788:

By the Diligence which leaves town tomorrow morning, you will receive a Box cont'g your Harness & Saddles. The Box likewise contains what further Books of your list Payne has been able to procure . . . a little case with two pictures, one of which I hope you will do me the honor to accept, & the other I beg you to be so good as offer to Miss Jefferson:—I almost dispair of its meeting her approbation, but it is all I can do until I have the happiness to see you again:—you would have rec'd both long since for the Vexation I have had with my larger picture, which has left me little Spirits to attend to anything else. . . .

Jefferson replied (letter now in the Princeton University Library) to Trumbull on 12 January 1789:

I am to thank you a thousand times for the portrait of Mr. Paine, which is a perfect likeness, and to deliver you, for the other, on the part of my daughter . . .

The "larger picture," which was causing such vexation, was, most probably, the *Declaration of Independence* (Fig. 158), for which the preliminary sketch was prepared in September 1786 (Fig. 157). The artist referred to this subject in these words:

I resumed my labors, however, and went on with my studies of other subjects of the Revolution,

* From *The Yale University Library Gazette, 30,* April 1956.

arranging carefully the composition for the Declaration of Independence, and preparing it for receiving the portraits, as I might meet with the distinguished men, who were present at that illustrious scene. . . . In the autumn of 1787, I again visited Paris, where I painted the portrait of Mr. Jefferson in the original small Declaration of Independence.[1]

From this original portrait in the *Declaration* the artist promptly made three replicas, all in miniature: the first, for Miss Jefferson, which has descended in the family and is now owned by "Monticello," Thomas Jefferson Memorial Foundation, Charlottesville, Va.; the second for Mrs. John Barker Church, daughter of Philip Schuyler, now in the Metropolitan Museum of Art, New York; and a third for Jefferson's friend Mrs. Richard (Maria Hadfield) Cosway, wife of the miniaturist, left by her to the Collegio Maria S. S. Bambina at Lodi, Italy. The first of these, one of the two pictures in the "little case" sent to Jefferson in December 1788 for his daughter, offered, therefore, the best stylistic parallel for its companion, the lost Paine miniature. It should be noted that the present to Miss Jefferson was apparently painted rapidly and on an oblong piece of mahogany upon which the oval was inscribed. This is rather unusual; the sixty Trumbull miniatures at Yale are all cut in oval shape (Fig. 119).

In 1947, through the good offices of Alexander Wall, Director of the New-York Historical Society, Mrs. Arthur M. Greenwood brought to my attention a loosely painted miniature, oval on a rectangular piece of mahogany, said to be of Trumbull's friend and companion-in-arms, Philip Schuyler. It was published in the *Works* (first ed., 1950, p. 68), under "Unidentified Men" as a "Miniature of an Unknown Man(?), possibly PHILIP SCHUYLER; Estate of Dr. Arthur M. Greenway, Marlboro, Mass." (containing a mistake in transcription, for the name was Greenwood). And there the matter rested.

When the Trumbull–Jefferson correspondence was brought to my attention, I searched my files of unidentified men and was immediately struck by the stylistic affinity to the "Unknown Gentleman," from the collection of the late Dr. and Mrs. Arthur M. Greenwood of "Time Stone Farm," Marlboro, Mass. The miniature had been acquired before 1912 by Dr. Greenwood from a family living in Concord, Mass., who had kept it for years in a button box. Some time in the past both eyes had been mutilated—possibly by a child.

Doubting the Schuyler attribution (Trumbull's one miniature of Schuyler, painted at Philadelphia, is now in the New-York Historical Society [Fig. 124]), I turned to the study, at the Frick Art Reference Library, of every known portrait of Tom Paine. The Greenwood miniature came closest to the destroyed portrait of Paine painted by George Romney in 1791–92, known through the fine engraving of 1793 by William Sharp. I next appealed to Colonel Richard Gimbel, United States Air Force, Retired,

---

1. *The Autobiography of Colonel John Trumbull, Patriot-Artist* (New Haven, Yale University Press, 1953) pp. 146–47, 152.

Curator of Aeronautical Literature at the Yale University Library, a great collector of Paine's work. After studying abundant prints, photographs of portraits, Paine's death mask, and even caricatures, and comparing them with the borrowed Greenwood miniature, I found the Paine attribution more or less convincing. It should be mentioned, parenthetically, that Paine left America for England in 1787 and that it is a simple matter to get artist and sitter together during that and the ensuing year, and that all of Trumbull's miniatures with one or two exceptions are painted in oils on mahogany.

Still unsatisfied, Colonel Gimbel and I went to the Boston Museum and there laid the Jefferson family miniature alongside the still questionable Paine. They fitted like two peas in a pod. Both were painted on rectangular pieces of mahogany (unusual for Trumbull), which appeared to come from the same plank, though the Greenwood one was on a slightly smaller piece. The painted ovals, however, were identical in size, 4⅞ by 3¾ inches. Even the character of the stains on the backs was the same for both. Stylistically, both were identical, the pigment and the manner of handling it coinciding exactly, except that the Jefferson had been cleaned and newly varnished and the other was dirty, dry, and mutilated. Both were painted in a more sketchy manner than Trumbull ordinarily employed, but then both were intended as presents and were not to be incorporated in historical compositions (as were the sixty at Yale), which were ultimately destined to be engraved. The crackling on the surfaces of both—unusually large—was the same. Both were examined under ultraviolet light—from the front, back, and sides—similitude was conclusively demonstrated. Greatly enlarged photographs were also studied. The writer is convinced that the Greenwood miniature—in oils on mahogany—is not only the work of Trumbull, but is the missing portrait of the pamphleteer, Colonel Gimbel concurring fully in this last. The "perfect likeness," as Jefferson put it, of Tom Paine, which disappeared in 1828, has been found.

A PORTRAIT OF
THE MYSTERIOUS SARAH TRUMBULL*

A little drama took place before the ancient Parish Church of St. Mary, Hendon[1] (seven miles from London), on a Monday, the first day of October 1800. A small group of puzzled men and women had just attended the unexplained marriage of the handsome, middle-aged Colonel John Trumbull and his strikingly beautiful bride of twenty-six. They were, one and all, seeking an answer to the question: why had the proud, painter-turned-diplomat,[2] a socially conscious member of one of the first families of Connecticut, suddenly, almost secretly, married an obscure, uneducated English girl? The group was composed of the Rev. Ralph Woseley, the Church of England priest who had just performed the wedding service; Elizabeth Halbrook, an official witness, presumably a friend of the bride; and two of the artist's old Harvard friends, Christopher Gore, later governor of Massachusetts and United States senator (another witness), and Rufus King, American Minister to Great Britain. The inquisitive wedding guests stood aside as the coach rumbled up to carry off the newly married pair. Rufus King, who had given the bride away, acting as spokesman, turned to Trumbull and inquired who the lady might be. The Colonel's curt reply was simply: "Mrs. Trumbull, sir."

We now know her name but little else. She was Sarah Hope Harvey of the parish of Hendon, daughter of William Hope of Perthshire, Scotland, born in the vicinity of London on the first of April 1774. But who was she? Her husband devoted less than three lines of type to his "faithful and beloved companion" in his *Autobiography* (1841). There was gossip, plenty of it, good and evil, but few facts. The Colonel admitted to his brother Jonathan that she was "not of the fashionable kind." To what extent she was literate is difficult to determine in the absence of samples from her hand. She was something of a watercolorist of flowers, but, again, we have nothing to go by. We do know, however, that she was socially unacceptable and that she, poor, unhappy girl, constantly partook more generously of the comforting contents of the punchbowl than was befitting a lady. Her presence among family and friends was too often embarrassing. Nonetheless, the Colonel loved her, protected and defended her, rarely be-

* From Winterthur Portfolio, II, 1965.

1. Considered today by Nikolaus Pevsner as "a rewarding building," *The Buildings of England: Middlesex* (Harmondsworth, Middlesex: Penguin Books, 1951), pp. 107–08. The church dates from the 13th to the 16th centuries.

2. The Colonel served as a commissioner concerned with the adjustment of claims under the Jay Treaty from 1794 to 1804.

coming exasperated by her conduct. The marriage was, obviously, the result of some involvement forever hidden from our eyes.[3]

The portrait of the unhappy Sarah, now at Winterthur (Fig. 69), is typical, technically, of the artist.[4] The surface is smooth, untampered, and in prime condition. There are several questions yet to be answered: why, when, and where was the portrait painted, and what is its history? Through whose hands has it passed?

The first of these has been partially answered: Sarah had one great asset—her beauty. During their twenty-four years of married life, Trumbull painted her portrait over a dozen times: as "Innocence" with a dove (Fig. 70); as "Sensibility" with a small spaniel; with winsome reticence and correct and charming classical accessories. He even recorded her last moments on her deathbed with hands stretched forth in final supplication (Fig. 71). She also modeled for her classically educated husband's less fortunate romantic, literary, allegorical, and religious subjects. Why so many portraits? Was it an artist's natural delight in and concern for a lovely form, a willing and handy sitter, lack of commissions—what? Or were the paintings destined for members of the Colonel's large, influential, and distinguished family, as defensive status symbols? On canvas the radiantly beautiful Sarah was silent, respectful, impeccable, ideal—in startling contrast to the agonies and embarrassments of actuality.

The questions of when and where are also partially answered. From stylistic evidence, costume, and from the age of the subject (twenty-six years), the portrait has every appearance of having been executed in London between 1800 and 1804 (when the pair left for New York). I believe that it can be narrowed further to the last four months of the year 1800—an early, if not the first, postnuptial tribute. It was during that year, probably before the October wedding, that Rufus King and his wife, Mary Alsop King, sat for the artist.[5]

Mrs. King wears a distinctive, jeweled comb in her hair (Fig. 36), identical with that in the portrait of Sarah Trumbull. What could be more natural than for Mrs. King to present, probably impulsively, the jeweled comb to the friendless Mrs. Trumbull at the time of her wedding, particularly since Rufus King gave the girl in holy matrimony? At all events, the Winterthur portrait was painted before the Kings re-

3. For the curious, I have collected and set down such flimsy facts as exist in an article, "Who was the Colonel's Lady? The Strange Case of Mrs. John Trumbull," first published in *The New-York Historical Society Quarterly, 36* (1952), 410–29, and reprinted in the Appendix, pp. 350–65, of *The Autobiography of Col. John Trumbull* (New Haven, Yale University Press, 1953), ed. T. Sizer.

4. There is a replica of the portrait, of a later date (formerly attributed to Samuel Lovett Waldo), at the Yale University Art Gallery, Cat. no. 1929.1.

5. CLARENCE WINTHROP BOWEN, *The History of the Centennial Celebration of the Inauguration of George Washington* (New York, Appleton, 1892), pp. 490–91, and illustrations opp. p. 121 and p. 260; also CHARLES R. KING, M.D., *The Life and Correspondence of Rufus King* (New York, Putnam, 1894), I, frontispiece. Portrait dated 1800 by Dr. King. The portrait of Mrs. King was formerly the property of Dr. Charles R. King of Andalusia, Pennsylvania, and is now owned by his grandson, Charles King Lennig, Jr., Chestnut Hill, Philadelphia.

turned to the United States in 1803. If the hair comb hypothesis holds, it was painted three years earlier. Portraits have often been dated by such accessories.

The history of the portrait is irreproachable. It came into the hands of George Brinley (1774–1857) and his wife Catherine Putnam; thence to their son, George Brinley II (1817–75), Hartford bibliophile, and his wife Frances Ellen Terry; then to their son, Charles A. Brinley (1847–1919), Yale 1869, engineer and scientist of Hartford and Philadelphia, and his wife, Mary Goodrich Frothingham, the parents of the last owner, Mary Frothingham Brinley (Mrs. John Wallingford Muir) of Chestnut Hill, Philadelphia; from whom it was acquired by The Henry Francis du Pont Winterthur Museum in 1960.[6]

The portrait of the mysterious Sarah Trumbull has numerous pleasing qualities— aesthetic, technical, romantic, and historic. As a simple but intimate human document, it is immensely revealing.

6. This paragraph has been rewritten and slightly changed as fresh information has come to hand.

PHILADELPHIA'S FIRST PRESBYTERIAN CHURCH BY "MR. TRUMBUL"*

Among the responses I received as a result of my article "John Trumbull, Amateur Architect" (JSAH, *8*, July–December, 1949, pp. 1–6), there was one of unusual interest. Charles E. Peterson of the United States Department of the Interior, National Park Service, Philadelphia, pointed out to me a reference in *Stephens's Philadelphia Directory, 1796,* in which, among a listing of prominent structures then being erected in that city, there is the following: "The first Presbyterian Church by Mr. Trumbul" (see Fig. 260). The intriguing question is whether the designer of this Roman Revival building, which no longer exists, could have been Col. John Trumbull.

This reference in *Stephens's Directory* to "Mr. Trumbul" is the only one I know. For the facts of the case I am largely indebted to Mr. Peterson and to Richard Norris Williams, 2nd, Director of the Historical Society of Pennsylvania at Philadelphia. The church, begun in 1793, took the place of an earlier edifice, which had been built in 1704 and enlarged in 1729. Worship in the new building commenced in 1796, the year of *Stephens's Directory,* and continued until 1821. J. Thomas Scharf and Thompson Wescott, in their *History of Philadelphia, 1609–1884* (Philadelphia, L. H. Everts & Co., 1884, vol. 2, p. 1270), state:

> In 1793 the ancient meeting-house of the First Church, commonly called the "Old Buttonwood," situate at the southeast corner of Market Street and White Horse Alley (now called Bank Street), was found to be too small for the accommodation of the congregation. It was resolved that "Old Buttonwood" should be torn down, and a larger and handsomer building erected in its place. The new church was one of the first in Philadelphia constructed upon the Greek [sic] model of architecture. The front was on Market Street, with four plain pillars, with Corinthian capitals, resting on a platform and supporting a pediment, upon the architrave of which was the inscription, "Founded MDCCIV. Rebuilt MDCCXCIV." The house was eighty-eight feet long, fifty-six feet broad, and forty feet high, having galleries. There were ninety-six pews upon the floor, holding six persons each, and altogether one hundred and sixty-three pews, having a seating capacity for nine hundred persons. The ascent to the main floor of the building was by eight marble steps. . . .

A little further on (pp. 1278–79) the authors continue:

> The First Presbyterian Church building, in Market Street, at the time it was finished was considered the handsomest religious edifice in the city. It was also eligibly situated. But the movement

* From *The Journal of the Society of Architectural Historians, 9* (3), 1950.

westward increased greatly in the early part of the century, and the Market Street Church became entirely surrounded with stores and places of business. In addition there was imposed upon the congregation, after some years, the necessity of expensive repairs. The showy portico on Market Street was supported by wooden pillars and exposed to decay, and fifteen thousand dollars was thought necessary to place the building in a tenable condition. A large number of the congregation thought it would be a waste to expend this amount upon the church edifice, and recommended that the lot be sold and a new church be erected at some other place. The point was not carried without controversy. A pamphlet, published in 1819, stated that all the pews were occupied. . . . These statements were adduced in argument to show that there was no necessity for removing the church, and that it was in a state of prosperity. The arguments in favor of a change were at length successful. On the 1st of May, 1820, the congregation held a meeting, and by a vote . . . ordered the trustees to purchase the lot at Seventh and Locust Streets. . . . The house was so far finished in July, 1821, that the congregation was enabled to assemble in the "prayer-room." . . . The new church building was the largest and finest yet erected in the city.

So much for the printed and written word. On the visual side, the best picture of the 1794–1821 church "by Mr. Trumbul" is the colored engraving by William Birch, one of his thirty views of Philadelphia (item no. 168 in David McNeely Stauffer's *American Engravers upon Copper and Steel,* New York, Grolier Club, 1907, vol. 2), first published in 1799, just three years after the completion of the building. It represents the white façade of a steepleless edifice with a heavy, projecting Roman portico, and a flattish roof relieved by urns at the corners. (Harold E. Dickson of the Pennsylvania State College points out to me that this "giant-order portico was surely the first within the city, preceded only by the one on 'The Woodlands' across the Schuylkill.") Four large Corinthian columns support the pediment, beneath which a central door is flanked by generous-sized windows with three windows of the same proportion above. Two single and two pairs of twin pilasters extend from base to cornice to match the columns in front. The classical edifice—whoever was responsible for its design—is an exceedingly interesting example of advanced architectural thinking in the new nation.

As to the possibility of the Trumbull authorship, this was the situation in 1792, when the plans for the church were undoubtedly prepared. After nearly nine years of schooling under the watchful eye of Benjamin West, Col. Trumbull returned from London in November, 1789. The artist knew his Paris well. He had last visited that city in the autumn of 1789. The Philadelphia church, designed three years later, recalls the Corinthian façade of the recently completed Panthéon by Soufflot, finished in 1781, which Trumbull greatly admired, and, to a lesser extent, the Church of Saint Philippe-du-Roule, with its four Doric columns and lettered frieze, designed by Chalgrin and finished in 1774. There is also, however, a strong suggestion of James Gibbs. The great Corinthian portico of St. Martins-in-the-Fields is reflected in the Presbyterian Church. This is what one might expect of the architectural style of the French-speaking, London-trained artist.

The thirty-six-year-old Trumbull, in 1791 and again in 1792, was actively engaged in collecting "heads" at Philadelphia, the capital of the new Republic, for his historical paintings, as well as thinking along architectural lines. James Hillhouse, a member of the Continental Congress and also Treasurer of Yale, had commissioned him to prepare a scheme for the further development of the College. Thus, besides being a belated pictorial reporter of the Revolution, the middle-aged artist, then at the height of his creative powers, was also actively engaged with architectural problems.

It is not inconceivable that this versatile New Englander, this outsider, fresh from Europe, conversant with the latest English and Continental fashions, would have been the choice of the church elders. "A prophet is not without honour, save in his own country and in his own house" (Matthew xiii, 57)—and Trumbull, a staunch Calvinist, was far from home. In Philadelphia, this former aide-de-camp of General Washington (now President) was moving in high political and social circles. Trumbull's celebrated father, the Colonial and Revolutionary Governor of Connecticut, had died a half-dozen years before; but his brother, another Jonathan, Washington's former Military-Secretary, was then a member of the Continental Congress and had been recently elected its Speaker. Trumbull was the "expert" from afar, socially correct, architecturally-minded, and a pious, God-fearing gentleman. Stylistically, the Church is what one would expect to come from the mind and hand of this amateur architect. Trumbull designed, it should be recalled, the Congregational Meetinghouse in his home town, Lebanon, Connecticut, in 1804 (see Figs. 261 and 262). The records of the First Presbyterian Church have been searched, through the kindness of Mr. Williams, who reports that although "there are a great many vouchers for digging and erection of the building, [there is] no mention of Trumbull"—nor of any other architect. Some readers might know the answer to the problem. My guess is Col. Trumbull.

AGAIN PHILADELPHIA'S FIRST
PRESBYTERIAN CHURCH*

The conjectural attribution for the design of this early example of neoclassicism to the painter and amateur architect, Col. John Trumbull, was set forth in the JSAH, *9,* no. 3, pp. 20–22 (see Fig. 260). The argument there presented has brought helpful hints from readers—but no positive answer. It might be well to incorporate these with the scanty facts, already sketched, with the hope of ultimately arriving at a definite conclusion.

The elegantly proportioned Classical-Georgian Presbyterian Church (illustrated by the 1799 William Birch engraving in the October number of the *Journal*) with its pedimented façade of the Corinthian order, recalls, as Henry-Russell Hitchcock, of Smith College, is good enough to point out, St. Georges, Hanover Square, London, designed by John James and built in 1724, church and newly laid-out square (1718), by appellation, doubly honoring George I. Trumbull, long resident of London, familiar with its fashionable quarters, with his keen eye for architectural niceties, must have known this church.

The name of Samuel Blodget was tentatively suggested by Oliver Larkin, also of Smith College, as the possible designer of the *wooden* Market Street church of 1794, pointing out its resemblance to his *stone* Girard Bank (the old Bank of the United States) of the same year, the first important building executed in marble in Philadelphia. Blodget, born in 1757, was Trumbull's junior by a year. Trumbull, the painter, was a self-trained amateur architect; Blodget, the merchant and real estate operator, can hardly be classed as a professional architect. Although the two men were, in many ways, alike and their architectural styles not dissimilar, it would appear to me that considerable weight should be attached to the 1796 statement in *Stephens's* two years or less after the completion of both buildings ascribing the wooden church to "Mr. Trumbul" and the marble bank to Blodget. Trumbull never built in stone. With the exception of the brick Congregational church at his home town, Lebanon, Connecticut (see Figs. 261 and 262), his work is all wood. But such arguments are inconclusive.

My attention was directed by Charles E. Peterson of Philadelphia to an engraving of the 1794 edifice which appeared in the Philadelphia publication, the *Port-Folio.* A search through the files of that magazine for the following year disclosed an unsigned article (1820, *9,* no. 2, 495–501) with an engraving by John Boyd (much employed by

* From *The Journal of the Society of Architectural Historians, 10* (2), 1951.

Philadelphia publishers from 1811 to 1827) of a projected house of worship, to take the place of the older, 1794 church situated on busy and noisy Market Street. This later church was built in the new residential district, on the corner of Seventh and Locust Streets by the architect, John Haviland (1792–1852). The Haviland Church, with its heavy Ionic façade, was finished in 1821 and is described in the *Port-Folio and New-York Monthly Magazine* for 1822 (2, no. 4, 339–41).

It is Mr. Peterson again to whom I am obliged for pointing out another engraving of the 1794 church. This one appeared in *The Ariel,* also of Philadelphia (2, no. 19), for 1829 (January 10th). It is, however, the identical plate, used in the *Port-Folio* of seven years earlier. The same engraved caption, "The First Presbyterian Church in Phila.," is followed by "As it stood corner of Market & Bank Streets" and in the place of "Engd. for the Port-Folio" "Published for the Ariel" has been substituted. The accompanying, leading article, likewise unsigned, refers to the "remarkable movement of classical taste in designing . . . of . . . the architects of Philadelphia," but gives no hint of the designer. How exasperatingly inconclusive these references of the 1820s are!

The late Joseph Jackson in his *Market Street, the Most Historic Highway in America,* Philadelphia, 1918, referred to the 1794 Market Street Church "with its row of Corinthian columns." In his *Early Philadelphia Architects and Engineers,* Philadelphia, 1923, he wrote that it was the "first . . . attempt . . . to transplant in Philadelphia the Greek form in its larger significance . . . (and that) . . . there does not appear to be any record of the name of the designer of this structure, but it is strongly suspected that it was the apprentice work of Samuel Blodget, whose greater and more successful effort was the façade of the First Bank of the United States, now the Girard National Bank" (pp. 69–70). The same author in his *Development of American Architecture,* 1783–1830, Philadelphia, 1926, reproduced (on p. 11) the engraving of the Market Street Church from the *Port-Folio* of 1822, below which he wrote, "Designed by an amateur, it was the first classic structure in Philadelphia." He stated (pp. 15–16):

> There does not appear to be any record of the designer of the First Presbyterian Church . . . more the pity because it was one of the first instances in this country where the classic temples of antiquity were drawn upon to furnish designs for Christian temples in this part of the world. It has been suggested that Dr. William Thornton, the architect of the Library of Philadelphia, was the author of the design . . . If Doctor Thornton was not the designer of the church edifice then the next most probable designer would have been Samuel Blodgett, who suggested the design of the first Bank of the United States, which building was started about the same time. There are similarities of design in both the façades, but the bank building was the better example of the Corinthian porch front. Also its columns were of marble, and fluted, while the others were of wood and plain.

There is mention of the 1794 Market Street Church with its "handsome portico, with Corinthian columns (which) distinguish the structure" in John F. Faris's *Old Churches and Meeting-Houses in and around Philadelphia,* Philadelphia, 1926, but no hint of authorship is given. So much for such past recordings which have come to light.

THE LEBANON MEETINGHOUSE, LEBANON, CONNECTICUT*

In June 1804 the versatile Col. John Trumbull . . . returned from London to this country after serving it well for a decade as a diplomat. After a stormy passage of a month's duration he finally arrived at New York accompanied by his strikingly beautiful English wife. There he set up, with much difficulty, as a portrait painter. Possibly it was because he was not pressed for time that the forty-eight-year-old historical painter accepted the invitation to prepare designs for a new Congregational meetinghouse in his home town (see Figs. 261 and 262).

He had always been interested in architecture. During his senior year at Harvard he had been set on fire when he first beheld the set of nine great volumes of prints of the monuments of ancient Rome by the Italian, Giovanni Battista Piranesi, which had arrived at the College Library a few years after their publication.[1] He never got over the impact which these Piranesis made. His concern with the problems of architectural form, proportion, and perspective continued before and after his military service. In London, while studying under the kindly Philadelphian painter Benjamin West, it was temporarily abandoned, only to be promptly revived during his eight months' imprisonment in reprisal, he so believed, for the hanging of the popular British officer, Major André.[2] Books were supplied to the incarcerated artist by that great friend of the wayward Colonies, Edmund Burke, who admonished him to give up painting in favor of architecture. The latent seeds of this early interest, pertinent advice, and undistracted study in prison ultimately blossomed forth. In 1791 the colonel designed (so I believe) the First Presbyterian Church in Philadelphia (Fig. 260), then the capital of the new Republic. A year later he produced comprehensive plans for Yale College at the request of James Hillhouse, Treasurer of the College and a delegate to the Continental Congress. He was not unprepared for his task at Lebanon.

The day after the colonel and his bride arrived at New York in 1804 the congregation at Lebanon voted to build a new meetinghouse. Two months later it was again

---

* From *The Journal of the Society of Architectural Historians, 14* (2), 1955.

1. The identical volumes are still in the Harvard College Library.

2. Trumbull regarded André as his "perfect pendant." It is interesting to note that years later, in 1821, he designed the casket in which the bones of the hanged André were placed, returned to England, and buried in Westminster Abbey. See Sizer, "The Perfect Pendant," *The New-York Historical Society Quarterly, 25,* no. 3, 400–04, and *Autobiography,* Appendix, pp. 365–368.

voted that it be "agreeable to the Plan which has been made by Col. John Trumbull."[3] A year later, on 30 June 1805, the latter wrote to his brother, Jonathan: "Our Meeting-house goes on very well and is in a fairway to be neatly and handsomely finished. Our workmen appear to know their business and the people are well disposed to have the work well executed."[4] The church dominates and lends its grace to the town in good New England fashion and is still its most cherished landmark. It was constructed of red brick with a vaulted entrance flanked by four engaged, Roman Doric brick columns, and surmounted by a white wooden steeple of graceful proportion. It differs in some ways from other contemporary churches in Connecticut, its designer having freshly arrived from England and having the classic examples of Wren, Gibbs, and other London ecclesiastical architects well in mind. It is chaste, restrained, and elegant in a homey way. The moldings are rich, delicate, and sparingly employed—in the manner of the brothers Adam of London[5] or, more closely, in that of the Connecticut architect, David Hoadley. The church was in use early in 1807, though it was not finished in all detail until 1809.

Only a year prior to the Centennial Exhibition at Philadelphia of 1876, that great turning point in the awakening of interest in America's past and in the full appreciation of the beauties of Colonial and Federal architecture, the interior of the meeting-house was made over in the Victorian manner. The balconies were joined in order to make a second floor and the fine Palladian pulpit-window removed (but fortunately preserved) to create two floors, in order to give extra space for the missionary society and other church activities. Only the handsome exterior, except for the bricked-up pulpit window on the rear wall, remained intact in its former quiet beauty after these unfortunate changes had taken place. And so it remained until the great hurricane of 21 September 1938.

In that catastrophe the steeple was blown across the ridge, smashing the shingled roof and demolishing the floor at the former gallery level. The four brick walls, the fine arched doorway, and the square brick tower above it alone remained. The rest lay in ruins.

Immediate action was taken by the pastor, Rev. Howard C. Champe, the congregation and citizens of Lebanon, as well as by interested groups throughout the state. Fortunately, Wilbur L. Cross, the governor, recognized the importance of preserving the historic church. He headed a state-wide body, which became known as The Committee on the Restoration of the Lebanon Meeting House, to undertake the difficult task. J. Frederick Kelly, New Haven architect, antiquarian, and architectural historian,

---

3. See J. Frederick Kelly, *Early Connecticut Meetinghouses* (New York: Columbia University Press, 1948), I (2 vols.), "Lebanon Congregational Church," pp. 260–274, for the most authoritative account of the construction and history of the church.

4. Trumbull Papers, Connecticut State Library, Hartford.

5. For Trumbull's architectural drawings in the Adam manner see those at the New-York Historical Society.

was propitiously commissioned in 1940 to carry out the program of restoration. No more admirable choice could have been made. Mr. Kelly was superbly equipped by temperament, scholarship, and foresight for the mission. Some years before the destruction of the stately old meetinghouse he had made accurate measured drawings of the whole structure and could, therefore, proceed on a solid basis without guesswork. I had acquired several pieces of the original trim and moldings in 1928 from an elderly woman in Lebanon whose brother had been a carpenter during the remodeling of the interior in 1875; these proved to be of some minor use. Fortunately, a master woodcarver, Gottlieb Laibrandt of Village Hill, was found. He and his fellow craftsmen "neatly and handsomely" executed the original Connecticut architect's designs as rescued, over a century later, by the farsightedness of another Connecticut architect. The laying of the cornerstone took place on 29 June 1941 with Governor Cross the principal speaker. The rebuilding proceeded as funds permitted with a loving care and pride in craftsmanship more characteristic of pre-Industrial Revolution days than of the present. Progress was slow but continuous. A serious blow was struck by the long illness and subsequent death in 1948 of the architect-in-charge. He was succeeded by his brother, Henry Schraub Kelly, his former partner, who, with great fidelity, aided by the enthusiastic and learned support of the pastor, Rev. Robert G. Armstrong, D.D., carried the whole to successful conclusion. The dedication, on 28 November 1954, of the William Williams Memorial Steeple marked the completion of the restoration of the meetinghouse at Lebanon (Figs. 261 and 262), the sole surviving example of the architectural work of her illustrious son, Col. Trumbull.

BENJAMIN SILLIMAN AND HIS
UNCLE-IN-LAW COLONEL TRUMBULL*

This paper is the outcome of a discussion about the once interdependence of science and art, their close relationship during the period of the Renaissance, and their separation since the Industrial Revolution. An era of cooperative speculation was followed by one of individualistic endeavor. The present period of specialization, of the division of labor, and of intense concentration in severely limited fields, has been enormously rewarding—but distressingly stultifying. But happy exceptions can be cited and it is of one of these that I would speak.

The fine arts at Yale were sired by science. They sprang, surprisingly, from a most unusual and inauspicious background, compounded of chemistry, mineralogy, geology, geography, and electricity. Let us examine this singular situation. It started with the benign Benjamin Silliman who, it will be remembered, was during his long and useful life the most prominent and influential scientist in America. What I have to say of him is drawn, for the most part, from a private (and but partially published) notebook which he started a few years after his well-earned retirement. He began with these words:

AE. 78—after August 8, 1857 I shall, if I live, have entered my 79th year. My children and some of my friends have often suggested to me, that, in the evening of a long life, I ought to commit to writing some reminiscences of my times and of my own life and of eminent and worthy persons whom I have known. . . . Having in the passing hour finished my historical recital of my extra labors in science, I have looked back to the first pages of my account of Col. Trumbull and his gallery (see Fig. 276).

He set down these words—then modestly crossed them out:

the establishment of the Trumbull Gallery of paintings in Yale College has been effected primarily through my agency, cooperating with colleagues and other friends.

This understatement is emphatically true. Without the imaginative and assiduous scientist, the Trumbull Gallery would not have come into being. When its doors were opened to the public in October 1832, it represented not only the first gallery connected with an institution of higher learning in this country but also one of the earliest art museums in the Anglo-Saxon world.

* From *The Art Quarterly,* Winter 1959.

Silliman first met the artist at New Haven in 1801. To quote from the notebook:

This was in one of the public rooms of Yale College, in which Institution I was then a tutor. It was
... during the autumnal session of the legislature, when his distinguished brother Jonathan Trumbull, Esq. was in attendance, as Governor of the State. He came to the College with Col. and Mrs.
Trumbull, and I was introduced in the old Philosophical Hall over the former Chapel, now the
Atheneum. The brothers were elegant graceful gentlemen of winning manners and their familiarity
with each other, manifested in little sallies of wit, was pleasing to me, who had regarded them only
as grave, dignified men. [Col. Trumbull was] already a man in full life twenty-three years old, when
I was born ... as I came into early manhood I heard his praise from eminent men, President
Dwight, Hon. James Hillhouse and others; for, his country was proud of him, and his fame as a
soldier of the revolution and a friend and aid of Washington, and his celebrity as an artist were
cherished at home, and especially in his native state of Connecticut. ... My acquaintance with him
ceased only with his life.

The year after this initial meeting, in 1802, Silliman was appointed a full professor of
chemistry and natural history at the age of twenty-three, a post which he held until his
retirement in 1853.

"Even after my introduction to this distinguished man," to continue quoting from
the notebook,

he treated me as a friend. He was soon established in New York, and when, in 1804, I was preparing
to visit England, he gave me valuable letters of introduction, and still more valuable written in-
structions, as to life in England and especially in London, embodying the results of his own long
experience of twenty years.

Silliman spent the year 1805–06 abroad, mostly in London, where he met important
people, visited instrument makers and explored churches, literary institutions, museums, and libraries. Among other things, he dined with Trumbull's old master, Benjamin West. A few years later, in 1809, the youthful professor married Harriet, Governor Jonathan Trumbull's second daughter, thus becoming the "Patriot-Artist's"
nephew-in-law. This last was a matter of future importance in the history of fine arts in
this country, for it ultimately led to the establishment of the Trumbull Gallery.

That event, which occurred but eight years after the initial organization of the
National Gallery in London, is described as follows:

In the summer of 1830, when returning from a journey, I called upon Col. Trumbull at his lodgings
at Miss Lentner's, corner of Walker Street and Broadway, New York, it being my habit to pay my
respects to him whenever I was in the city. The house was large, the apartments spacious and two
contiguous parlors, of uncommon dimensions, were adorned by the paintings of Col. Trumbull,
which were advantageously suspended all around upon the walls. I had seen many of them singly
before, but had never seen them all together and some of them never before. I was, therefore,
strongly impressed and delighted by this unexpected vision, and had the good fortune to find the
venerable artist in the midst of his treasures.
Friendly salutations were followed by fuller explanations of some of the subjects than I had before

received, but I was sorry to find that the great artist, at seventy-four years of age, was in a position far from eligible, and although surrounded by the splendid productions of his own skill, talent and taste, he was without a sure foundation upon which he might repose the evening of life. . . . He . . . lamented his poverty in manly but energetic and eloquent language, which painfully touched my feelings. The very expressions which he used . . . are still with me at this moment. . . . Referring to the paintings around us, which he stated were his chief resource, I said:

"And what, Sir, do you intend to do with them?"

He instantly replied, "I will give them to Yale College to be exhibited forever for the benefit of poor students provided the College will pay me a competent annuity for the remainder of my life."

"Are you in earnest, Sir?"

"Certainly I am."

"Am I then at liberty to go home and act upon this suggestion?"

"You are at liberty and I authorise you to say so from me."

"The proposition, Sir, is as grateful to me as it is surprising."

Would that we could know the motives which prompted Silliman to act; kindness and compassion, pride and patriotism, opportunism, recognition of the unique historical and educational value of the subject matter, all of these; beauty, aesthetic consideration, probably played but a minor part. Whatever they might have been, the energetic professor undertook the problem with enthusiasm and zeal. "Our president, The Revd. Jeremiah Day," he recorded,

and my immediate colleagues among the older members of the College Faculty, as well as of the officers of the fiscal department were men of liberal minds, and I found no difficulty in exciting in them a lively interest and a strong desire to obtain the prize that was thus, unexpectedly, offered to us.

Having won over his colleagues the next step was to procure pledges for the underwriting of the annuity in case the expected entrance fees failed to suffice. In this he was greatly aided by his brother-in-law, Daniel Wadsworth—again family ties. That Hartford banker, merchant, philanthropist, and amateur artist was the husband of Faith, the eldest of Governor Trumbull's daughters. "It was proposed," Silliman noted,

and for some months favored by Col. Trumbull, to divide his paintings and establish two galleries —one in New Haven and the other in Hartford—both to inure to the benefit of the artist by an annuity to him during life; and after his death, the net income to be appropriated towards the support of poor and meritorious students in Yale College. . . . The duty of correspondence, of course, fell to my lot. . . . I have now lying before me about forty letters addressed by me to Col. Trumbull . . . and other letters . . . to persons more or less interested. . . . It soon became obvious that Col. Trumbull himself felt the increasing difficulty of the case, and his leaning to a single gallery became more and more apparent. . . . At length he proposed in a letter to me that the collection of pictures should not be divided.

Mr. Wadsworth had the magnanimity to acquiesce, founding, it will be remembered, some years later, in 1844, the Atheneum which proudly bears his name.

The securing of building funds was the next formidable problem undertaken by the resourceful Silliman, who "having been duly authorized . . . resorted to Hartford in May 1831 and made application to the Legislature then in season for aid to Yale College." He devoted his entire summer vacation to highly intelligent lobbying. It took considerable courage to attempt to extract funds from the State for the College and much more for an art museum, for such were then unknown in America. Art itself, too, was held under suspicion in Calvinistic Connecticut. The undaunted scientist was aided in his bold, unprecedented demands by "friends of the cause," in particular by two well-placed Yale alumni in the legislative halls, "in obtaining a grant for seven thousand dollars," out of which was "enough to erect a Building." "At a meeting of the Corporation in September 1831," he wrote, "the proposals for the Gallery were received with unanimous approbation"—as, indeed, they should have been! A formal indenture was drawn up conveying the pictures to the President and Fellows of Yale, provided that the College "shall erect . . . a fire-proof building for the reception of said paintings . . . of such form and dimensions as shall be approved by the said John Trumbull." What might have been a difficult problem was solved by having the aging artist, an amateur architect of merit, design the building himself. It was a happy selection.

It is not the place here to enter into an architectural description of the well-proportioned little neoclassical gallery on the old Yale Campus, except to note that the busy professor was consulted on each and every detail. It contained two exhibition galleries, each approximately thirty feet square and fifteen feet high to the base of the skylight. The ground floor of the near-fireproof building was initially used as a "Repository of Records" for the Treasurer and as a Theological Lecture Hall (beneath which, in later years, the colonel and his wife were buried). It was not long, however, before Silliman moved his "Cabinet of Minerals" to this convenient location, thereby combining the arts and sciences under a single roof.

When, at last, the building was opened, Silliman noted with considerable satisfaction that the creation of "an era of the arts in Connecticut" was at hand—as, indeed, it was!

At precisely the same time that the doors of the new gallery were thrown open to the public, the scientist's former pupil, Samuel F. B. Morse, a graduate in 1810, painter and inventor, had worked out a method of transmitting a message over an electric wire. It is interesting to reflect that the birth of this early art museum and that of the telegraph occurred simultaneously in the month of October 1832.

The relationship between the aging artist and the vivacious and virtuous scientist did not stop there. Five years later Silliman, the kindest of men, invited his proud and petulant uncle-in-law, then living alone in a New York boarding house, to make his home in New Haven with him and his family. Could anything be kinder or more Christian? The moment was well chosen. The dictatorial old gentleman was lonely, misunderstood, and disappointed. He had long ceased to be the leader in the arts in New York. His painting rooms in the American Academy of Fine Arts, of which he had been perpetual president, were partially destroyed by fire and no longer available; he had, finally, resigned from that moribund institution. A dozen years earlier the younger members, led by S. F. B. Morse, had walked out to found the rival National Academy of Design, of which Morse became the president, leaving Trumbull the captain of a crewless ship. His wife had died; he was companionless. The warm and generous invitation was, understandably, irresistible.

How far the professor, who was not a wealthy man, was prepared to go to make his old uncle-in-law comfortable may be gathered from his letter to his daughters Maria and Faith, dated New Haven, January 30, 1836:

If everything should go well, I have some thought of raising a story on the woodhouse for a library and miscellaneous room and for a repository and painting room for Uncle Trumbull, who now appears very well and in very good spirits and most pleased with the prospect of coming to us.[1] We can enter the painting and library gallery at the window where the clock stands and light the passage from the roof. The gallery will be 50 feet long, 13½ wide—9 or 10 high at the sides and arched 12 or 13 in the middle, and with side windows for ventilation. If divided, it will give a room of 18 feet long at the north end—with a chimney between the rooms and ample closets and leave a gallery 30 feet long. I think Uncle Trumbull can never paint in peace in the gallery at college.

Mrs. Silliman wrote her daughters July 19, 1837:

We heard the day before that Uncle Trumbull would come up. Your Papa went down to the boat to meet and bring him up and we waited dinner for him. . . . There were seven truck loads of boxes and he brought no articles of apparel and his bed has not yet come. He has many boxes of books.

and on November 6, 1837:

Just as we rose from dinner . . . Uncle Trumbull came upon us quite unexpectedly. . . . Mr. Underwood came up with him to look after his effects, of which he had enough to load 2 trucks. He brought his own bedstead and bed. . . . He seems satisfied with the accommodations provided for him and I hope he will be comfortable and happy.

But all was not happy. William Dunlap, Trumbull's old fellow pupil at Benjamin West's London studio, and one of the founders of the rival National Academy of Design, had visited the Gallery and had written disparagingly of Trumbull (*The Arts of Design*, 2 vols., 1834) and his work. The artist's friend, Philip Howe, the diarist, wrote the Colonel (March 16, 1835):

1. The white clapboarded Silliman house then stood on the northeast corner of Hillhouse Avenue and Trumbull Street in New Haven. Although badly mauled by further and less fortunate additions, it still stands, but on a new site, number 87 Trumbull Street.

I have this moment finished reading of Mr. Dunlap's Book . . . [I am] vexed and annoyed . . . by the bad temper which characterizes every page of it . . . The ill-natured remarks in which he has indulged, his bad feeling toward you, have excited my Indignation.

Some years before he left New York the Colonel, smarting under Dunlap's vindictiveness, had begun a self-defensive autobiography. (Dunlap, by the way, had New Haven connections, having married Elizabeth Woolsey in 1789, the aunt of President Theodore Dwight Woolsey of Yale.) Comfortably ensconced on Hillhouse Avenue and gently but firmly prodded by the kindly professor-editor, Trumbull finished the story of his long life as a soldier, artist, and diplomat. "Col. Trumbull wrote most of his *Autobiography* in my house," Silliman wrote the art historian C. Edward Lester (March 17, 1846). As chapter followed chapter he tried them out on family and patient friends. From the Silliman family correspondence we learn such details as: "Uncle Trumbull commenced reading a memoir about himself. . . . It is elegantly written and very interesting" (Mrs. Silliman, November 20, 1837); and "In the evening Uncle Trumbull read to us again and continued his interesting narrative." Faith Silliman gives a charming picture of these proceedings in a letter to her sister Maria (December 23, 1838):

Have we ever told you that Uncle is reading again to some friends his manuscript? The Hillhouses, Skinners, Whitneys, Mrs. Pritchard, Susan, Mr. Bakewell, come here Saturday evenings. Uncle reads till about nine o'clock and then he furnishes grapes and champagne and we a basket of cake. They are very pleasant evenings.

The *Autobiography,* it should be remembered, was the earliest extended account of an individual artist written and published in the United States.

It will be recalled that Professor Silliman founded and became the first editor of the *American Journal of Science* in 1818, one of the world's great scientific journals, to which he alluded at the beginning of his notebook. He noticed Trumbull and his work in its pages on no less than five separate occasions. It was still another instance of science serving the arts.

It is interesting to note, also, that both Col. Trumbull and Professor Silliman were among the earliest members elected to the Connecticut Academy. The artist painted the portraits of thirteen members. They were of President Timothy Dwight of Yale (Fig. 17); his brother Theodore Dwight, Sr., lawyer, editor and author; Professor Chauncey Allen Goodrich of Yale (Fig. 20); Professor Silliman; the banker and philanthropist Daniel Wadsworth (see Fig. 85); John Adams (Fig. 108), the second President; Chauncey Goodrich, United States Senator from Connecticut; Oliver Ellsworth (Fig. 110), Chief Justice; Oliver Wolcott, Jr. (Fig. 127), Governor of Connecticut; Jonathan Trumbull, Jr. (Fig. 113), Governor of the State; John Langdon (Fig. 107), United States Senator from New Hampshire; the Revolutionary officer Jedediah Huntington of Norwich, Connecticut, who married the artist's sister Faith Trumbull; as well as the artist himself (Figs. 63–66).

Silliman not only got the old Colonel to write and publish but to teach. Mrs. Silliman wrote her daughter Maria Trumbull (October 16, 1839): "Uncle is quite busy with committees from college requesting him to address them on the subject of his pictures. He meets with the Senior Class on Saturday, the Sophomores on Wednesday next. He laughs a good deal at his having taken up the trade." These were, without doubt, the earliest "art history" lectures given at Yale.

The crusty old Colonel, after spending four years in New Haven, returned to New York to be close to his physician Dr. James Augustus Washington. He died there on November 10, 1843. Silliman's kindnesses did not cease. Trumbull's remains were brought to New Haven by steamer and placed in the front parlor of his Hillhouse Avenue home, long familiar to the departed. Silliman wrote:

The next day being the Sabbath, the funeral solemnities took place in the afternoon in the College Chapel . . . Professor [Eleazar Thompson] Fitch [Livingston Professor of Divinity] was very interesting and touching . . . After the exercises the procession proceeded to the tomb [prepared some years before beneath the Gallery]. The relatives and particular friends of the deceased, the College Faculty, professional students, undergraduates, and citizens went through College to Chapel and High Streets to the Trumbull Gallery and in a bleak blowing evening of November deposited the body in its last resting place.

Silliman, as might be expected, became the chief executor of Trumbull's will and, as if that were not enough, became Curator of the Trumbull Gallery. The scientist, therefore, has the distinction of being among the earliest, if not the first, art museum curator in America.

THE FAILURE OF A FALSEHOOD*

Forgery is a by-product of collecting. Objects created for a definite use, be they cult statues, painted altarpieces, drawings, or postage stamps, are not falsified so long as they are employed for the immediate purpose for which they were made. It is only when that use disappears, or is altered, that such objects become "collectors' items," valued for their historical association, rarity, aesthetic merit, snob appeal, and for a hundred other valid or trivial reasons. When the *nouveaux riches* Romans carried off Greek votive figures to ornament their gardens, and the supply of such ran low, clever imitations—forgeries, the earliest known to us—came into being. It was the same with Renaissance and, recently, modern painting, medieval ivories and enamels, and artists' sketches. The pattern is uniform when demand exceeds supply. Collectors of the collectible, too often swayed by the fluctuations of fashion, unwittingly aid and abet the forger. The legitimate dealer, as well as the fraudulent fabricator, must be constantly attuned to the mode of the moment.

A change of fashion occurred in this country, as the result of two highly nationalistic expositions, during the last decade or two of the nineteenth century. The new taste was made as the direct result of the Centennial at Philadelphia in 1876, followed, in 1889, by the celebration marking the hundredth anniversary of President Washington's inauguration held in New York. We became conscious of our background, our history, and heroic past. The glamor of the Revolution, having receded for a century, was now revived. Arms, military accoutrements, drawings, maps, and prints—their original usefulness having long since passed—suddenly became desirable items, worthy of consideration by the collector. The setting was perfect for the sale of the genuine and the false.

The producer of the latter had his task enormously simplified. There were few accessible examples of Americana in the museums; comparison was difficult if not impossible. Illustrated art journals devoted most of their space to the art of Europe. There was an enthusiastic and uninformed public. The forger, on his part, had readily available sound source material providentially provided by Henry Alexander Ogden's monumental *Army of the United States,* published by the Quartermaster General's Office in 1888, and Clarence Winthrop Bowen's huge *History of the Centennial Celebration of the Inauguration of George Washington* of 1892. The stage was set.

* From *The Princeton University Library Chronicle, 32,* Winter 1961.

One Edouard Frossard, a self-styled "Numismatist and Archaeologist," made the most of it. That he finally failed is a tribute to the critics and collectors of the nineties. The tale of his unsuccessful efforts is, however, worth telling.

On an April day in 1894 that eminently respectable New York bookstore, Dodd, Mead and Company, of 5 East 19th Street, opened an exhibition called the "Trumbull Collection." This, so the catalogue stated, consisted "of original studies in india ink . . . of George Washington and the generals, statesmen and celebrities of the Revolutionary period . . . A unique collection of one hundred and one pieces by John Trumbull." Provenance and name of owner were omitted. The price of the entire collection, actually of 122 items, was set at fifteen thousand dollars. As Yale possessed a hundred or more paintings and miniatures (but no drawings or sketches) by Trumbull, eyes were turned in the direction of New Haven. At a dinner held at the Yale Club in New York on May 8, purchase at the indicated price was suggested. Although "subscriptions were solicited," happily for posterity nothing happened. This might have been due to indifference or to the fact that Professor John Ferguson Weir, then director of the Yale School of the Fine Arts, harbored some doubts, especially about the "uniformity of the signature 'J.T.' on the face of all of the sketches."

Some months later that year the collection was again exhibited, this time at Ed. Frossard's place of business (108 East 14th Street), now called "The Trumbull Gallery," and a new and more ambitious catalogue (No. 128) published, bearing the name of the owner. In a prefatory note it was explained that "up to about 1824 the collection remained in the possession of John Trumbull. It then passed, together with a number of Revolutionary uniforms, arms, and other objects, the paraphernalia of an artist's studio, into the hands of a Virginian, a close friend of Trumbull, whose grandchildren were the last recent owners. In 1892, 1893, and 1894 the collection was broken up. . . . The cataloguer . . . became deeply interested and soon applied all his money, time and energy to purchasing . . . the collection. . . . The authenticity of the collection as the original work of John Trumbull is fully and emphatically guaranteed. . . ." There were now 160 items; the price of the entire collection was newly set at eight thousand dollars. (A four-page supplement was added later, bringing the total to 193, which was again, informally, increased to a total of 203 items.) It is items 175 and 177 in the addition which concern us here. They read:

175. David Ramsay, M. D. The Life of George Washington. New York, 1807. 8vo.
    On fly-leaf a pen-and-ink portrait of Washington in military uniform, 1807, J.T.; below this was the autog. inscription: *After my 1776 Sketch on hide from life. J.T.*
177. The Revolutionary Plutarch, etc., London, 1806. 8vo.
    On fly-leaves of Vol. II are the following pen-and-ink portraits:
    1. Napoleon Bonaparte with autog. inscription: *Napoleon after my sketch from life on hide 1808. J.T.*

2. Talleyrand with autog. inscription: *Tallerand* [sic] *from pencil sketch from life—sketch lost. 1808. J.T.*

3. Military bust; under autog. inscription: *Josh. Barney. 1808. J.T.*

Again nothing happened—except a storm in the press.

Articles, pro and con, about the genuineness of the sketches appeared in *The Collector* (October 1894 to April 1896), *The Nation* (September 1894, in which the sketches are referred to as "crude, badly drawn, and worse proportioned . . . dealing often with trivial matters . . .), and the New York *Evening Post* (of the same date). Kenyon Cox, the academic painter, was among the first to damn the whole collection as a fraud. There were no takers.

The entire collection was, therefore, sent to a less heated climate. It went to Boston —but met with no success. Charles Greely Loring, Director of the Museum of Fine Arts, wrote to Professor Weir in December 1894: "Will you tell me what your final judgment is in regard to the Trumbull drawings, whether done by Trumbull. . . . I have grave reasons for questioning the authenticity of several of them, and if one begins to doubt the doubt is apt to spread from the known factors to the unknown." Some days later, he again wrote to the painter Weir: "your letter [is] a well put, excellent criticism for the artist's point of view, which no one is more competent to give than you. From other evidence I have no hesitation in pronouncing the collection to be fraudulent." He cited such inconsistency as a drawing, dated 1786, of Martha Washington dressed in the fashion of the French Empire of twenty years later. Still the game was not up.

Perhaps Mr. Frossard could think of no other way of disposing of his ever growing collection, or, possibly in pure desperation, he had the whole put up for auction. A twenty-seven-page catalogue announced that "The Frossard Revolutionary Collection" would go under the hammer. The sale was to take place on March 19 and 20, 1896, at the American Art Galleries, Madison Square, South, New York. There were now 346 Trumbull items—the familiar sketches of Revolutionary heroes, battle and camp scenes, the extra-illustrated David Ramsay, *Washington* (now no. 209), *The Revolutionary Plutarch* (numbered 211), and an extraordinary assortment of "mementoes," all suitably engraved, marked, ticketed, and labeled. Among these were Trumbull's inkstand, saddle pistols (*My own pair, J.T.*), sword (*My sword from 1776, J.T.*), a knife sheath (*from Capt. John Paul Jones, J.T.*), a blunderbuss (*From Washington, J.T.*), and a pewter basin (*Gen. Washington's wash-pan; all through the war. N. Y. July 1790, J.T.*). The whole thing was overdone. The result was disastrous. For instance, a copper tray (*brought from Scotland by P. Henry's Father, P. Henry gave it to me. J.T.*) went for $3.00, a sketch of David Wilkie for $2.00, one of Benjamin West for $8.00, George Washington, "Head . . . bold brush work . . . entirely unlike any portraits heretofore known . . . ," for $3.00, another Washington (*One of my strongest sketches of Gen. W. on thick cow-hide. Made in Boston. J.T.*) for $17.00. The highest price, $225.00, was paid for a *Life Size Bust Portrait of Gen. Washington in 1776 exhibit in N. York and admired very much. Taken by me to Eng.—and had to hide it away with my friend B* [Benjamin] *W* [West] *J.T.* The average per item was $11.25 and the total $2,766.25. Less than two years previous the price of the less expanded collection had been fifteen thousand dollars. It was a sad end for Mr. Frossard and his efforts. He died in Kings County on April 12, 1899, just three years later. Few had been fooled but the forger.

What were the reasons for the failure, especially as the ground had been so beautifully prepared? The writer believes that it was simply too good; everything was there—including the hair of heroes. There were locks of Washington, Benjamin Franklin, General Lafayette, General Israel Putnam, General Benedict Arnold, and others, all verified by the initials "*J.T.*" Stylistically, it seems ridiculous to us now (with our superior knowledge of Trumbull's work) that the portraits ever fooled anyone. Trumbull drew, carefully and correctly on paper, reserving sepia wash for landscape sketches. The Frossard drawings in sepia are on deerskin, vellum, wood, the "inside covers of old Revolutionary report books," and such like material. They are all signed, on the face, with the initials "*J.T.*" and dated; this the colonel never did. Trumbull drew for the purpose of obtaining visual information; he did not regard his portrait sketches as independent works of art. Mr. Frossard included miniatures, executed in watercolor-on-ivory, in his great collection. Trumbull invariably used an older technique, oil-on-wood (mahogany). And then, too, the forger sometimes got mixed with his dated drawings (the sitter mistakenly being represented as being in America when the artist was actually in England). Trumbull never saw nor drew the Emperor Napoleon, nor Major André, for that matter. A more competent counterfeiter would have avoided such blunders.

Who was this "Master of the Frossard Forgeries" anyway? We shall probably never know. Perhaps he was some poor, ill-paid artist working, conceivably, in good faith. The dates and signatures may not have been his. (Professor Weir had said they looked as if they had been added later.) The late John Hill Morgan, a New York lawyer and a close student of the Revolutionary period, thought the man might have worked in Brooklyn, where Frossard lived. Whoever he was, his *oeuvre* was vast. That contained in the three catalogues cited is but a part. All of it can be readily identified, stylistically, from the listed and documented forgeries.

What has become of the collection? The curious may see examples, all properly identified as forgeries, at Fort Ticonderoga (15); the Yale Art Gallery (an excellent collection of 21 sketches); the New-York Historical Society (3 sketches, plus "Capt. Paul Jones' knife holder"); the Society for the Preservation of New England Antiquities, at Boston (4); the Carnegie Institute, Pittsburgh; the Annmary Brown Memorial, Providence; and so on. The bulk of the collection is still in private hands, the largest single group being in Florida. The Yale University Library has recently acquired, through gift, from the second sale referred to above, item 175, Ramsay's *Life of George Washington,* with the fraudulent sketch of the general (Fig. 263). Item 177 from the same sale, *The Revolutionary Plutarch,* containing the three false portrait drawings (the Emperor Napoleon (Fig. 267), Talleyrand, and Joshua Barney), is now in the possession of the Princeton University Library.[1]

It is possible that many of the drawings still held in private hands will, at some future time, come on the market. Would that prospective buyers might check with the many excellent examples of the work of the unknown "Master of the Frossard Forgeries" before adding to their collections. *Caveat emptor!*

POSTSCRIPT

It is somewhat ironic that nine months, almost to the day, after the "Frossard Revolutionary Collection" was dispersed at auction, genuine Trumbulls, of irreproachable provenance, came to light in a Philadelphia auction room (1110 Chestnut Street). The drawings, 138 in number, may be found listed in Stan. V. Henkels' catalogue, no. 770, for December 17, 1896. Colonel Trumbull had given them to Professor Benjamin Silliman of Yale, with whom the old artist had lived for some years before his death. Subsequently they were bequeathed to Benjamin Silliman, II, his son, and then to Benjamin Silliman, III, his grandson. The last sold both the Trumbull drawings and the letters and papers (Henkels' catalogue, no. 778, February 11, 1897). Some of the drawings can now be seen at the Cooper Union, Fordham University, and the Metropolitan Museum of Art, New York; the Addison Gallery, Andover; the Historical Society of Pennsylvania, Philadelphia; the Yale University Art Gallery; and the Princeton University Library. Princeton possesses the most complete set of drawings extant for a major composition (Figs. 175–81). The Princeton Library has, therefore, the two extremes—typical examples of the forger's art and excellent, genuine sketches from the hand of the artist.

1. The gift in 1928 of the late James Barnes '91.

TRUMBULL'S PAINTINGS ON POSTAGE STAMPS*

Col. John Trumbull was the visual recorder of the Revolution. He depicted the chief events of that heroic episode and painted the prominent participants so effectively that it is through his eyes that we, today, envision such scenes as the "Battle of Bunker's Hill," the "Surrender of Burgoyne at Saratoga," and of "Cornwallis at Yorktown," the "Declaration of Independence" and the "Resignation of Washington." It was through young John's ability as a draughtsman (he made accurate sketches of British gun emplacements before Boston) that he was made an early member of Washington's military "family," as second aide-de-camp. He was later Adjutant to Gen. Gates at Ticonderoga, with the rank of colonel—at the age of twenty—a title to which he clung throughout his long life. Thus an ideal opportunity of witnessing military operations and observing the chief actors of the drama presented itself, and it was not missed. Trumbull painted a large full-length portrait of the Commander-in-Chief, which today is regarded as the finest representation of Washington in his military character, just as Gilbert Stuart's celebrated "Athenaeum" portrait is considered the best of the first President. Typical of his post-Revolutionary portraits is that of his friend, Alexander Hamilton, familiar to millions of Americans, reproduced on the face of the ten dollar bill (national currency, series of 1929, Federal Reserve note, series of 1928 and 1934, and silver certificates, series of 1933 and 1934). The head on the bill was engraved after the posthumous full-length portrait in the New York City Hall (Fig. 27), which Trumbull, a staunch Hamiltonian Federalist, painted in 1805, shortly after the famous Hamilton–Burr duel, using the marble bust of the visiting Italian sculptor, Ceracchi, as a model. He had painted the dead statesman once from life, before 1792 (the picture is now owned by the National Gallery in Washington), for John Jay (Fig. 22). It is a pity that the latter, rather than the posthumous portrait was not used on the bill.

The source material for the postage stamps could likewise have been selected with more discrimination. Too often the second best has been used, such as engravings after the original paintings or Trumbull's own dull replicas of his early vigorous work. A list of the Trumbull paintings represented on United States postage follows:

GEN. GEORGE WASHINGTON, no. 39, A19, 90¢ blue, 1860; head turned three-quarters to the left, bust only, from the half-length engraving by Asher Brown Durand, (frontispiece in The National Portrait Gallery, Philadelphia and New York, 1834, vol.

* From *The American Philatelist*, 62, June 1949.

1.), after the large full-length portrait of "Washington at Trenton," painted from life in 1792 at Philadelphia, now at the Yale University Art Gallery, New Haven, Conn. (Figs. 95 and 96)

GEN. GEORGE WASHINGTON, no. 72, A31, 90¢, blue, 1861; same source as #39.

THE DECLARATION OF INDEPENDENCE, no. 20, A41, 24¢, green and violet, 1869; slightly cut down from the large replica painted between 1818 and 1824 at New York (after the small-scale original begun in 1786 at London and now at Yale University) in the Rotunda of the Capitol, Washington, D.C. (See Figs. 158–163)

THE SURRENDER OF GEN. BURGOYNE AT SARATOGA, no. 644, A192, 2¢, carmine rose, 1927, the "Burgoyne Campaign Issue"; from the large replica painted between 1817 and 1824 at New York (after the small-scale original painted in 1816 at New York and now at Yale University) in the Rotunda of the Capitol, Washington, D.C. (See Figs. 184–186)

GEN. GEORGE WASHINGTON, no. 703, A209, 2¢, carmine rose and black, 1931, "York-town Issue"; same source as no. 39.

GEN. GEORGE WASHINGTON, no. 711, A217, 6¢, red orange, 1932, "Washington Bi-Centennial Issue"; same source as no. 39.

GEN. GEORGE WASHINGTON, no. 712, A218, 7¢, black, 1932, "Washington Bi-Centennial Issue"; head turned slightly to the left, bust from the small full-length portrait painted in 1780 from memory at London, now in the Metropolitan Museum of Art, New York. (Fig. 90)

GEN. GEORGE WASHINGTON, no. 785, A258, 1¢, green, 1936, "Army Issue"; same source as no. 39, but head is reversed and turned to the right.

MAJ. GEN. NATHANAEL GREENE, no. 785, A258, 1¢, green, 1936, "Army Issue," on same stamp as above; head three-quarters to the right, after the engraving of Ion B. Forrest (The National Portrait Gallery, Philadelphia and New York, 1834, vol. 1), after an oil miniature painted posthumously in 1792 at Philadelphia, now in the Yale University Art Gallery, probably after Charles Willson Peale's portrait, painted from life in 1783. (Fig. 104)

BRIG. GEN. RUFUS PUTNAM, no. 795, A268, 3¢, red violet, 1937, "Ordinance of 1787 Sesquicentennial Issue"; head turned three-quarters to the left, from an oil miniature painted from life in 1790 at New York, now in the Yale University Art Gallery. (Fig. 111)

ALEXANDER HAMILTON, no. 1047, A494, $5.00, black, 1956.

NOTE: A somewhat similar article, "Works of John Trumbull on United States Stamps," by the author in cooperation with Professor Deane Keller, appeared in *Linn's Weekly Stamp News, 29,* 28 Jan. 1957.

ILLUSTRATIONS

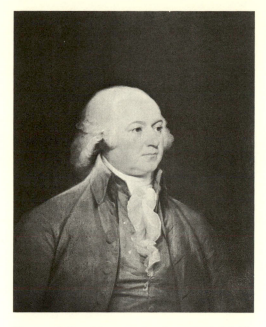

Fig. 1. *John Adams,* painted at Philadelphia about 1793, in the artist's happiest manner, a gift to Harvard College in 1794.
Courtesy of Harvard University.

Fig. 2. *Major Roger Alden,* painted fifteen years earlier than Fig. 1.
Owned by Mrs. Roger Alden Derby. Photograph courtesy of Frick Art Reference Library.

Fig. 3. *Goldsbrow Banyer,* painted in 1806.
Owned by The New-York Historical Society.

Fig. 4. *Robert Benson,* painted in 1804.
Owned by The New-York Historical Society (bequest of Robert Benson, Jr., 1885).

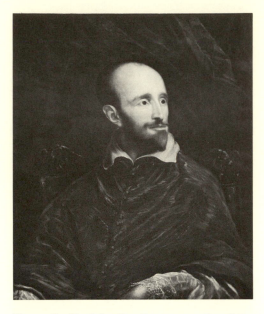

Fig. 5. *Cardinal Bentivoglio*, a copy after John Smibert's copy of Van Dyck's original, painted in 1778 in Smibert's old studio in Boston. The twenty-two-year-old artist had few pictorial guides. Trumbull gave the picture to his alma mater in 1791.
Courtesy of Harvard University.

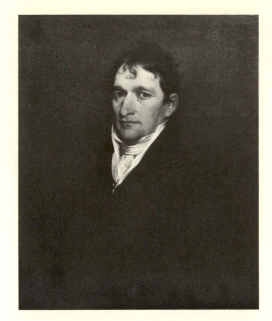

Fig. 6. *Isaac Bronson*, painted *ca.* 1805. Owned by Bronson W. Griscom.

Fig. 7. *Mrs. Isaac Bronson*, painted *ca.* 1805. Owned by Bronson W. Griscom.

Fig. 8. *William Brown*. The artist spent the years 1794 to 1804 in London on a diplomatic mission. Most of his best work was done prior to 1794. This portrait painted 1804–1806.
Owned by The Art Institute of Chicago.

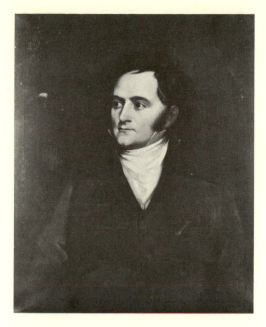

Fig. 9. *William Gedney Bull*, painted at New York in the 1840s.
Owned by Sir Chester Beatty.

Fig. 10. *Philip Church*, son of a London banker, painted in that city in 1784.
Owned by Mrs. Philip Schuyler Church.

Fig. 11. *De Witt Clinton*, painted in 1805 for the New York City Hall along with a dozen or more similar commissions.
Owned by City Hall, New York.

Fig. 12. *George Clinton*, painted in 1791.
Owned by City Hall, New York.

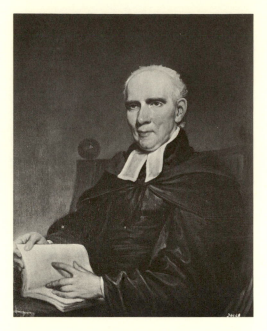

Fig. 13. *Rev. William Cochran,* a late portrait.
Owned by Columbia University.

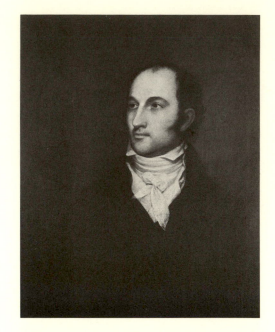

Fig. 14. *Bartholomew Dandridge,* painted at London prior to the subject's death in 1802.
Yale University Art Gallery.

Fig. 15. *James Duane,* 1805, another New York
City Hall portrait.
Owned by City Hall, New York.

Fig. 16. *Asher Brown Durand,* engraver of Trumbull's *Declaration of Independence,* a good late portrait, painted in 1826.
Owned by The New-York Historical Society.

Fig. 17. *Rev. Timothy Dwight,* President of Yale, painted for the College in 1817.
Yale University Art Gallery.

Fig. 18. *Dr. John Wakefield Francis,* done in 1819 in New York.
Owned by Columbia–Presbyterian Medical Center.

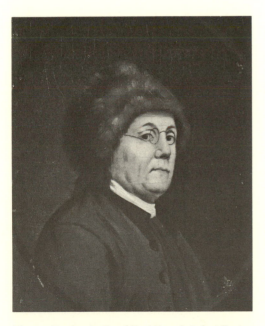

Fig. 19. *Benjamin Franklin* (A), painted at Boston in 1778 after the 1777 engraving by Augustin de Saint-Aubin after the portrait by Charles Nicholas Cochin (B) (see Appendix).
Yale University Art Gallery.

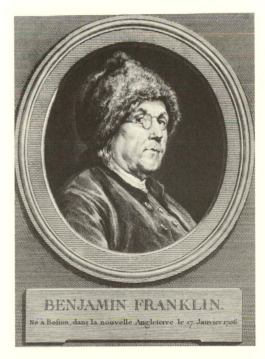

BENJAMIN FRANKLIN.

Né à Boston, dans la nouvelle Angleterre le 17 Janvier 1706

(B)

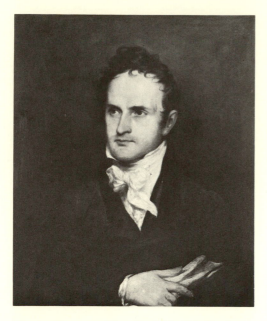

Fig. 20. *Chauncey Allen Goodrich,* Yale Professor, painted in 1827 at New Haven.
Owned by Bowdoin College Museum of Art.

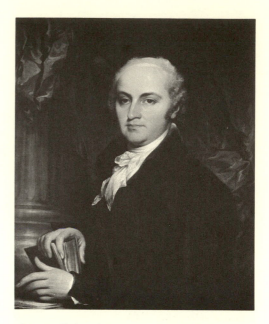

Fig. 21. *Christopher Gore,* a close friend of the artist, painted at London in 1800.
Yale University Art Gallery.

Fig. 22. *Alexander Hamilton,* painted from life for John Jay *ca.* 1792.
Owned by National Gallery of Art (gift of the Avalon Foundation).

Fig. 23. *Alexander Hamilton,* posthumous replica of 1832, one of five or six such portraits, known as the "Jay type."
Yale University Art Gallery.

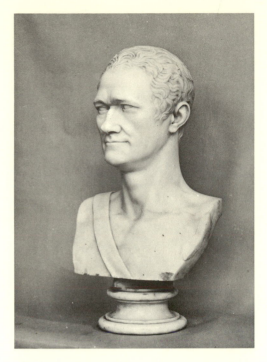

Fig. 24. *Alexander Hamilton*, one of several marble busts, of 1791, by the visiting Italian sculptor Giuseppe Ceracchi.
Owned by the Museum of the City of New York.

Fig. 25. *Alexander Hamilton*, posthumous, after the bust, known as the "Ceracchi type," of which some six or eight copies exist.
Owned by Museum of Fine Arts, Boston (bequest of Robert C. Winthrop).

Fig. 26. *Alexander Hamilton*, "Ceracchi type," 1804–1808.
The White House Collection, Washington, D.C.

Fig. 27. *Alexander Hamilton*, painted for City Hall, New York, in 1805.
Owned by City Hall, New York.

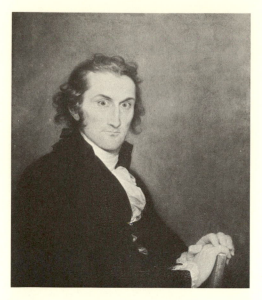

Fig. 28. *Dr. Lemuel Hopkins.*
Yale University Art Gallery.

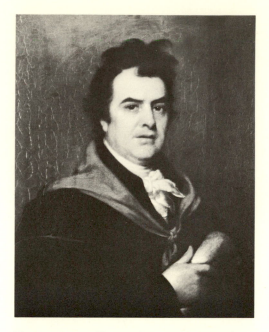

Fig. 29. *Dr. David Hosack,* a close friend of the artist.
Owned by The Society of The New York Hospital.

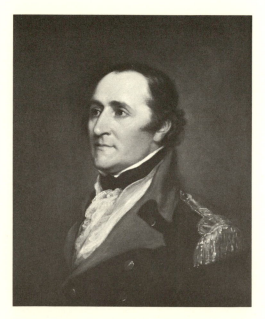

Fig. 30. *Brig. Gen. Ebenezer Huntington,* painted in 1806.
Owned by James Graham and Sons, Inc., New York.

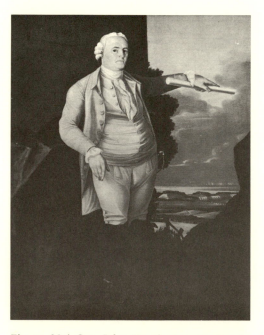

Fig. 31. *Maj. Gen. Jabez Huntington,* standing in a heroic attitude, derived from a seventeenth-century Italian print by Salvator Rosa, which in turn was taken from the celebrated statue of Augustus Caesar in the Vatican Museum. Trumbull picked up visual information when and where he could.
Owned by the Connecticut State Library.

Fig. 32. Print by Salvator Rosa (1615–73).

Fig. 33. *Jabez Huntington,* grandson of Maj. Gen. Jabez Huntington, painted the same year, 1777, at the artist's home in Lebanon, Connecticut, when he was twenty-one. Family and friends served as convenient and willing models.
Yale University Art Gallery.

Fig. 34. *John Jay,* painted in 1805 for the New York City Hall.
Owned by City Hall, New York.

Fig. 35. *Rufus King,* 1800, at London.
Yale University Art Gallery.

Fig. 36. *Mrs. Rufus King*, 1800, at London (see Sarah Trumbull portrait at Winterthur and Appendix).
Owned by Charles King Lennig, Jr.

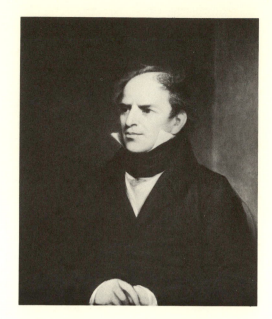

Fig. 37. *Peter Lanman*, 1828.
Yale University Art Gallery.

Fig. 38. *Mrs. Peter (Abigail Trumbull) Lanman.*
Yale University Art Gallery.

Fig. 39. *Robert Lenox*, 1805.
Owned by The New York Public Library.

Fig. 40. *Mrs. Robert Lenox*, 1805.
Owned by The New York Public Library.

Fig. 41. *Morgan Lewis*, 1808.
Owned by City Hall, New York.

Fig. 42. *Edward Livingston*, 1805.
Owned by City Hall, New York.

Fig. 43. *Dr. Edward Preble Marcellin, ca.* 1830.
Owned by Thomas M. Evans.

Fig. 44. *Stephen Minot.*
Owned by Museum of Fine Arts, Boston (gift of
Miss Susan I. Minot).

Fig. 45. *Mrs. Stephen Minot,* both 1806.
Owned by Museum of Fine Arts, Boston (gift of
Miss Susan I. Minot).

Fig. 46. *John Murray, ca.* 1806.
Owned by The Metropolitan Museum of Art
(Morris K. Jessup Fund, 1922).

Fig. 47. *Mrs. John Murray, ca.* 1806.
Owned by The Metropolitan Museum of Art
(Morris K. Jessup Fund, 1922).

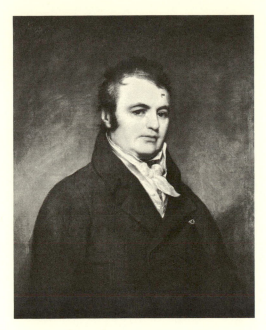

Fig. 48. *John Pintard*, 1817.
Owned by The New-York Historical Society.

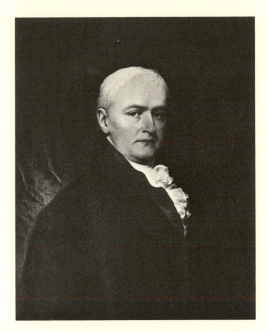

Fig. 49. *Jacob Radcliff*, 1816.
Owned by City Hall, New York.

Fig. 50. *Sergeant Bryan Rossetter*.
Owned by New York State Society of the Cincinnati.

Fig. 51. *Maj. Winthrop Sargent*.
Owned by M. Knoedler and Co., Inc.

Fig. 52. *Lydia Sigourney,* painted in 1838 at New Haven; possibly the artist's last portrait. Owned by Wadsworth Atheneum, Hartford.

Fig. 53. *Bartholomew Skaats, ca.* 1816. Owned by City Art Museum of Saint Louis.

Fig. 54. *Deborah Skaats, ca.* 1816. Owned by International Business Machines Corporation.

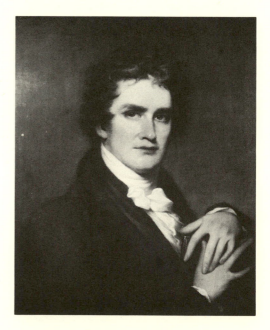

Fig. 55. *William Leete Stone, ca.* 1821. Owned by Mrs. Charles H. Higgins.

Fig. 56. *Peter Stuyvesant*, a copy made in 1808 for the New York City Hall.
Owned by City Hall, New York.

Fig. 57. *Mrs. Thomas Sully*, 1806.
Owned by Amherst College.

Fig. 58. *Maurice Swabey*, painted *ca.* 1800 at London.
Owned by The New-York Historical Society.

Fig. 59. *Sir John Temple*, painted in 1784 at London. A certain softness of handling here begins to supplant the rigidity of colonial portraiture.
From the Collection of Bartlett Arkell, Yale 1886, at Canajoharie Art Gallery, Canajoharie, N.Y.

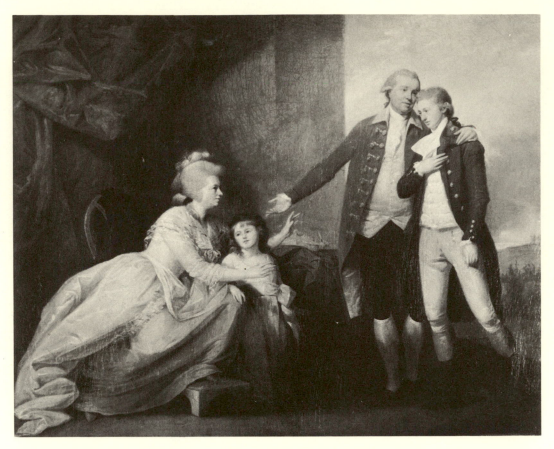

Fig. 60. *Sir John Temple and Family*. One of the artist's earliest pictures in the current English manner. Owned by George Temple Bowdoin.

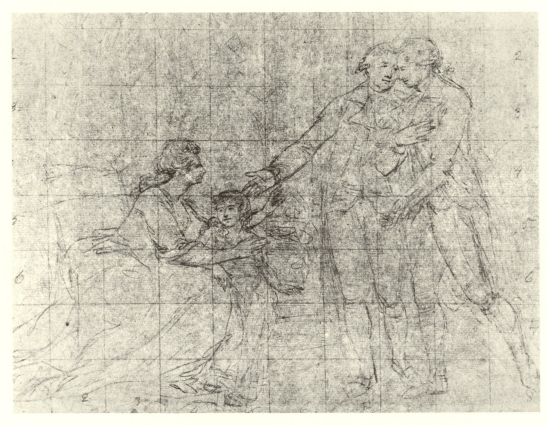

Fig. 61. A study (not used) for the 1784 family group. Yale University Art Gallery.

Fig. 62. *Daniel D. Tompkins,* another 1808 New York City Hall Portrait. Owned by City Hall, New York.

Fig. 63. *John Trumbull,* self-portrait of the serious young artist, painted at his home in Lebanon, Conn., in 1774, the year after his graduation from Harvard.
Owned by John McClellan.

Fig. 64. *John Trumbull,* a self-portrait of 1777. Note Hogarth's *Analysis of Beauty* (1753, pp. 116–17) supporting the young artist's palette, on which the pigments are arranged in the manner recommended by the English master.
Owned by Museum of Fine Arts, Boston (bequest of George Nixon Black in 1929).

Fig. 65. *John Trumbull,* self-portrait painted at London in 1801.
Owned by Wadsworth Atheneum, Hartford.

Fig. 66. *John Trumbull,* self-portrait also painted at London about the year 1812. Observe hand resting on the hilt of his sword and his brushes ("pencils"). "To his Country he gave his SWORD and his PENCIL" (from his tomb in the Yale University Art Gallery).
Owned by Marshall Hill Clyde, Jr.

Fig. 67. *Sarah Trumbull,* the artist's wife, painted at London about the time of his wedding in 1800. Owned by Mrs. Charles H. Higgins. Photograph courtesy of Frick Art Reference Library.

Fig. 68. *Sarah Trumbull,* painted at London *ca.* 1812.
Owned by Marshall Hill Clyde, Jr.

Fig. 69. *Sarah Trumbull,* the beautiful and mysterious Sarah (see Appendix), painted at London between 1800 and 1804.
Owned by Henry Francis du Pont Winterthur Museum.

Fig. 70. *Sarah as "Innocence,"* painted at New York, *ca.* 1816.
Yale University Art Gallery.

Fig. 71. *Sarah Trumbull on her Deathbed,* New York 1824. Owned by Joseph Lanman Richards.

Fig. 72. *John Trumbull, Poet,* is often confused with his second cousin, John, the painter. The portrait was painted at Hartford in 1793 in the artist's happiest style. Owned by Detroit Institute of Arts.

Fig. 73. *John "M." Trumbull*, the artist's nephew, painted at London *ca.* 1800.
Owned by Heyward Isham.

Fig. 74. *Governor Jonathan Trumbull, Senior*, the artist's father, painted at his home in Lebanon, Conn.
Yale University Art Gallery.

Fig. 76. *Nicholas Boylston*, painted by John Singleton Copley in 1773, the year of Trumbull's graduation from Harvard. Compare with Fig. 75. Copley's predominant influence on the young painter lasted until the latter reached London in 1784.
Owned by Harvard University (bequest of Ward Nicholas Boylston in 1828).

Fig. 77. *Governor Trumbull* with his (deceased) wife, painted at Lebanon in 1783.
Yale University Art Gallery.

Fig. 75. *Governor and Mrs. Trumbull,* the artist's father and mother painted at Lebanon in 1778. Owned by The Connecticut Historical Society.

Fig. 79. *Jonathan Trumbull, Junior, and His Family* (the artist's brother), painted at Lebanon in 1777. Yale University Art Gallery. Compare with Ralph Earl's forceful portrait, *Roger Sherman,* painted about 1776. (Fig. 80)

Fig. 78. *Governor Trumbull,* a posthumous portrait of the Governor (died 1785), painted at New York 1820.
Yale University Art Gallery.

Fig. 80. *Roger Sherman,* by Ralph Earl.
Yale University Art Gallery.

Fig. 81. *Joseph Trumbull,* the artist's oldest brother, a posthumous portrait of 1778 in the Copley manner.
Owned by Mrs. Clifton M. Bockstoce.

Fig. 82. *Stephen van Rensselaer,* painted also in 1778. Yale University Art Gallery.

Fig. 84. *The Vernet Family,* painted at Norwich, Conn., in 1806 in the artist's English manner. Yale University Art Gallery.

Fig. 83. *Richard Varick,* painted in 1805 for the
New York City Hall.
Owned by City Hall, New York.

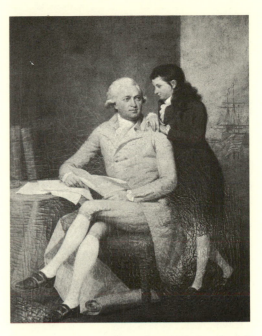

Fig. 85. *Jeremiah Wadsworth and His Son Daniel,*
painted at London in 1784, shown to Sir Joshua
Reynolds who pronounced it "bent tin." Trumbull's last portrait in the Copley manner.
Owned by Faneuil Adams.

Fig. 86. *Rev. Jonathan Mayhew Wainwright,*
painted at New York about 1822.
Owned by New Britain Museum of American
Art.

Fig. 87. *Mrs. Wainwright.* In the Collection of
the Corcoran Gallery of Art (purchase and gift of
Ruth Wainwright Wallace).

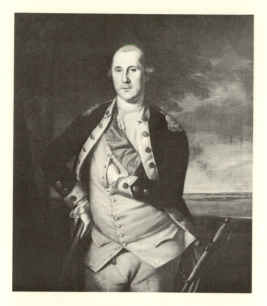

Fig. 88. Charles Willson Peale's portrait of General Washington of 1776.
Owned by The Brooklyn Museum.

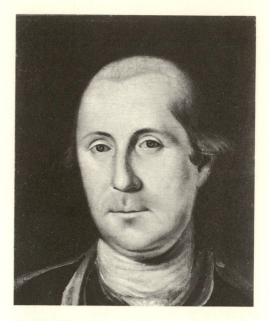

Fig. 89. Young Trumbull's copy of 1778 after Peale's portrait, then hanging in John Hancock's mansion on Beacon Hill, Boston.
Yale University Art Gallery.

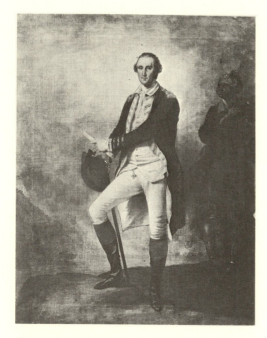

Fig. 90. *General Washington*, painted from memory at London in 1780.
Owned by The Metropolitan Museum of Art (bequest of Charles Allen Munn, 1924).

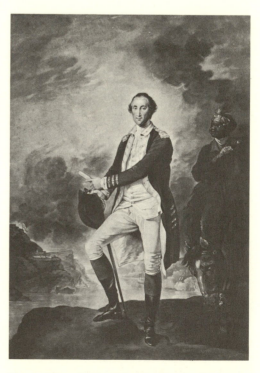

Fig. 91. Mezzotint by Valentine Green of 1781.
Owned by The Metropolitan Museum of Art (gift of William H. Huntington, 1882).

Fig. 92. Small-scale study for the large official portrait of General Washington for the New York City Hall. Both were painted at New York in 1790. The thirty-four year old painter, then at the height of his powers, gave the study to Martha Washington. Trumbull had but one good eye. With near monocular vision he is best in his small-scale studies and particularly in his miniatures.
Owned by Henry Francis du Pont Winterthur Museum.

Fig. 93. Signature on Fig. 92. Trumbull signed but few of his paintings, in general those that especially pleased him.
Owned by Henry Francis du Pont Winterthur Museum.

Fig. 94. The life-size portrait in City Hall, which lacks the brilliance of the small original study. Owned by City Hall, New York.

Fig. 95. *General Washington at the Battle of Trenton*, painted two years later at Philadelphia. Yale University Art Gallery.

Fig. 96. Detail of Fig. 95.
Yale University Art Gallery.

Fig. 97. *President Washington*, painted at Philadelphia in 1793.
Yale University Art Gallery.

Fig. 98. *James Watson,* painted about 1789, probably in New York.
Owned by Munson-Williams-Proctor Institute.

Fig. 99. *Brig. Gen. Samuel Blachley Webb,* painted about 1790, probably at New York.
Owned by The New-York Historical Society.

Fig. 100. *The Duke of Wellington,* after a marble bust by the English sculptor, Joseph Nollekens, painted *ca.* 1814 at London.
Yale University Art Gallery.

Fig. 101. Portrait of an "Unknown Gentleman" (Wilkes or Wilks?), probably painted at New York 1804–08.
Owned by Thomas Gilcrease Institute, Tulsa, Okla.

Fig. 102. *Marinus Willett,* another New York
City Hall portrait; this one painted in 1808.
Owned by City Hall, New York.

Fig. 103. *"Lady in White,"* probably painted at
New York, at the same time as Fig. 101.
Owned by Victor D. Spark.

MINIATURES

Owing to an accident to his left eye in his infancy, the painter's vision was in a measure monocular. He is at his best with his miniatures and small compositions, and worst with his large-scale pictures. Figures 104–15 are framed miniatures; Yale University Art Gallery.

Fig. 104.

Nathanael Greene

Thomas Y. Seymour

Ebenezer Stevens

William Hull

John Brooks

Fig. 105.

Otho H. Williams

Charles C. Pinckney

John Rutledge

Thomas Pinckney

William Moultrie

Fig. 106.

Thomas Mifflin

Laurence Manning

Samuel Livermore

Richard Butler

Arthur Lee

Fig. 107.

Rufus King   "The Infant" (Chief of the Seneca Indians)   Fisher Ames

John Langdon   John Brown

Fig. 108.

Henry Laurens

George Hammond

John Adams

John Jay

William Temple Franklin

Fig. 109.

Thomas J. Oakley

William Allen

John C. Calhoun

Henry Dwight

David B. Ogden

Fig. 110.

Giuseppe Ceracchi

"The Young Sachem" (A Chief of the Six Nations)

Tristram Dalton

Theodore Sedgwick

Oliver Ellsworth

Fig. 111.

William Smith　　　　　　　　　Jacob Read　　　　　　　　　Rufus Putnam

Ralph Izard　　　　　　　　　　　　　　　　　　　　　John F. Grimké

Fig. 112.

William Smallwood

Daniel Morgan

Elnathan Haskell

Egbert Benson

Philip Schuyler

Fig. 113.

Jonathan Trumbull, Jr.

"Good Peter" (Chief of the Oneida Indians)

Jonathan Trumbull, Sr.

Lemuel Hopkins

John Trumbull

Fig. 114.

Eleanor Custis

Cornelia Schuyler

Martha Washington

Sophia Chew

Harriet Chew

Fig. 115.

Harriet Wadsworth

Mrs. Jonathan Trumbull

Faith Trumbull

Catherine Wadsworth

Julia Seymour

Fig. 117. *Harriet Chew*. Compare with
the following.
Yale University Art Gallery.

Fig. 116. *Joel Barlow*.
Owned by Museum of Fine Arts, Boston (Ellen Kelleran Gardner Fund).
Photograph courtesy of Frick Art Reference Library.

Fig. 118. Mme. Vigée-Lebrun's portrait
of her daughter (see Appendix).
Owned by Museum of Fine Arts, Boston (bequest of Mrs. Robert Dawson
Evans).

Fig. 120. *Thomas Mifflin*, painted in
1790 at Philadelphia.
Owned by Mr. and Mrs. J. William
Middendorf, II.

Fig. 119. *Thomas Jefferson*, a gift from
the artist to Jefferson's oldest daughter,
Martha (see article on page 154).
Owned by Thomas Jefferson Memorial
Foundation, Charlottesville, Va.

Fig. 121. *Robert Morris,* 1790 at Philadelphia.
Owned by Mrs. Philip L. Poe.

Fig. 122. *Mrs. Robert Morris,* 1790 at Philadelphia.
Owned by Mrs. Philip L. Poe.

Fig. 123. *Thomas Paine,* Trumbull's gift to Thomas Jefferson. Painted at London in 1788 (see Appendix).
Owned by Thomas Jefferson Memorial Foundation, Charlottesville, Va.

Fig. 124. *Philip John Schuyler,* painted at Philadelphia in 1792.
Owned by The New-York Historical Society.

Fig. 125. *Mrs. Jonathan Trumbull, Junior,* painted in 1793, probably in Connecticut.
Yale University Art Gallery.

Fig. 126. *Harriet Wadsworth*, beloved by the artist, painted posthumously from memory in 1793, the year of her death.
Owned by Mrs. Catherine Aikman.

Fig. 127. *Oliver Wolcott, Jr.*, probably painted in 1790 at Philadelphia.
Yale University Art Gallery.

Fig. 128. *Unknown Gentleman,* possibly late 1790s at Philadelphia.
Unlocated.

Trumbull collected visual information as opportunity arose. His pencil sketches done directly from life are sensitive and satisfying documents.

Fig. 129. *Indian Chief, Hopothle Mico.*
Owned by Fordham University Library. Photograph courtesy of Frick Art Reference Library.

Fig. 130. *Indian Chief, Tuskatche Mico.* Both pencil sketches made in New York in 1790.
Yale University Art Gallery, deposited in the Yale Library.

Fig. 131. *Samuel Chase,* about 1790.
Owned by estate of Hall Park McCullough. Photograph courtesy of Frick Art Reference Library.

Fig. 132. *Maj. Gen. Horatio Gates,* 1790.
Owned by The Metropolitan Museum of Art (gift of Robert W. deForest, 1906).

Fig. 133. *Maj. Gen. Nathanael Greene,* drawn at Providence in 1791.
Owned by estate of Hall Park McCullough. Photograph courtesy of Frick Art Reference
Library.

Fig. 134. *Mlle. Rosamonde,* drawn in Paris in 1787.
Yale University Art Gallery, deposited in the Yale
Library.

Fig. 135. *Maj. Gen. Arthur St. Clair*, New York in 1790.
Owned by The Metropolitan Museum of Art (gift of Robert W. deForest, 1906).

Fig. 136. Joseph Trumbull, a posthumous drawing of 1783.
Owned by estate of Hall Park McCullough. Photograph courtesy of Frick Art Reference Library.

Fig. 137. *Brig. Gen. Anthony Wayne*, drawn between 1790 and 1792 at Philadelphia or New York. Owned by Fordham University Library. Photograph courtesy of Frick Art Reference Library.

Fig. 138. *Brutus and his Friends at the Death of Lucretia,* after a print. Yale University Art Gallery.

Fig. 139. *The Death of Paulus Aemilius,* painted in 1774 at the artist's home in Lebanon, Conn., his earliest attempt at composition. Dramatic death scenes are subjects that interested the artist. Compare this to his Revolutionary scenes of a decade or more later.
Yale University Art Gallery.

Fig. 140. *The Blind Belisarius.* The artist, who received a classical education at Harvard (class of 1771), was always interested in Roman History. This was painted in 1778 after an engraving.
Owned by Wadsworth Atheneum, Hartford.

Fig. 141. *Peter the Great at the Capture of Narva,* a crowded composition painted as an exhibition piece in London 1812. Yale University Art Gallery.

Fig. 142. Benjamin West's celebrated *Death of Wolfe,* of 1770, made a strong impact on the sensitive and impressionable young painter. Note similarity of grouping in this and other battle pieces.
Owned by The National Gallery of Canada.

Fig. 143. *Battle of La Hogue,* painted by West in 1778. (Copied by Trumbull, his pupil and studio assistant, in 1785, enlarged, "retouched and harmonized by Mr. West.")
Owned by The Metropolitan Museum of Art (P. Harris Brisbane Dick Fund, 1964).

Fig. 144. *The Death of Major Peirson*, by John Singleton Copley. Exhibited with great fanfare and success at the time of Trumbull's arrival at London in 1784, this picture influenced such subsequent paintings by Trumbull as *The Death of Montgomery* and *The Sortie from Gibraltar*.
Owned by The Tate Gallery, London.

Fig. 145. *The Battle of Bunker's Hill, Charlestown, Mass., 17 June 1775.* An engagement which the artist witnessed from across Boston Harbor. It was painted in Benjamin West's London studio, "finished March 1786." As English engravers were unwilling to celebrate the American victory, Trumbull took the picture to Stuttgart, Germany, where it was engraved by Johann Gotthard (von) Müller (1747–1830). It was published in London by Antonio C. de Poggi in 1788, twenty-three years—a generation—after the battle. The long delay in publishing this and other prints was the probable cause of their commercial failure. Yale University Art Gallery.

Fig. 146. Key. Yale University Art Gallery.

KEY

1. Maj. Gen. Joseph Warren, Massachusetts Militia (killed)
2. Col. Israel Putnam, 3rd Connecticut Regt.
3. Col. William Prescott, Massachusetts Militia
4. Col. Thomas Gardner, Massachusetts Regt. (mortally wounded)
5. Lieut. Col. Moses Parker, Bridge's Massachusetts Regt. (mortally wounded)
6. Capt. Thomas Knowlton, 3rd Connecticut Regt.
7. Maj. Andrew McClary, 1st New Hampshire Regt. (killed)
8. Maj. Willard Moore, Doolittle's Massachusetts Regt. (killed)
9. 2nd Lieut. Thomas Grosvenor, 3rd Connecticut Regt., and Peter Salem, his Negro servant
10. Rev. Samuel McClintock, Chaplain, 2nd New Hampshire Regt.
11. Maj. Gen. Sir William Howe, K.B., British
12. Lieut. Gen. Sir Henry Clinton, British
13. Lieut. Col. Sir Robert Abercromby, British, 37th Regt. of Foot
14. Maj. John Pitcairn, British, Royal Marines (mortally wounded)
15. Maj. John Small, British, 84th Regt. of Foot
16. Lieut. William Pitcairn, British, Royal Marines
17. Lieut. Francis, Lord Rawdon, British, 63rd Regt. of Foot

Fig. 147. Detail. Yale University Art Gallery.

Fig. 148. Detail. Yale University Art Gallery.

Fig. 149. Detail. Yale University Art Gallery.

Fig. 150. Detail. Yale University Art Gallery.

Fig. 151. Group Study: Lieut. Grosvenor and his Negro servant, Peter Salem. Yale University Art Gallery.

Fig. 152. *The Death of General Montgomery in the Attack on Quebec, Canada, on the Night of 31 December 1775.* Painted at London and "finished June 1788" (the same year as David's rigid, classical *Oath of the Horatii*). *Quebec* was engraved at London in 1792 by Johann Frederik Clemens of Copenhagen, Denmark. It was later re-engraved by Christian Wilhelm Ketterlinus of Stuttgart, Germany, a pupil of J. G. Müller. Both *Quebec* and *Bunker's Hill* were repeatedly re-engraved on copper and wood.
Yale University Art Gallery.

Fig. 153. Key. Yale University Art Gallery.

KEY

1. Maj. Gen. Richard Montgomery, Continental Army (killed)
2. Capt. Jacob Cheeseman, Aide-de-Camp to Gen. Montgomery (killed)
3. Capt. John MacPherson, Aide-de-Camp to Gen. Montgomery (killed)
4. Lieut. Col. Donald Campbell, Deputy Quartermaster General, New York Department
5. Col. William Thompson, Thompson's Pennsylvania Regt.
6. "Colonel Joseph Lewis," Chief of the Oneida Indians
7. Maj. Return Jonathan Meigs, 2nd Connecticut Regt.
8. Capt. William Hendricks, Thompson's Pennsylvania Regt. (mortally wounded)
9. Capt. Samuel Ward, 1st Rhode Island Regt.
10. 1st Lieut. John Humphries, Morgan's Company of Virginia Riflemen (killed)
11. 1st Lieut. Samuel Cooper, 2nd Connecticut Regt. (killed)
12. Lieut. Matthias Ogden, Volunteer

Fig. 154. Detail. Yale University Art Gallery.

Fig. 155. Detail. Yale University Art Gallery.

Fig. 156. Detail. Yale University Art Gallery.

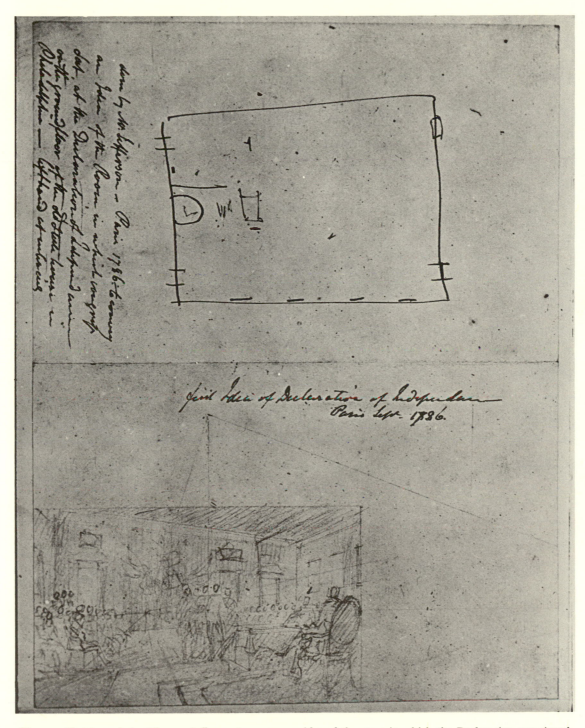

Fig. 157. Sketch made by Thomas Jefferson to convey an idea of the room in which the Declaration was signed. Below is Trumbull's pencil sketch of the general layout.
Yale University Art Gallery.

Fig. 158. *The Declaration of Independence, 4 July 1776 at Philadelphia.* This, the original version of the *Declaration* was painted between 1786 and 1797 at London for the engraving, which was done by the young American engraver and future landscape painter, Asher Brown Durand of New York, whose reputation was established thereby. The print, dated 1820, was published in 1823, forty-seven years after the historic event. The familiar replica of this picture in the Rotunda of the Capitol at Washington was painted in 1818 and installed in 1824. The original painting of the *Declaration* at Yale measures 21⅛ by 31⅛ inches.
Yale University Art Gallery.

Fig. 159. Key. Yale University Art Gallery.

KEY

1. George Wythe, Virginia
2. William Whipple, New Hamphsire
3. Josiah Bartlett, New Hampshire
4. Thomas Lynch, South Carolina
5. Benjamin Harrison, Virginia
6. Richard Henry Lee, Virginia
7. Samuel Adams, Massachusetts
8. George Clinton, New York
9. William Paca, Maryland
10. Samuel Chase, Maryland
11. Richard Stockton, New Jersey
12. Lewis Morris, New York
13. William Floyd, New York
14. Arthur Middleton, South Carolina
15. Thomas Heyward, Junior, South Carolina
16. Charles Carroll of "Carrollton," Maryland
17. Robert Morris, Pennsylvania
18. Thomas Willing, Pennsylvania
19. Benjamin Rush, Pennsylvania
20. Elbridge Gerry, Massachusetts
21. Robert Treat Paine, Massachusetts
22. William Hooper, North Carolina
23. Stephen Hopkins, Rhode Island
24. William Ellery, Rhode Island
25. George Clymer, Pennsylvania
26. Joseph Hewes, North Carolina
27. George Walton, Georgia
28. James Wilson, Pennsylvania
29. Abraham Clark, New Jersey
30. Francis Hopkinson, New Jersey
31. John Adams, Massachusetts
32. Roger Sherman, Connecticut
33. Robert R. Livingston, New York
34. Thomas Jefferson, Virginia
35. Benjamin Franklin, Pennsylvania
36. Thomas Nelson, Junior, Virginia
37. Francis Lewis, New York
38. John Witherspoon, New Jersey
39. Samuel Huntington, Connecticut
40. William Williams, Connecticut
41. Oliver Wolcott, Connecticut
42. Charles Thomson, Pennsylvania
43. John Hancock, President, Massachusetts
44. George Read, Delaware
45. John Dickinson, Pennsylvania
46. Edward Rutledge, South Carolina
47. Thomas McKean, Delaware
48. Philip Livingston, New York

Fig. 160. Detail. Yale University Art Gallery.

Fig. 161. Detail, one of the best portraits of Jefferson in miniature scale. Yale University Art Gallery.

Fig. 162. The *Declaration* and the *Surrender at Saratoga*. The painter was in his mid-sixties when he painted these enlarged replicas. The scale of the pictures can be determined by the figures in the foreground.
Rotunda of Capitol, Washington, D.C.
Photograph courtesy of Sturgis Warner.

Fig. 163. The Rotunda picture. It is a pity that Trumbull's reputation largely rests upon these late, heavy-handed replicas. Courtesy of the Library of Congress.

Fig. 164. *The Capture of the Hessians at Trenton, New Jersey, 26 December 1776.* Painted between 1786 and 1797 at London. Yale University Art Gallery.

Fig. 165. Key. Yale University Art Gallery.

KEY

1. Col. Edward Wigglesworth, 13th Massachusetts Regt.
2. Col. William Shepard or Shepherd, 3rd Continental Infantry
3. Lieut. Col. Josiah Parker, 5th Virginia Regt.
4. 1st Lieut. James Monroe, 3rd Virginia Regt.
5. Col. Johann Gottlieb Rall of the Hessians (killed)
6. Maj. William Stephens Smith, Aide-de-Camp to Gen. Sullivan
7. Lieut. Col. Robert Hanson Harrison, Military Secretary to Gen. Washington
8. Capt. Tench Tilghman, Military Secretary to Gen. Washington
9. Gen. George Washington, Commander-in-Chief
10. Maj. Gen. John Sullivan
11. Maj. Gen. Nathanael Greene
12. Brig. Gen. Henry Knox, Chief of Artillery
13. Brig. Gen. Philemon Dickinson, New Jersey Militia
14. Col. John Glover, 14th Continental Infantry
15. Col. George Weedon, 3rd Virginia Regt.
16. Capt. William (Augustine) Washington, 3rd Virginia Regt.

Fig. 166. Detail. Yale University Art Gallery.

Fig. 167. Detail. Yale University Art Gallery.

Fig. 168. Detail. Yale University Art Gallery.

Fig. 169. *The Death of Gen. Mercer at the Battle of Princeton, New Jersey, 3 January 1777.* Yale University Art Gallery.

Fig. 170. Key. Yale University Art Gallery.

KEY

1. Brig. Gen. Thomas Mifflin, Continental Army
2. 2nd Lieut. Charles Turnbull, Proctor's Battalion, Pennsylvania Artillery
3. Dr. Benjamin Rush, Military Surgeon, Pennsylvania
4. Col. John Cadwalader, Pennsylvania Militia
5. Gen. George Washington, Commander-in-Chief
6. Brig. Gen. Hugh Mercer, Continental Army (killed)
7. Capt. Hon. William Leslie, British, 17th Regt. of Foot (killed)
8. Lieut. Col. Benjamin G. Eyre, 2nd Battalion, Pennsylvania Militia

Fig. 171. Detail. Yale University Art Gallery.

Fig. 172. Detail. Yale University Art Gallery.

Fig. 173. Detail. Yale University Art Gallery.

Fig. 174. Preliminary composition. Yale University Art Gallery.

Fig. 175. Preliminary drawing. Figures 175–180 are in Princeton University Library.

Fig. 176. Preliminary drawing.

Fig. 177. Preliminary drawing.

Fig. 178. Preliminary drawing.

Fig. 179. Preliminary drawing.

Fig. 180. Preliminary drawing.

Fig. 181. Preliminary study. Owned by Princeton University Library. These sketches form the most complete series of studies that has survived, for the makeup and composition of a historical event by Trumbull. He was not only a careful composer and skilled craftsman, but a documentary artist of great importance. (See Appendix).

Fig. 182. Detail, John Mercer, who posed for his deceased father, Gen. Hugh Mercer.
Owned by Fordham University Library. Photograph courtesy of Frick Art Reference Library.

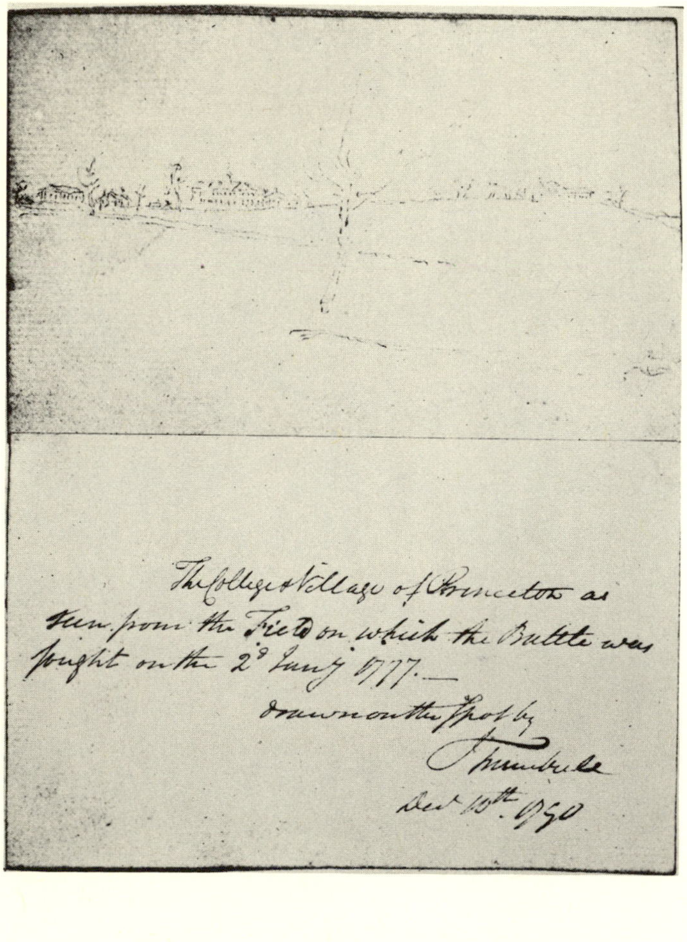

Fig. 183. Sketch of the field of battle.
Owned by estate of Hall Park McCullough.

Fig. 184. *The Surrender of Gen. Burgoyne at Saratoga, New York, 17 October 1777*. The Yale version, one of the later and less fortunate pictures in the historical series, planned in 1786, started in 1816 and finished a few years later.
Yale University Art Gallery.

Fig. 185. Key. Yale University Art Gallery.

KEY

1. Maj. William Lithgow, 11th Massachusetts Regt.
2. Col. Joseph Cilley, 1st New Hampshire Regt.
3. Brig. Gen. John Stark, New Hampshire Militia
4. Capt. Thomas Youngs Seymour, 2nd Continental Dragoons
5. Maj. William Hull, 8th Massachusetts Regt.
6. Col. John Greaton, 3rd Massachusetts Regt.
7. Lieut. Col. Henry Dearborn, 3rd New Hampshire Regt.
8. Col. Alexander Scammell, 3rd New Hampshire Regt.
9. Col. Morgan Lewis, Deputy Quartermaster General, Northern Department
10. Maj. Gen. William Phillips, British, Royal Regt. of Artillery
11. Lieut. Gen. John Burgoyne, British
12. Maj. Gen. Friedrich Adolf Riedesel, Baron Eisenbach, German
13. Lieut. Col. James Wilkinson, Deputy Adjutant General, Northern Department
14. Maj. Gen. Horatio Gates
15. Col. William Prescott, Massachusetts Militia
16. Col. Daniel Morgan, 11th Virginia Regt.
17. Col. Rufus Putnam, 5th Massachusetts Regt.
18. Lieut. Col. John Brooks, 8th Massachusetts Regt.
19. Rev. Enos Hitchcock, Chaplain, 10th Massachusetts Regt.
20. Lieut. Col. Robert Troup, Aide-de-Camp to Gen. Gates
21. 1st Lieut. Elnathan Haskell, Adjutant, 14th Massachusetts Regt.
22. Maj. John Armstrong, Aide-de-Camp to Gen. Gates
23. Philip John Schuyler
24. Brig. Gen. John Glover, Continental Army
25. Brig. Gen. William Whipple, New Hampshire Militia
26. Maj. Matthew Clarkson, Aide-de-Camp
27. Maj. Ebenezer Stevens, Independent Battalion of Artillery, Continental Army

Fig. 186. The enlarged replica in the Rotunda of the Capitol at Washington. Courtesy of the Library of Congress.

Fig. 187. *The Surrender of Lord Cornwallis at Yorktown, Virginia, 19 October 1781.* Painted at London, finished there before 1797. Curiously, all of Trumbull's American historical pictures—celebrating victories over the mother country—were painted in the British capital. The large replica in the Rotunda of the Capitol at Washington was completed in 1824. A lithograph print of it was made by N. Currier in 1852. Trumbull's Revolutionary subjects were popularized by cheap Currier and Ives prints. Yale University Art Gallery.

Fig. 188. Key. Yale University Art Gallery.

KEY

1. Col. Christien, or Col. Guillaume, both marquis des Deux-Ponts, French
2. Brigadier Matthieu Paul Louis, vicomte de Laval, French
3. Brigadier Adam Philippe, comte de Custine, French
4. Brigadier, Duc de Lauzun, French
5. Lieut. Gen. Claude Gabriel de Choisy, French
6. Maréchal-de-Camp Charles Joseph Hyacinthe du Houx, marquis de Vioménil, French
7. Lieut. Gen. Claude Anne, marquis de Saint Simon, French
8. Col. Hans Axel, comte de Fersen, Aide-de-Camp to Gen. Rochambeau, French
9. Col. Joseph François Louis Charles, comte de Damas, Aide-de-Camp to Gen. Rochambeau, French
10. Maj. Gen. François Jean, marquis de Chastellux, French
11. Lieut. Gen. Antoine Charles du Houx, baron du Vioménil, French
12. Admiral Louis, comte de Barras, French
13. Admiral François Joseph Paul, comte de Grasse-Tilly, French
14. Lieut. Gen. Jean Baptiste Donatien de Vimeur, comte de Rochambeau, General-in-Chief of the French forces
15. Maj. Gen. Benjamin Lincoln
16. Lieut. Col. Ebenezer Stevens, 2nd Continental Artillery
17. Gen. George Washington, Commander-in-Chief
18. Thomas Nelson, Junior, Commander of the Virginia State Forces
19. Maj. Gen. Marie Joseph Paul Yves Roch Gilbert du Motier, marquis de Lafayette, Continental Army
20. Maj. Gen. Friedrich Wilhelm Ludolf Gerhard Augustin, Baron von Steuben, Continental Army
21. Lieut. Col. David Cobb, Aide-de-Camp to Gen. Washington
22. Lieut. Col. Jonathan Trumbull, Junior, Military Secretary to Gen. Washington
23. Brig. Gen. James Clinton, Continental Army
24. Brig. Gen. Mordecai Gist, Continental Army
25. Brig. Gen. Anthony Wayne, Continental Army
26. Brig. Gen. Edward Hand, Adjutant General, Continental Army
27. Brig. Gen. John Peter Gabriel Muhlenberg, Continental Army
28. Brig. Gen. Henry Knox, Chief of the Artillery, Continental Army
29. Lieut. Col. Ebenezer Huntington, 3rd Connecticut Regt., acting Aide-de-Camp to Gen. Lincoln
30. Col. Timothy Pickering, Quartermaster General, Continental Army
31. Lieut. Col. Alexander Hamilton, principal Aide-de-Camp to Gen. Washington
32. Lieut. Col. John Laurens, Aide-de-Camp to Gen. Washington
33. Col. Walter Stewart, 2nd Pennsylvania Regt.
34. Maj. Nicholas Fish, 2nd New York Regt.

Fig. 189. Detail. Yale University Art Gallery.

Fig. 190. Detail. Yale University Art Gallery.

Fig. 191. Detail, Lieut. Col. Alexander Hamilton.
Yale University Art Gallery.

Fig. 192. Detail. Yale University Art Gallery.

Fig. 193. Detail, Lieut. Gen. du Houx. Yale University Art Gallery.

Fig. 194. Detail, Lieut. Gen. Rochambeau. Yale University Art Gallery.

Fig. 195. Replica in the Rotunda of the Capitol. Courtesy of the Library of Congress.

Fig. 196. The Rotunda picture (with figures to give scale). Photograph courtesy of Sturgis Warner.

Fig. 197. *The Sortie made by the Garrison of Gibraltar on the night of 26/27 November 1781*. This picture, celebrating a British victory, was painted at London at the suggestion of his publisher, Antonio C. de Poggi.
Collection of the Cincinnati Art Museum.

Fig. 198. A monumental picture (72 by 108 inches), painted at London in 1789. It is Trumbull's most successful large-scale picture of a historical scene. The arrangement of the four hands in the center of the composition is reminiscent of those in Tintoretto's celebrated *Bacchus, Ariadne and Venus* (1578) in the Doge's Palace, Venice, a print of which he might have seen in Benjamin West's well-supplied studio.

On deposit at the Museum of Fine Arts, Boston; courtesy, Boston Athenaeum.

REFERENCES to the SORTIE.

1 Gen Elliot, late Lord Heathfield Governor of Gibraltar
2 Major Gen! Ross. Major Gen! Reg!
3 Commodore Sir Roger Curtis Volunteer
4 Lieut Col! Hugo Hanoverian
5 Lieut Col! Trigge 12th Regiment
6 Lieut Col! Maxwell 71st Regt
7 Lieut Col! Hardy 56th Reg!
    Quarter master General of the Garrison
8 Major Vallotton, 56th Reg!
    first aid du camp to Gen! Elliot
9 Capt! Whitham, commanding a detachment
    of the Royal Artillery who served as artificers.

10 Major Tipping, Manchester Volunteers
11 Capt! Gillidge, Royal Artillery.
12 Capt!n Alex Mc Kenzie 71st Reg!
13 Lieut Koehler, Royal Artillery.
    Aid du Camp to Gen! Elliot.
14 Lieut C. B. Frederic } Manchester volunteers, acting as
15 Mr Budworth } Aids du Camp to Gen! Ross
16 Capt Hay, Engineer, commanding a party of Pioneers.
17 Don Joseph Barbosa, Capt!n in the Spanish Artillery
18 Baron Von Helmstadt of the Walloon guards, who was
    wounded and died soon after in the Garrison of Gibraltar

Fig. 199. Key. Yale University Art Gallery.

The above Head was sketched in 1789, from Sir Thomas Lawrence, with whom I was then intimate; and who did me the Favour to act as Model for my dying Spaniard, in the bar-picture.

I have lately been told by Mr. Robert Gilmor that Sir Thomas informed him that He had never set for his portrait, except on this occasion to me: — this therefore may be regarded as a unique remembrance of that very eminent and estimable Man.

Fig. 200. Sir Thomas Lawrence obligingly posed for "the Dying Spaniard," the central figure in the composition.
Owned by Boston Athenaeum.

Fig. 201. The engraving by William Sharp (1746–1824) of London.
Owned by Museum of Fine Arts, Boston (gift of George W. Wales).

Fig. 202. A late replica by the aging painter, probably after the Sharp engraving.
Yale University Art Gallery.

Fig. 203. *"The Resignation of General Washington, at Annapolis, Maryland, 3 December 1783."* Painted in New York between 1816 and 1822. The poorest of the historical pictures; the fire and dash, and drawing and perspective of the first two of the series are lacking. The large replica of this wretched performance is in the Rotunda of the Capitol.
Yale University Art Gallery.

Fig. 204. Key. Yale University Art Gallery.

KEY

1. Thomas Mifflin, President, Member of Congress, Pennsylvania
2. Charles Thomson, Secretary, Member of Congress, Pennsylvania
3. Elbridge Gerry, Member of Congress, Massachusetts
4. Hugh Williamson, Member of Congress, North Carolina
5. Samuel Osgood, Member of Congress, Massachusetts
6. Eleazer McComb, Member of Congress, Delaware
7. George Partridge, Member of Congress, Massachusetts
8. Edward Lloyd, Member of Congress, Maryland
9. Richard Dobbs Spaight, Member of Congress, North Carolina
10. Benjamin Hawkins, Member of Congress, North Carolina
11. Abiel Foster, Member of Congress, New Hampshire
12. Thomas Jefferson, Member of Congress, Virginia
13. Arthur Lee, Member of Congress, Virginia
14. David Howell, Member of Congress, Rhode Island
15. James Monroe, Member of Congress, Virginia
16. Jacob Read, Member of Congress, South Carolina
17. James Madison, Spectator, Virginia
18. William Ellery, Member of Congress, Rhode Island
19. Jeremiah Townley Chase, Member of Congress, Maryland
20. Samuel Hardy, Member of Congress, Virginia
21. Cadwalader Morris, Member of Congress, Pennsylvania
22. Gen. George Washington, Commander-in-Chief
23. Lieut. Col. Benjamin Walker, Aide-de-Camp to Gen. Washington
24. Lieut. Col. David Humphreys, Aide-de-Camp to Gen. Washington
25. Maj. Gen. William Smallwood, Spectator, Maryland
26. Brig. Gen. Otho Holland Williams, Spectator, Maryland
27. Lieut. Col. Samuel Smith, Spectator, Maryland
28. Lieut. Col. John Eager Howard, Spectator, Maryland
29. Charles Carroll of "Carrollton" and his two daughters, Spectators, Maryland
30. Mrs. George (Martha Custis) Washington, and her three grandchildren, Spectators, Virginia
31. Daniel of St. Thomas Jenifer, Spectator, Maryland

Fig. 205. The Rotunda picture. Courtesy of the Library of Congress.

Fig. 206. The figures in the foreground give scale. Photograph courtesy of Sturgis Warner.

Fig. 207. The Rotunda.
National Geographic photographer George F. Mobley. Courtesy of The United States Capitol Historical Society.

Fig. 208. *Priam Receiving the Body of Hector,* an exhibition piece in the grand manner, 1785 at London. Owned by Boston Athenaeum.

Fig. 209. *Maternal Affection,* another exhibition picture painted at London in 1809. Yale University Art Gallery.

Fig. 210. Sketch for Fig. 209 made at Paris in 1786—thus did
Trumbull collect visual material.
Yale University Art Gallery.

Fig. 211. *The Death of Hotspur*, London 1786.
Owned by Vassar College Art Gallery.

Fig. 212. Subject from Macpherson's *Ossian*. Owned by The Toledo Museum of Art.

Fig. 213. *Lamderg and Gelchossa,* from *Ossian.* Yale University Art Gallery.

Fig. 214. *The Earl of Angus,* from Scott's *Marmion.* Yale University Art Gallery.

Fig. 215. *The Grief of Andromache Over the
Body of Hector,* after J. L. David; Paris 1786.
Yale University Art Gallery, deposited in the
Yale Library.

Fig. 216. *The Last Family Who Perished in the Deluge,* painted at New Haven, Conn., 1838–39, when the artist was 83 years old. Yale University Art Gallery.

Fig. 217. *Joshua at the Battle of Ai,* New Haven, 1839–40. Trumbull painted religious subjects throughout his long life. Yale University Art Gallery.

Fig. 218. *Elisha Restoring the Shunammite's Son,* painted in 1777 by the religious-minded Connecticut Congregationalist at his Lebanon home, at the age of 21.
Owned by Wadsworth Atheneum, Hartford. Photograph courtesy of Frick Art Reference Library.

Fig. 219. *Holy Family.* Another New Haven-painted picture of 1839–40, destined for the Trumbull Gallery which was opened on the old Yale campus in 1831.
Yale University Art Gallery.

Fig. 220. *Madonna and Child with St. John the Baptist,* after a copy after Raphael's *Madonna au Corset Rouge,* painted at London in 1801.
Yale University Art Gallery.

Fig. 221. *The Infant Savior and St. John the Baptist*, dressing the lamb with flowers. London 1801.
Owned by Wadsworth Atheneum, Hartford.

Fig. 222. *St. John and the Lamb*, London 1800. Yale University Art Gallery.

Fig. 223. *Our Saviour with Little Children,* an exhibition piece painted at London in 1812. Yale University Art Gallery.

Fig. 224. *Christ and the Woman Taken in Adultery*, London 1811.
Yale University Art Gallery.

Fig. 225. *St. Jerome of Parma,* copy after Benjamin West's copy after Correggio, 1780 at London.
Yale University Art Gallery.

Fig. 226. *Preparation for the Entombment of the Saviour,* after a copy after Annibale Cerracci, painted in 1826 at New York.
Yale University Art Gallery.

Fig. 227. *"I was in Prison and Ye Came unto me,"* painted at New York in 1834 and after. Yale University Art Gallery.

Fig. 228. Study for Fig. 227. Yale University Art Gallery, deposited in the Yale Library.

A View of Part of the City Rome. J. Trumbull.

Fig. 229. Trumbull was always interested in landscape. This imaginary view of Rome is the earliest surviving work of the artist in any medium.
Yale University Art Gallery.

Fig. 230. *Shakespeare Cliff, Dover,* drawn on shipboard in 1781. Yale University Art Gallery, deposited in the Yale Library.

Fig. 231. *Bilbao, Spain*, drawn on shipboard in 1781. Yale University Art Gallery, deposited in the Yale Library.

Fig. 232. *Cohoes Falls*, near Albany on the Mohawk River, 1791.
Owned by Addison Gallery of American Art, Phillips Academy, Andover.

Fig. 233. *The Great Falls of the Connecticut River at Walpole,* 1791.
Owned by Fordham University Library. Photograph courtesy of Frick Art Reference Library.

Fig. 234. *Monte Video, Avon, Connecticut,* probably painted in 1791.
Yale University Art Gallery.

Fig. 235. *Falls at Norwich, Connecticut*, 1806. Yale University Art Gallery.

Fig. 236. *Niagara Falls*, 1807. Owned by Wadsworth Atheneum, Hartford.

Fig. 237. *Niagara Falls*, 1807. Owned by Wadsworth Atheneum, Hartford.

Fig. 238. Panorama of Niagara Falls, 14½ feet long, 1808.
Owned by The New-York Historical Society.

Fig. 239. Panorama of Niagara Falls, 14½ feet long, 1808.
Owned by The New-York Historical Society.

Fig. 240. Owned by Paul A. Frederick.

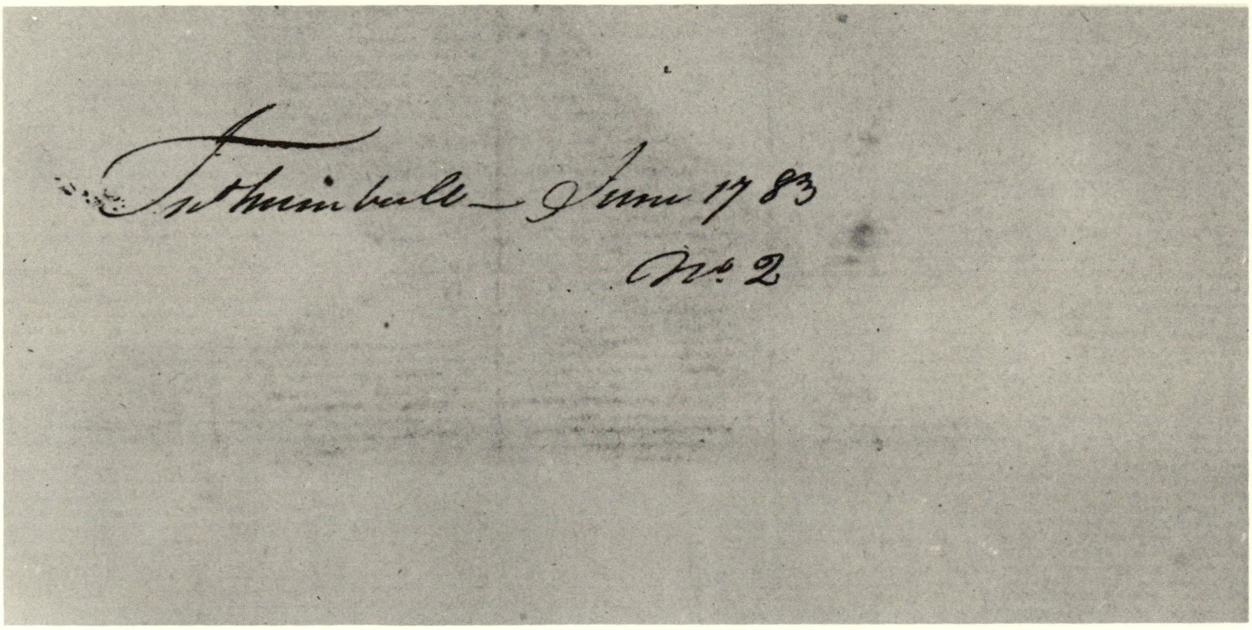

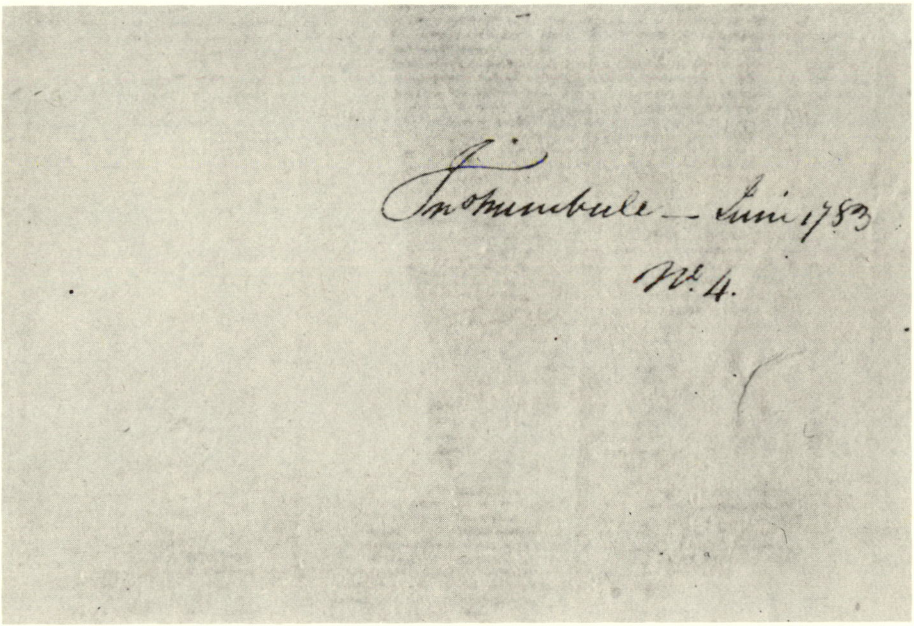

Fig. 241. Trumbull signatures from drawings on facing page.
Owned by Paul A. Frederick.

Fig. 242. Yale University Art Gallery.

Fig. 243. Yale University Art Gallery.

Fig. 244. Yale University Art Gallery.

Fig. 245. Yale University Art Gallery, deposited in the Yale Library.

Fig. 246. Indian Peace Medals, designed at London in 1796.
Yale University Library.

Fig. 247.

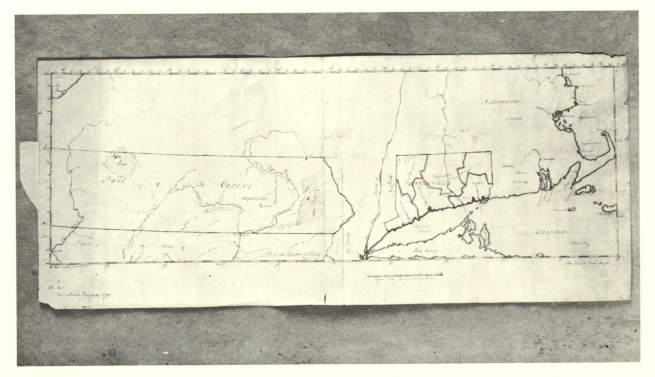

Fig. 248.

Maps prepared in 1774 and 1775 under the direction of the artist's father, Governor Trumbull, showing the Colony's claims to the West—documents of considerable historic importance.

Owned by Massachusetts Historical Society.

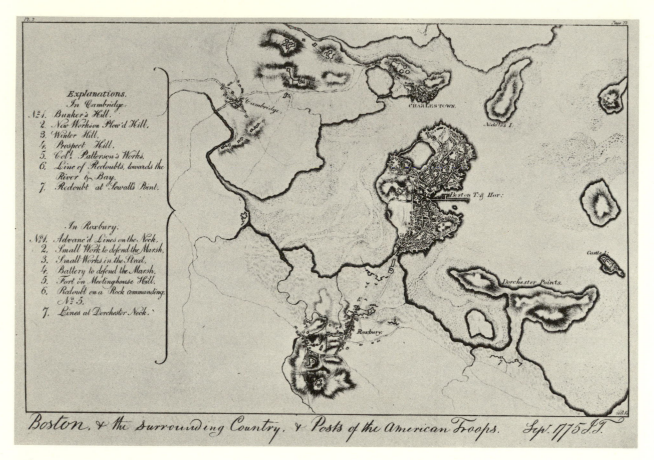

Fig. 249. Engraving, after a lost original, showing the British and American positions at Boston in 1775. It was as a military mapmaker that Trumbull was commissioned a colonel and became an aide-de-camp of General Washington.

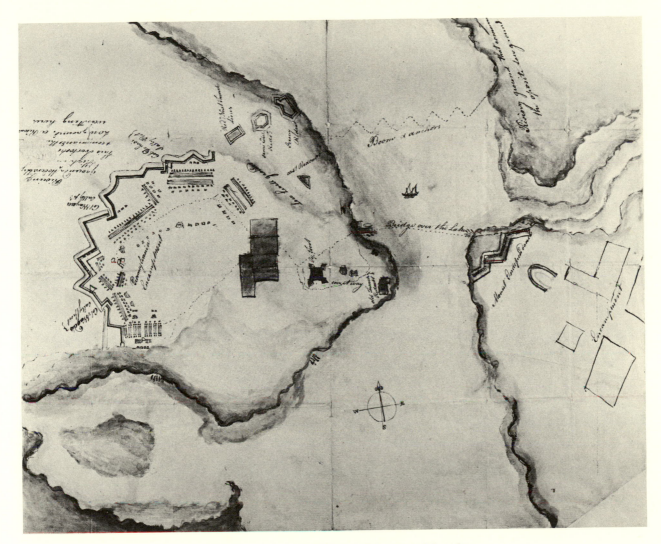

Fig. 250. Fortifications and disposition of troops at Ticonderoga.
Owned by estate of Hall Park McCullough.

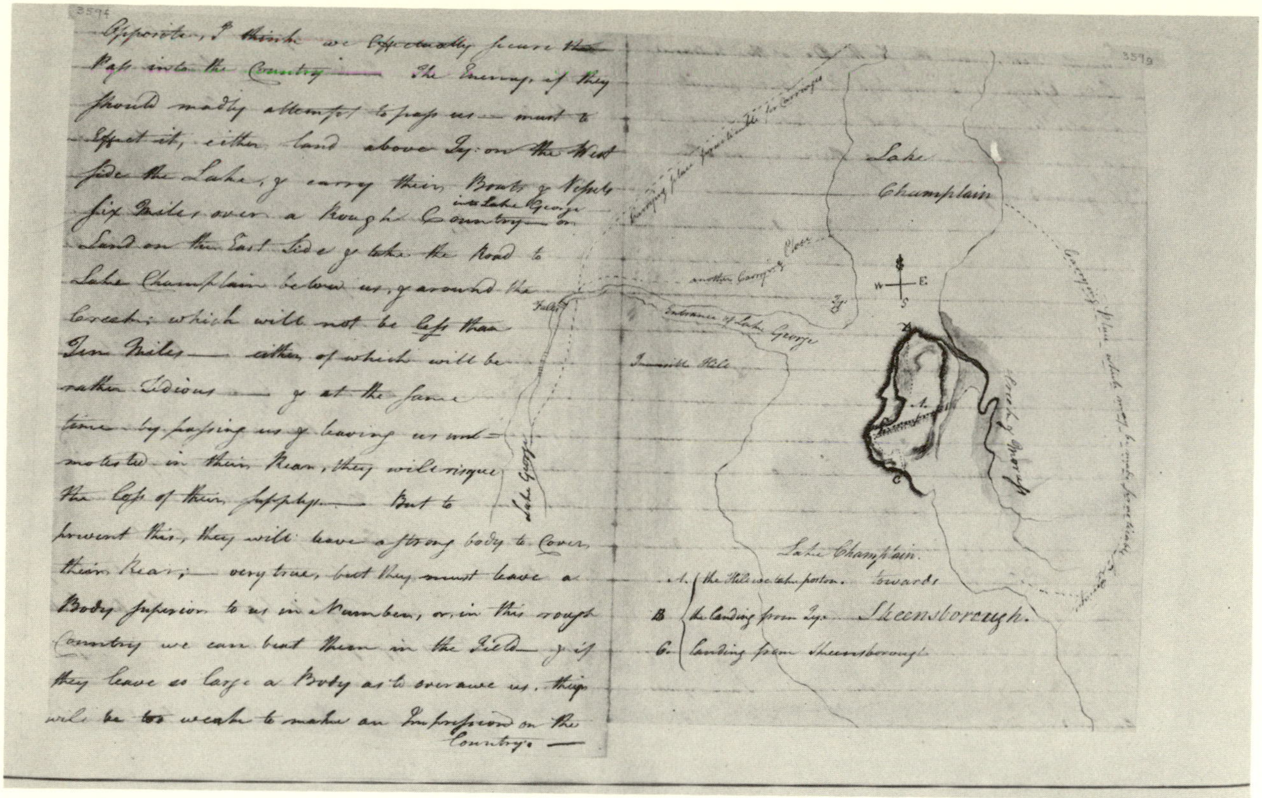

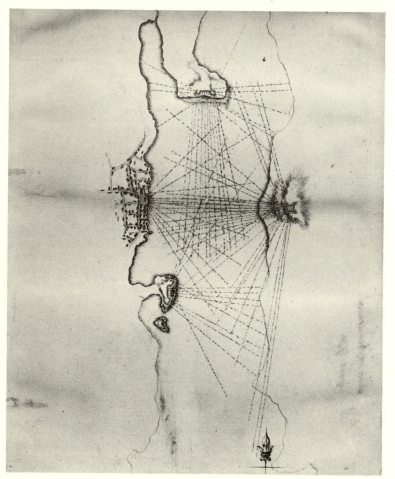

Fig. 251. Military map of Ticonderoga prepared by the young colonel for his brother Joseph, Commissary General of the Continental Forces.
Joseph Trumbull Collection, Connecticut State Library.

Fig. 252. Chart of New London Harbor, indicating fire capability. Military engineers were in short supply in the Colonial forces. Jonathan Trumbull Papers, Connecticut State Library.

Fig. 253. *An Anglo-Palladian Villa,* 1777 at Boston, possibly the artist's earliest architectural study. Owned by The New-York Historical Society.

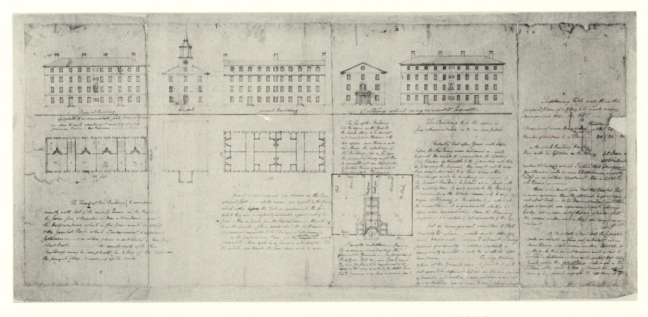

Fig. 254. *Plan for the Development of Yale College,* drawn at Philadelphia in 1792. Yale University Library.

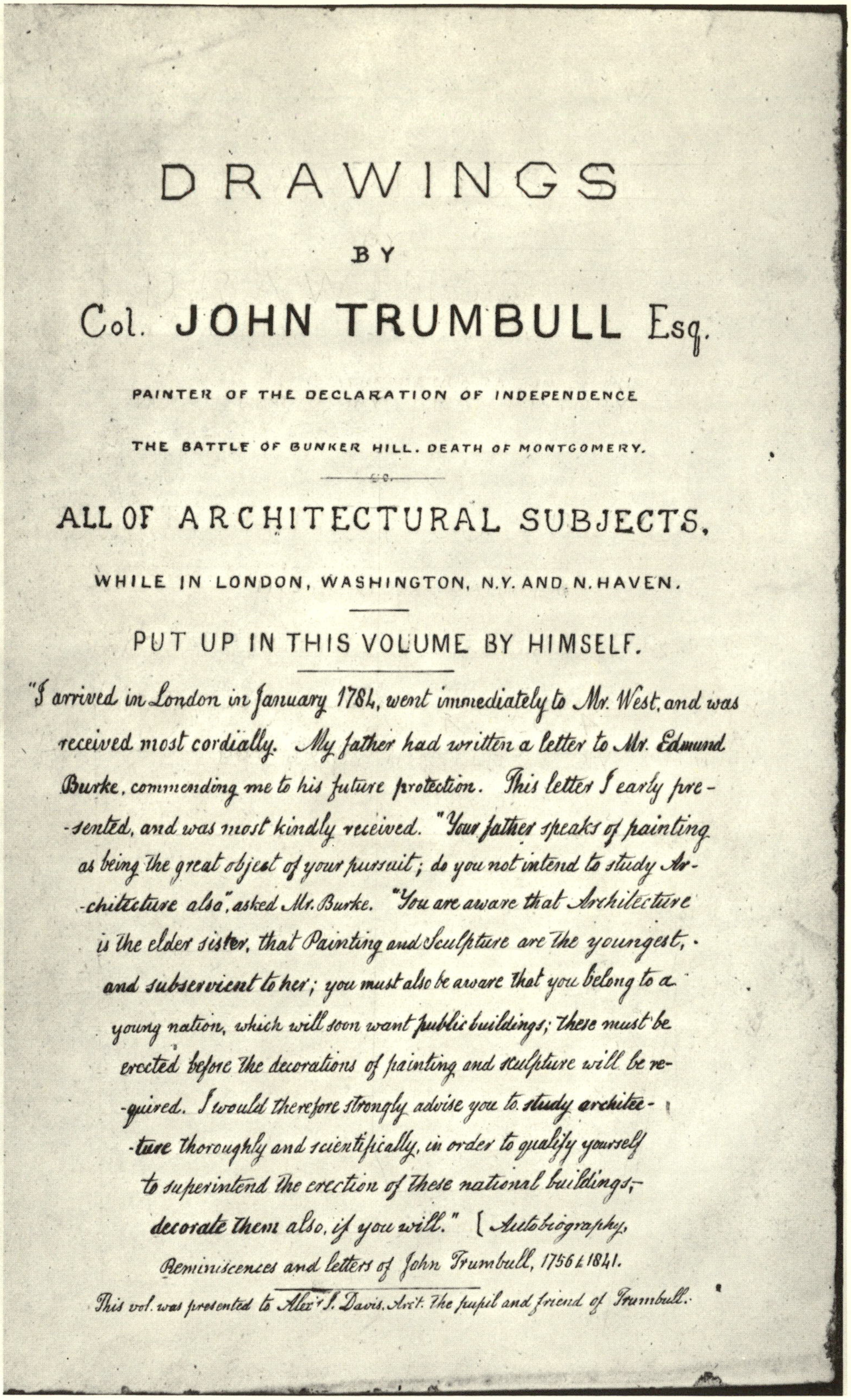

DRAWINGS

BY

Col. JOHN TRUMBULL Esq.

PAINTER OF THE DECLARATION OF INDEPENDENCE

THE BATTLE OF BUNKER HILL. DEATH OF MONTGOMERY.

ALL OF ARCHITECTURAL SUBJECTS,

WHILE IN LONDON, WASHINGTON, N.Y. AND N. HAVEN.

PUT UP IN THIS VOLUME BY HIMSELF.

"I arrived in London in January 1784, went immediately to Mr. West, and was received most cordially. My father had written a letter to Mr. Edmund Burke, commending me to his future protection. This letter I early presented, and was most kindly received. "Your father speaks of painting as being the great object of your pursuit; do you not intend to study Architecture also", asked Mr. Burke. "You are aware that Architecture is the elder sister, that Painting and Sculpture are the youngest, and subservient to her; you must also be aware that you belong to a young nation, which will soon want public buildings; these must be erected before the decorations of painting and sculpture will be required. I would therefore strongly advise you to study architecture thoroughly and scientifically, in order to qualify yourself to superintend the erection of these national buildings, decorate them also, if you will." (Autobiography, Reminiscences and letters of John Trumbull, 1756 & 1841.

This vol. was presented to Alex'r S. Davis, Arc't. The pupil and friend of Trumbull.

Fig. 255. Scrapbook kept by Alexander Jackson Davis, wherein he describes himself as "The pupil and friend of Trumbull." Davis was a partner of Ithiel Town of New Haven and later of New York; Town and Davis was a celebrated architectural firm.
Owned by The New-York Historical Society.

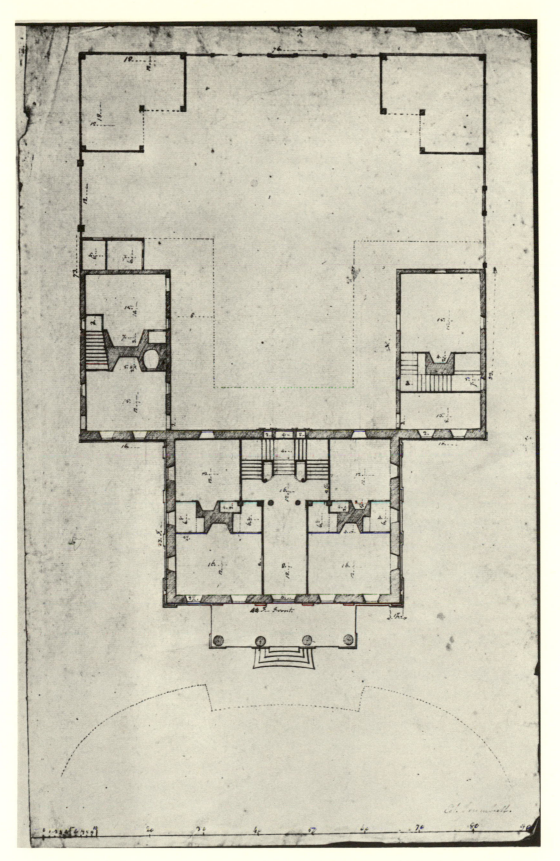

Fig. 256. Study, "Presented to Alex^r J. Davis." Owned by The New-York Historical Society.

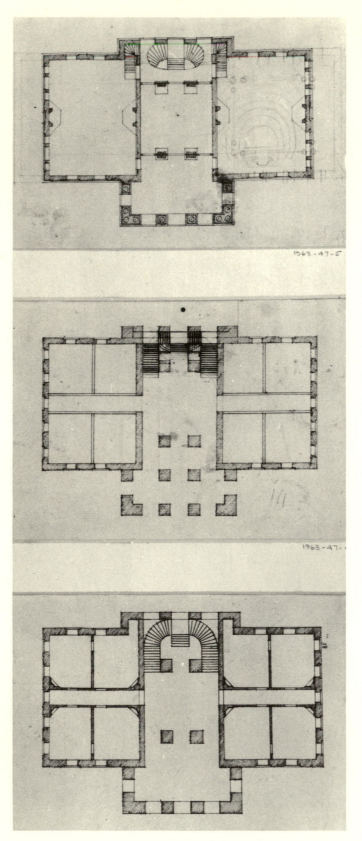

Fig. 257. Studies, possibly drawn during Trumbull's incarceration at the Bridewell Prison in London in 1781. Owned by The Cooper Union Museum.

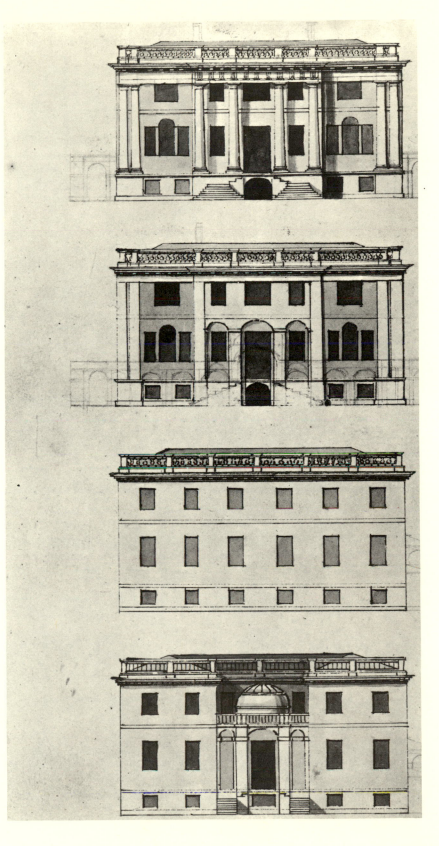

Fig. 258. Studies, 1790 to 1794.
Yale University Art Gallery, deposited
in the Yale Library.

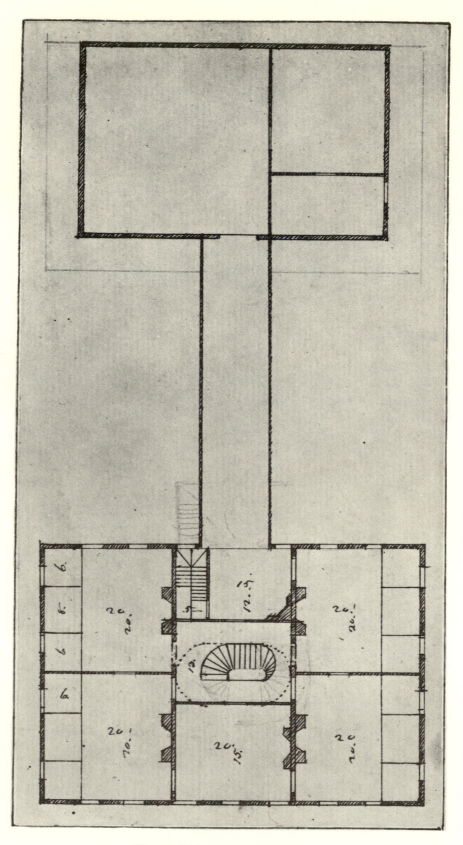

Fig. 259. Study, 1790 to 1794.
Yale University Art Gallery, deposited
in the Yale Library.

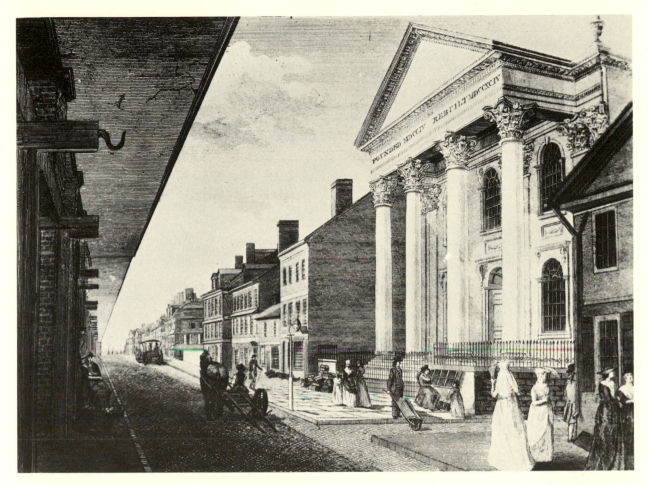

Fig. 260. *The First Presbyterian Church, Philadelphia,* designed in 1792. Engraved by William Birch, published in 1799 (see article Appendix).
Yale University Art Gallery.

Fig. 261. *Meetinghouse at Lebanon, Connecticut,* planned in 1804 and finished in 1806, the sole extant example of the artist's architectural efforts. Partially destroyed in the hurricane of 1938; restored in 1954.
Photograph, courtesy of Connecticut United Church Center.

Fig. 262. *Meetinghouse at Lebanon, Connecticut,* interior.
Photograph, courtesy of Connecticut United Church Center.

Fig. 263. *General Washington.* Yale University Art Gallery.

Fig. 264. *Self-portrait*. Yale University Art Gallery.

Fig. 265. *Rochambeau*. Yale University Art Gallery.

Fig. 266. *General St. Clair*. Yale University Art Gallery.

Fig. 267. *Napoleon*. Owned by Princeton University Library.

Fig. 268. The John Trumbull medal, designed and modeled by P. P. Duggan, dies cut by C. C. Wright. Published by the American Art-Union, New York, 1849.

Fig. 269. *John Trumbull* by Gilbert Stuart, painted at Boston in December 1818. Yale University Art Gallery.

Fig. 270. *The "Patriot-Artist,"* with his palette resting on his Revolutionary sword, at the age of sixty-five, by Samuel Lovett Waldo.
Yale University Art Gallery.

Fig. 271. *John Trumbull* by Samuel Lovett Waldo and William Jewett, painted at New York, 1832. Yale University Art Gallery.

Fig. 272. *John Trumbull* by his young friend Ball Hughes, executed about 1839. Note the badge of the Society of the Cincinnati attached to his Roman toga.
Yale University Art Gallery.

20414

Fig. 273. The painter at the age of seventy-seven, by George W. Twibill, Jr., at New York in 1833. Owned by National Academy of Design. Photograph courtesy of Frick Art Reference Library.

Fig. 274. The artist's son, *Lieut. John Trumbull Ray* of the British Army, the 45th (Nottinghamshire) Regiment of Foot; miniature painted at London in 1814 by Andrew Robertson.
Yale University Art Gallery.

Col. JOHN TRUMBULL,
Patriot and Artist,
Friend and Aid
OF WASHINGTON,
Died in New-York, Nov. 10, 1843,
ÆE. 88.
He reposes in a Sepulchre
Built by himself, beneath
THIS MONUMENTAL GALLERY;
where in Sept. 1834,
He deposited the remains of
SARAH his WIFE,
who died in N.Y. Apr. 12, 1824, ÆE. 51.

To his Country he gave his
SWORD and his PENCIL.

Fig. 275. Stone in the Yale University Art Gallery marking the grave of artist and his wife. Yale University Art Gallery.

TRUMBULL GALLERY OF PAINTINGS:

YALE COLLEGE.

By agreement between the College and Colonel TRUMBULL, this valuable collection of Paintings became the property of the Institution, on the death of the venerable artist,—which occurred in November, 1843. This agreement requires that the income of the Gallery, after paying his annuity, be forever applied towards the education of needy and meritorious students in Yale College.

The Gallery is contained in a stone edifice, built expressly for the object: and comprises two rooms each 30 feet square, 24 feet high, and lighted from above.

The TRUMBULL GALLERY *proper* occupies the North Room, and contains 53 Paintings from the pencil of Col. T., including all his original historical pictures of Scenes of the American Revolution. The following is a summary of the collection.

Battle of Bunker's Hill.	Declaration of Independence.
Death of Gen. Montgomery, at Quebec.	Capture of the Hessians at Trenton.
Death of Gen. Mercer, at battle of Princeton.	Surrender of General Burgoyne.
Resignation of Gen. Washington.	Surrender of Lord Cornwallis.
Our Savior with little children.	Preparing the body of our Savior for the tomb.
Our Savior bearing the cross.	Infant Savior and St. John.
Holy Family.	St. John and Lamb.
Communion of St. Jerome.	St. Jerome, (copy from Correggio.)
Madonna della Sedia.	Madonna au corset rouge.
Transfiguration, (copy from Raphael.)	Woman accused of adultery.
Earl of Angus, conferring Knighthood on De	Peter the Great at the capture of Narva.
Wilton.	Death of Paulus Emilius.
Lamderg and Gelchossa.	Last Family which perished in the Deluge.
Joshua at the battle of Ai.	Portrait of Duke of Wellington.
"I was in prison and ye visited me."	Gov. Trumbull, sen.
Portrait of Mrs. Trumbull.	Gen. Washington.
Timothy Dwight.	Rufus King.
Stephen Van Rensselaer.	Alexander Hamilton.
Christopher Gore.	12 Groups, comprising 58 portraits.

The South Room comprises a collection of portraits of the past and present officers and benefactors of the College, besides many other paintings of historic interest, the whole number being about fifty. It also includes the celebrated group in marble of *Jephthah and his Daughter* by AUGUR, several busts of distinguished persons,—ancient coins, medals, and other memorials of antiquity.

The Gallery is open for visitors generally throughout the day, except the hour from 1 to 2 P. M. *Price of admission*, 25 cts. Access to the *Cabinet of Minerals*, the *Library*, and the other public Rooms of the College, is *without charge*. Directions for finding these rooms may be obtained by visitors, on inquiry at the Treasurer's Office under the Trumbull Gallery.

N. B. *Visitors are earnestly requested not to touch the paintings or the statuary. Canes, whips, umbrellas, fruit, tobacco and dogs are excluded.*

B. SILLIMAN, *Curator.*

Fig. 276. Poster issued by Professor Benjamin Silliman, the Yale scientist, Trumbull's nephew-in-law.
Yale University Art Gallery.